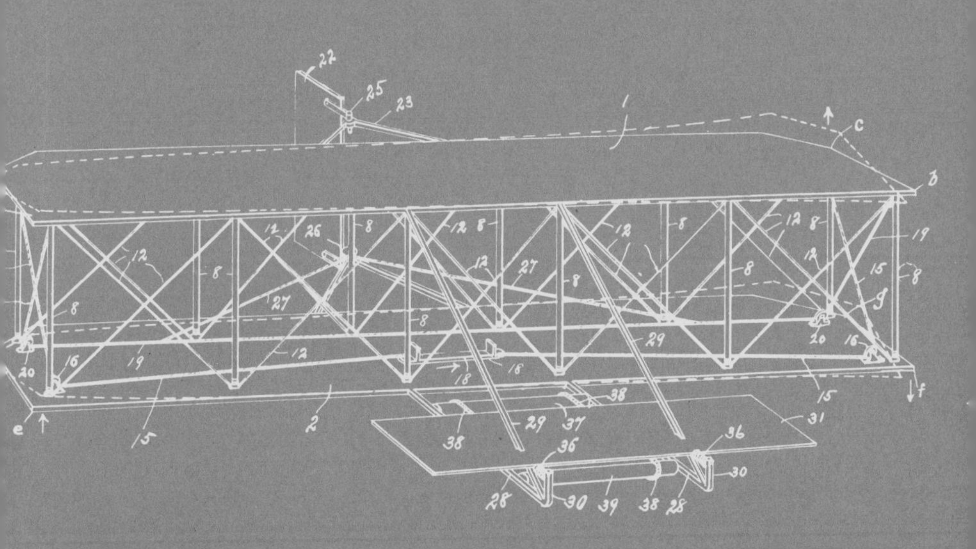

WILBUR & ORVILLE WRIGHT

A Bibliography

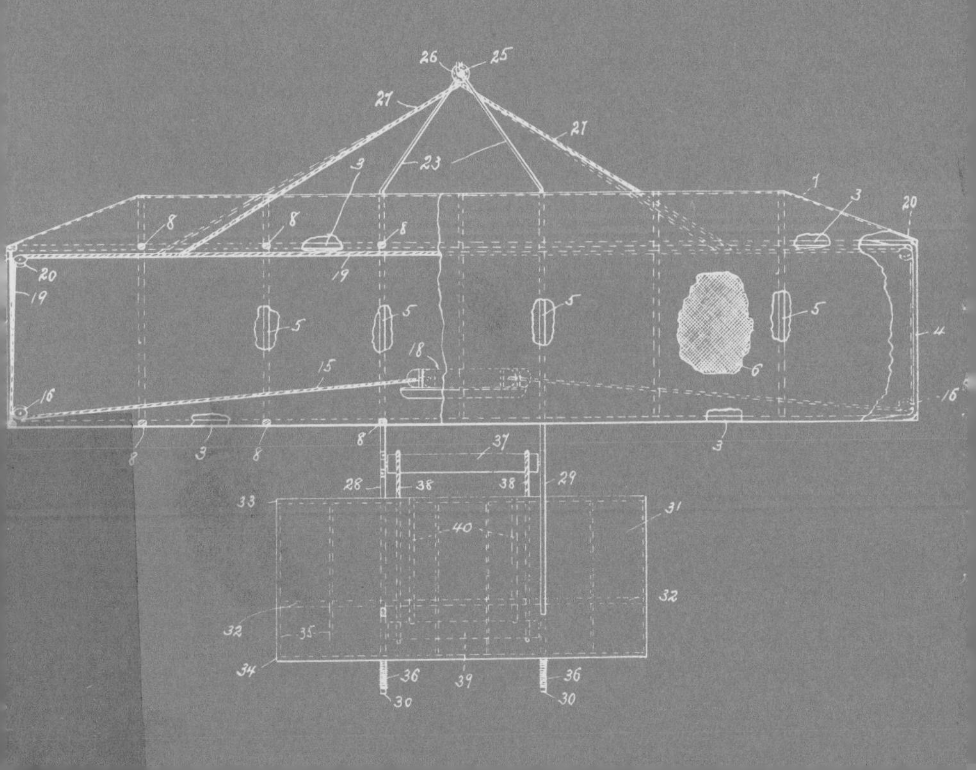

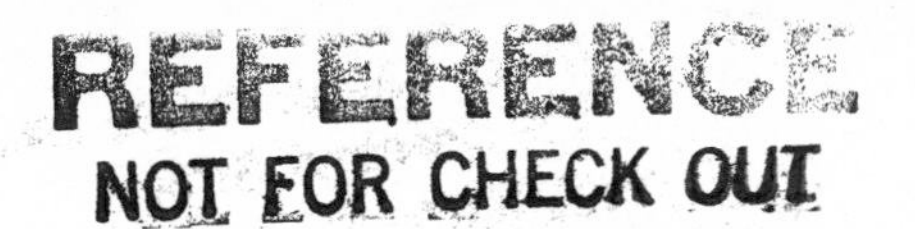

WILBUR & ORVILLE WRIGHT

A Bibliography Commemorating

the Hundredth Anniversary of the Birth of

WILBUR WRIGHT • APRIL 16, 1867

Compiled by Arthur G. Renstrom

SCIENCE AND TECHNOLOGY DIVISION

Reference Department

LIBRARY OF CONGRESS

Washington : 1968

L.C. Card 68–60013

Cover: Drawings from Wilbur and Orville Wright's patent no. 821,393 on their flying machine.

Preface: Photographs of the Wilbur and Orville Wright medal, courtesy of the Hall of Fame for Great Americans at New York University.

For sale by the Superintendent of Documents, U.S. Government Printing Office
Washington, D.C. 20402 - Price 55 cents

Contents

Preface

The year 1967 marks two great anniversaries in the history of aviation —the hundredth anniversary, on April 16, of the birth of the co-inventor of the airplane, Wilbur Wright, and the 40th, on May 20–21, of Charles A. Lindbergh's epochal flight from New York to Paris. The Lindbergh event has been celebrated, very appropriately, by lavish public ceremonies in Europe and the United States. The Wilbur Wright centenary, regrettably, evoked but a few scattered observances, the most notable of which took place on May 7 when, with colorful and impressive exercises, the busts and commemorative tablets of Wilbur and his brother Orville, inseparable colleagues and companions in all things, were installed in the Hall of Fame for Great Americans.

This publication is issued not only as a bibliographic service to scholars and others interested in aeronautical history but also as a tribute in this centennial year to Wilbur and Orville Wright by the Library of Congress. The Library's concern with Wrightiana is of long standing, dating back at least to 1932 when the Wright-Chanute correspondence was acquired as a part of the papers of Octave Chanute. The main body of Wright papers was received by the Library in May 1949, 16 months after the death of Orville. As a concomitant of the gift of the papers by the Orville Wright estate, the then Librarian of Congress agreed to their preparation for publication under Library auspices, an objective realized in the two-volume edition brought out by McGraw-Hill in 1953 to mark the 50th anniversary of the achievement of powered flight by the Wrights.

The bibliography presented here is a revision and expansion of that published in 1953 as part of "The Papers of Wilbur and Orville Wright." At that time it was feasible to publish only 191 references from the exhaustive list that had been compiled. Appearing in volume 2, pages 1221–1243, of "The Papers," these were grouped under six headings: "Published Writings of Wilbur and Orville Wright," "Patents," "Court Records," "General References," "Wind Tunnel," and "Powerplant."

The complete bibliography, comprising the published and unpublished references compiled in 1952 and 1953 and those compiled later, totals 2,055 entries, including books, periodical articles, pamphlets, patents, government documents, and court records in English and eight foreign languages. Brief annotations have been provided for most of the references cited. To avoid revising the entries, which had been prepared in the style prescribed by the publisher of "The Papers," the bibliography is being published in the same style rather than according to Library of Congress bibliographical practices and rules. Likewise the spelling "aeroplane" has been retained. The bibliographical information, however, is essentially the same as in other Library publications.

The titles listed are based primarily on examination of the extensive aeronautical holdings of the Library of Congress, including the Wright papers and collection bequeathed to the Library by the Orville Wright estate, and of many bibliographical sources. Supplementary sources and collections were consulted during visits to other libraries in Washington, D.C.—the National Air and Space Museum, the National Archives, the Department of Justice Library, and the Patent Office Library—as well as the Institute of the Aeronautical Sciences (now American Institute of Aeronautics and Astronautics) Library and the Science and Technology Division of the New York Public Library in New York City.

The references are grouped under 22 subjects, indicated in the contents, reflecting published materials dealing with Orville or Wilbur Wright or relating to aviation affairs with which they were associated. Arrangement in most sections is chronological, as in "The Papers," since this seems best suited to document the early gliding and wind-tunnel experiments and the design and production of successive models of aeroplanes and motors. The sections consisting primarily of book materials, however, such as "Bibliographical References—Wright Brothers," "Poetry," and "Juvenile Publications," are arranged alphabetically by author. The sections "Monuments and Museums," "Memorials," "Medals and Honors," and "Memorabilia" have been further subdivided for greater ease in locating materials under specific subjects. An index to authors and to persons and institutions referred to is provided to facilitate use of the bibliography.

THE HALL OF FAME FOR GREAT AMERICANS AT NEW YORK UNIVERSITY

Published Writings of Wilbur and Orville Wright

Wilbur Wright

Wright, Wilbur. Angle of Incidence. *The Aeronautical Journal*, July 1901, vol. 5, pp. 47–49.

As far as can be ascertained, this brief article and "Die Wagerechte Lage Während des Gleitfluges" (see below) by Wilbur Wright constitute the first aeronautical writings of the brothers to appear in print.

——— The Earliest Wright Flights—A Letter from Wilbur Wright. *Scientific American*, July 16, 1910, vol. 103, p. 47.

Comment on an editorial in the June 25th issue of the magazine and the use of the term "open flights" with reference to the Wrights.

——— *Experiments and Observations in Soaring Flight.* [Preprint of *Journal of the Western Society of Engineers.*] Chicago: Western Society of Engineers, 1903, 18 pp., illus.

Published also in *Journal of the Western Society of Engineers*, Aug. 1903, vol. 8, pp. 400–417; translation of selected excerpts with title, "Versuche und Beobachtungen im Schwebeflug" [signed *A. S.*, *i.e.*, Arthur Stenzel], *Illustrierte Aeronautische Mitteilungen*, Oct. 1903, vol. 7, pp. 331–334; abstract *Engineering Magazine*, Nov. 1903, vol. 26, p. 272; abstract *Le Génie Civil*, Nov. 7, 1903, vol. 44, pp. 9–10; with title, "The Later Experiments of the Wright Brothers in Soaring Flight," *The Aero Manual*, 1909, pp. 22–33 (also 1910 ed.).

Paper presented before the Western Society of Engineers, June 24, 1903, giving an account of gliding experiments at Kitty Hawk, N.C., September and October 1902. Discussion and questions by O. Chanute and others.

——— The Experiments of a Flying Man. *Independent*, Feb. 4, 1904, vol. 56, pp. 242–246, illus.

Abridged with title, "Experiments in Flying," *Science*, Feb. 12, 1904, vol. 119 (n. s.), pp. 269–270; with title, "The Wright Experiments in Flying," *Scientific American Supplement*, Mar. 12, 1904, vol. 57, pp. 23571–23572; reprinted in Humphreys, Pauline A., and Gertrude Hosey, *Romance of the Airmen*, Boston: Ginn and Company, 1931, pp. 197–205.

The use of Wilbur Wright's signature on this article was unauthorized. See editor's retraction, with apologies, in *Independent*, February 25, 1904, page 455 and March 10, 1904, page 574.

——— Flying as a Sport—Its Possibilities. *Scientific American*, Feb. 29, 1908, vol. 98, p. 139.

Reprinted in part with title, "The Fun of Flying," by Wilbur Wright and others, *Life* [Melbourne], Apr. 1909, vol. 11, pp. 368–369.

Contributed to a "Sportsman's Number" of the magazine.

——— Flying from London to Manchester. Specially Written for "The London Magazine." *London Magazine*, Feb. 1909, vol. 21, pp. 617–625, illus.

Abridged *L'Aviation illustrée*, Mar. 20, 1909, vol. 1, no. 9, p. 4; *La Conquête de l'air*, Apr. 1, 1909, vol. 6, no. 7, p. 3.

Discussion of "Daily Mail" prize of $10,000 offered to first flyer to complete journey from London to Manchester within a period of twenty-four hours and with only two stops en route.

——— How to Glide and Soaring Flight. *Flight*, Oct. 2–Nov. 27, 1909, vol. 1, pp. 607–608, 621–622, 647–648, 672–673, 693–694, 721–723, 757–758, illus.

In this, "Experiments and Observations in Soaring Flight" and "Some Aeronautical Experiments" are abridged and combined.

——— [in part]. Octave Chanute's Work in Aviation. *Aeronautics*, Jan. 1911, vol. 8, no. 1, p. 4.

Tribute written shortly after Chanute's death on November 24, 1910.

——— Otto Lilienthal. *Aero Club of America Bulletin*, Sept. 1912, vol. 1, no. 8, pp. 20–21, illus.

Wilbur Wright's last article, written May 1912, a day or two before he was stricken with typhoid fever. Attempts to define Lilienthal's place in aeronautical history. Published posthumously.

——— *Some Aeronautical Experiments*. Reprint from *Journal of the Western Society of Engineers*. [Chicago: Western Society of Engineers, 1901], 22 pp., illus.

Published also in *Journal of the Western Society of Engineers*, Dec. 1901, vol. 6, pp. 489–510; abstract *Engineering Magazine*, Feb. 1902, vol. 22, pp. 773–774; abstract *Scientific American*, Feb. 22, 1902, vol. 100, p. 125; *Automotor Journal*, Feb.–Mar. 1902, vol. 4, pp. 196–198, 240–243; summarized with title, "Recent Aeronautic Experiments," *Feilden's Magazine*, Mar. 1902, vol. 6, pp. 261–272; *Flying*, Mar., June, Oct. 1902, Jan. 1903, vol. 1, pp. 87–94, 138–140, 189–191, 226–229; translation with title, "Die Gleitversuche der Brüder Wright," *Wiener Luftschiffer-Zeitung* May 1903, vol. 2, pp. 95–99; *Annual Report of the Smithsonian Institution, 1902*, Washington: Government Printing Office, 1903, pp. 133–148, and reprinted as *Smithsonian Publication* 1380, Washington: Government Printing Office, 1903; with title, "Some Classical Aeronautical Experiments," *Aero*, May 25, June 1–15, 1909, vol. 1, pp. 3–4, 23–24, 39–40, 57–58; with title, "The Wright Brothers' First Gliding Experiments," *The Aero Manual*, 1909, pp. 4–21 (also 1910 ed.); *The Aeronautical Journal*, July/Sept. 1916, vol. 20, pp. 86–97; *Orville Wright Dinner of the Society of Automotive Engineers, Inc., July [June] 17, 1918, Dayton, Ohio*, New York: Society of Automotive Engineers, 1918, pp. 23–32; reprinted in part in *The Early History of the Airplane*, Dayton: The Dayton-Wright Airplane Co., [1922], pp. 16–24.

Paper presented before the Western Society of Engineers, September 18, 1901. First extensive public account of the Wrights' gliding experiments at Kitty Hawk, N.C., October 1900 and July and August 1901. Introduction by Octave Chanute, president of the Society, at whose invitation the address was made. Few other articles on the subject of flight have been so frequently reprinted or widely quoted.

——— W. Wright on Altitude and Fancy Flying. *Aero*, Dec. 17, 1910, vol. 1, no. 11, p. 3.

Published also in *Flight*, Dec. 31, 1910, vol. 2, p. 1083.

Letter to the editor of *Aero* objecting to editorial in same, November 26, 1910, page 12, which distorted Wrights' views. States Wrights believed in "all kinds of flying which demonstrate the *merits of the machine*."

——— Die W a g e r e c h t e Lage Während des Gleitfluges. *Illustrierte Aeronautische Mitteilungen*, July 1901, vol. 5, pp. 108–109.

Cites advantages of the horizontal position of the operator during gliding flights as opposed to the upright position used by earlier experimenters.

——— What Clément Ader Did. *Aero Club of America Bulletin*, May 1912, vol. 1, no. 4, pp. 17–19, illus.

Published also in *The Aeronautical Journal*, July/Sept. 1916, vol. 20, pp. 110–115.

Depreciation of French claims for Ader as the first to achieve heavier-than-air flight. Quotes extensively from *Report of the Trials of Mr. Clément Ader's Aviation Apparatus*, General Mensier, Chairman of the Committee, October 21, 1897.

——— What Mouillard Did. *Aero Club of America Bulletin*, Apr. 1912, vol. 1, no. 3, pp. 2–4, illus.

Published also in *The Aeronautical Journal*, July/Sept. 1916, vol. 20, pp. 107–110.

Prompted by the erection of a monument to Louis-Pierre Mouillard at Heliopolis, Egypt, February 25, 1912, under the sponsorship of the so-called Ligue Aérienne. It had been claimed that Mouillard conceived the use of wing warping and its application to lateral control, and that this concept had been communicated to the Wrights by Octave Chanute.

For discussion by A. Henry-Coüannier see *La Revue aérienne*, May 10, 1912, vol. 5, pp. 241–243; for another by Paul Hamelle, see *La Vie au grand air*, July 6, 1912, vol. 15, p. 532.

Orville Wright

Wright, Orville. Air Routes to the National Parks. In *Proceedings of the National Parks Conference, held in the Auditorium of the New National Museum, Washington, D.C., January 2, 3, 4, 5, and 6, 1917*, Washington: Government Printing Office, 1917, pp. 280–283.

Published also in *Flying*, Feb. 1917, vol. 6, no. 1, p. 64.

Address by Orville Wright, January 5, citing advantages of air travel for reaching national parks and need for additional landing facilities in or near them. Includes introductory remarks by the presiding officer, Dr. H. M. Rowe.

——— Amazing Records. *Popular Science Monthly*, June 1929, vol. 114, no. 6, p. 18.

Interview statement by Orville Wright in answer to question submitted to leading American aviation experts: "What is Ahead in Aviation?"

——— The Commercial Airplane. In *New York Aero Show Program*, [New York: 1920,] 1 p.

A résumé of the postwar developments in the use of the aeroplane for pleasure and commerce.

——— Diary of the First Flight. *Collier's*, Dec. 25, 1948, vol. 122, pp. 32–33, illus.

Published also in Kelly, Fred C., *Miracle at Kitty Hawk*, New York: Farrar, Straus and Young, 1951, pp. 114–116; with title, "At Kitty Hawk—Dec. 17, 1903," in *Air Force*, Sept. 1953, vol. 36, p. 18; in McFarland, Marvin W., ed., *The Papers of Wilbur and Orville Wright*, New York: McGraw-Hill Book Company, 1953, vol. 1, pp. 394–397; and in Dunaway, Philip, and George de Kay, *Turning Point; Fateful Moments That Revealed Men and Made History*, New York: Random House, 1958, pp. 245–249.

Entry of December 17, 1903, Orville Wright's Diary D.

——— [in part.] L'Empire des airs et son avenir. *Figaro illustré*, Feb. 1909, no. 227, p. 30, ports.

Contributed to a roundup of opinion on one of the important questions of the day. Contains facsimile signature of Orville Wright.

——— First Flight. *American Legion Monthly*, Sept. 1926, vol. 1, no. 3, pp. 14–15, illus.

Published also in *Congressional Record*, Feb. 8, 1927, vol. 68, pp. 3281–3282.

Brief account contributed by Orville to article "Winged Pioneers," which includes statements by thirteen noted aviators and aeronautical engineers.

——— [Fortieth Year Anniversary Statement.] In *Aerosphere, 1943*, New York: Aerosphere, Inc., 1944, p. CV.

Brief comment on the general use of the aeroplane.

——— Future of the Aeroplane. *Country Life*, Jan. 1909, vol. 15, pp. 252–253.

Predicts commercial future for the aeroplane.

——— The Future of Civil Flying. *Aviation*, Jan. 1, 1919, vol. 5, p. 676.

States that future development of private flying will depend upon development of aircraft capable of flying at low speeds and provision of adequate landing fields.

——— How I Learned to Fly. As told by him to Leslie W. Quirk, for the readers of Boys' Life. *Boys' Life*, Sept. 1914, vol. 4, no. 7, pp. 2–4, illus.

Reprinted *Boys' Life*, Dec. 1928, vol. 28, no. 12, pp. 10–11, 81–82: in the *Boy Scout's Book of True Adventure*, New York, London: G. P. Putnam, 1931, pp. 29–40.

Résumé of early flying experiments at Kitty Hawk, N.C., culminating in the first power flights, December 17, 1903.

——— *How We Invented the Aeroplane*. Edited and with Commentary by Fred C. Kelly. Drawings by James MacDonald. New York: David McKay, 1953, 78 pp.

Originally published (in part) under this title in *Harper's Magazine*, June 1953, vol. 206, pp. 25–33. A translation of this article appeared in *Argentina Aérea*, Dec. 1953, vol. 8, pp. 4–5, 12–13.

Edited extracts from Orville Wright's depositions, January 13, 1920, and February 2, 1921, in the suit brought by the heirs of John J. Montgomery against the Government, originally published as a part of Court of Claims case, *Regina Cleary Montgomery et al. vs. The United States, Evidence for Defendant*, Washington: Government Printing Office, 1923, pages 651–691, 694–714, 857.

——— How We Made the First Flight. *Flying*, Dec. 1913, vol. 2, pp. 10–12, 35–36.

Also in *Orville Wright Dinner of the Society of Automotive Engineers, Inc., July* [*June*] *17, 1918—Dayton, Ohio.* Dayton: Society of Automotive Engineers, 1918, pp. 14–22; *Flying*, New York, Dec. 1918, vol. 7, pp. 1020–1024; *Flying*, London, Jan. 8–15, 1919, vol. 5, pp. 24–25, 44–46; *Aircraft Year Book, 1919*, New York: Manufacturers Aircraft Association, 1919, pp. 304–309; *The Early History of the Airplane*, Dayton: The Dayton-Wright Airplane Co., 1922, pp. 9–15; *Aviation*, Dec. 17, 1923, vol. 15, pp. 737–741; reprinted with title, *Twenty-Five Years Ago*, Washington: International Civil Aeronautics Conference, 1928, 23 pp.; *Science News Letter*, Dec. 8, 1928, vol. 14, pp. 353–354; *U.S. Air Services*, Dec. 1937, vol. 22, no. 12, pp. 10–13, 28–30; *Federal Architect*, Apr./June 1941, vol. 11, no. 4, pp. 34–35; in Kelly, Fred C., *The Wright Brothers*, New York: Harcourt, Brace & Co., 1943, pp. 96–102, and same New York: Farrar, Straus and Young, 1950, pp. 96–102.

First extensive authentic account of the Kitty Hawk flights of December 17, 1903.

——— Introduction to Hayward, Charles B. *Practical Aeronautics*, Chicago: American School of Correspondence, 1912, p. xv.

Also in 2d ed., Chicago: American Technical Society, 1919.

Approves of Hayward's account [pp. 107–126] of Wrights' early work, especially the chapter on their patent litigation [pp. 505–524]. This chapter was omitted from the 2d ed.

——— Introduction to Jacobs, Anne Marguerite. *Knights of the Wing*, New York, London: The Century Co., 1928, pp. vii–viii.

——— Inventor of the Airplane Details Some of Early Experiences in Radio Message to the World. *National Aeronautic Association Review*, Jan. 1, 1924, vol. 2, no. 1, p. 3.

Published also in *Air Service News Letter*, Jan. 7, 1924, vol. 8, no. 1, pp. 2–4.

Text of speech written by Orville Wright on the twentieth anniversary of the December 17, 1903, flights and broadcast over radio station WLW, Cincinnati, December 16, 1923.

——— Inverted Aeroplane Stresses. *Aeronautics*, Apr. 1912, vol. 10, no. 4, p. 119.

Opinion as to cause of Lieut. Henry P. Seville's fatal accident, March 13, 1912.

——— Low-Speed Landing is First Need of Aviation. *Popular Science Monthly*, Feb. 1922, vol. 100, no. 2, p. 68, illus.

Contributed by Orville Wright to symposium on question: "What is the most pressing scientific achievement now required in the field of your special interest and deserving the first attention of American inventive genius during 1922?"

——— My Narrowest Escape in the Air. As told by him to Leslie W. Quirk for the readers of Boys' Life. *Boys' Life*, Aug. 1914, vol. 4, pp. 5, illus.

Account of the Ft. Myer accident, September 17, 1908.

——— The Mythical Whitehead Flight. *U.S. Air Services*, Aug. 1945, vol. 30, p. 9.

Published also in *U.S. Air Services*, Apr. 1953, vol. 38, no. 4, p. 7.

Comment on statement in *Reader's Digest*, July 1945,

page 57, in an article "The man who knows everything," by Mort Wesinger (abridged from *Liberty*, April 28, 1945), reregarding "Gustave Whitehead, the first man to fly a heavier-than-air machine, two years, four months and three days previous to the Wright flight at Kitty Hawk."

——— Our Early Flying Machine Development. *Slipstream*, Jan. 1925, vol. 6, no. 1, pp. 11–15, illus.
Published also in *Slipstream*, Sept. 1927, vol. 8, no. 9, pp. 15–16; *Wright Engine Builder*, Dec. 1928, vol. 10, no. 12, pp. 3–5.
Brief statement on the 1903 Kitty Hawk flights.

——— Our Life in Camp at Kitty Hawk. *U.S. Air Services*, Dec. 1943, vol. 28, no. 12, pp. 12–17, illus.
"Made up entirely of excerpts from letters written at Kitty Hawk by Wilbur and me to our sister Katharine . . . The story of the first flight is not included."

——— Our Recent Experiments in North Carolina. By Wright Brothers (Orville Wright). *Aeronautics*, June 1908, vol. 2, no. 6, pp. 4–6, ports.
Brief note on flights of May 6–14, 1908.

——— Possibilities of Soaring Flight. *U.S. Air Services*, Dec. 1922, vol. 7, no. 11, pp. 7–9.
Presents view that the importance of soaring flight was being exaggerated as result of the experiments in Europe in 1922, and that the powered aeroplane would remain unrivalled as a means of transportation as would the wind tunnel as a source of precise aerodynamic knowledge.

——— Le Premier vol d'un aéroplane (17 décembre, 1903), par Orville Wright. *L'Aéronautique*, Dec. 1923, vol. 5, p. 494.
Translated excerpts from "The Wright Brothers' Aeroplane" by Orville and Wilbur Wright.

——— Sporting Future of the Aeroplane. *U.S. Air Services*, Feb. 1919, vol. 1, no. 1, pp. 4–5, illus.
Emphasizes reduced landing speeds as an essential factor.

——— Stability of Aeroplanes. *Journal of the Franklin Institute*, Sept. 1914, vol. 78, pp. 249–258.
Published also in *Aeronautics*, Sept. 15, 1914, vol. 14, pp. 67–68, 78; *Scientific American Supplement*, Sept. 26, 1914, vol. 78, pp. 206–207; abstract *Aeroplane*, Oct. 9, 1914, vol. 6, pp. 1024–1026; reprinted Philadelphia: J. B. Lippincott Company, 1914; *Annual Report of the Smithsonian Institution, 1914*, Washington: Government Printing Office, 1915, pp. 209–216, and reprinted as *Smithsonian Publication 2328; Aerial Age Weekly*, July 19, 1915, vol. 1, pp. 428–429; abstract *Scientific American Supplement*, May 13, 1916, vol. 81, p. 320.
Address presented at the Franklin Institute, May 20, 1914.

——— [Statement to National Aeronautic Association, August 1928.] *Aeronautic Review*, Aug. 1928, vol. 6, no. 8, p. 114, illus.
Published also in *Dayton Motor News*, Dec. 1928, vol. 6, no. 12, p. 3.
Brief twenty-fifth anniversary statement.

——— The Story of the Wright Brothers' Early Developments. In "*Dayton-Wright*" *Airplanes, Commercial and Pleasure Air-*

craft of Distinction, Dayton: The General Motors Corporation, Dayton-Wright Division, 1920, pp. [5–10].

On Orville Wright's copy of this publication, he ruled out his name and wrote in that of F. C. Makeley as the author.

——— Sun Power Motor. *Science News Letter*, Apr. 16, 1932, vol. 21, p. 239.

Very brief statement by Orville Wright, one of eleven opinions by eminent American inventors answering the question submitted to them by Science Service: "The Next Great Invention: What Does the World Need Most?"

——— Why the 1903 Wright Airplane Is Sent to a British Museum. *U.S. Air Services*, Mar. 1928, vol. 13, pp. 30–31.

Also *U.S. Air Services*, Feb. 1948, p. 33, no. 2, pp. 14–15.

——— Wilbur Wright. [Signed O. W.] In *The Encyclopædia Britannica*, 14th ed., London, New York: 1929, vol. 23, pp. 808–809.

Continued in later editions.

——— [in part]. The Wright-Langley Controversy. *Aviation*, May 1925, vol. 18, pp. 550–551, illus.

Orville Wright and Dr. Charles D. Walcott, Secretary of the Smithsonian Institution, present both sides of the controversy.

——— Wright's First Statement Since the War. *U.S. Air Services*, Dec. 1921, vol. 6, no. 5, p. 8.

Statement submitted to the Aeronautical Chamber of Commerce on the eighteenth anniversary of the first flight. Stresses importance of the 1901 wind-tunnel experiments.

Wilbur and Orville

Wright, Wilbur, and Wright, Orville. [Letter Report to the Aero Club of America, March 2, 1906.] New York: Aero Club of America, 1906, 2 pp.

Published also in *Scientific American Supplement*, Apr. 7, 1906, vol. 61, p. 25203; *The Aeronautical News*, May, 1906, vol. 1, no. 1, p. 17; *Technical World Magazine*, June 1906, vol. 5, pp. 332–333; *Revue d'artillerie*, Oct. 1906, vol. 69, pp. XII–XV; *American Magazine of Aeronautics*, July 1907, vol. 1, no. 1, pp. 23–24; *Navigating the Air*, New York: Doubleday and Company, 1907, pp. 6–8; translation by L. Ferrus, with title, "Les expériences d'aviation des frères Wright," Paris: Berger-Levrault, 1907, 7 pp.; *Greater Dayton*, June 1909, vol. 2, no. 6, pp. 218–219; *U.S. Air Services*, Dec. 1928, vol. 13, no. 12, pp. 27–29; *Aeronautica*, Jan. 1929, vol. 3, pp. 10–11; *National Aeronautics*, Dec. 1943, vol. 21, no. 12, pp. 15, 41.

Publication of the Wrights' letter of March 2, 1906, to Augustus Post, Secretary of the recently created Aero Club of America, summarizing their 1905 experiments.

——— *Miracle at Kitty Hawk; the Letters of Wilbur and Orville Wright*, edited by Fred C. Kelly. New York: Farrar, Straus and Young, 1951, 482 pp., illus.

Also excerpts in *Atlantic Monthly*, May–July 1950, vol. 185, May, pp. 23–29, June, pp. 64–70, July, pp. 68–74.

Selections from approximately 500 letters in the Wilbur and Orville Wright Papers in the Library of Congress.

——— *The Papers of Wilbur and Orville Wright, Including the Chanute-Wright Letters and Other Papers of Octave Chanute.*

Marvin W. McFarland, Editor. New York, Toronto, London: McGraw-Hill Book Company, Inc., 1953. 2v. (1278p.), illus.

Excerpts published in *New York Times*, Oct. 11, 1953, Sec. 10, p. 3, with title "The Wright Brothers' Story—Told in Their Private Papers" and in *Life*, Dec. 7, 1953, vol. 35, pp. 162–176, in article entitled "The Day That Man First Flew; Wrights' Papers Recall Great Event 50 Years Ago," by Ernest Havemann.

Comprises selections from the Wright collection bequeathed to the Library of Congress by the Orville Wright Estate in 1949 and from the Octave Chanute papers deposited in the Library in 1932 by his daughters, Elizabeth C. and Octavia. Included are the correspondence between Wilbur and Octave Chanute (1900–1910), early leader in the aeronautics field; excerpts from 33 Wright diaries and notebooks (1900–1919) and from Wright family correspondence; wind-tunnel tables, propeller notebooks, and many other selected articles, lectures, and writings by the brothers.

Technical data are presented in four appendices (Notes on Nomenclature, Wright Wind Tunnel, 1901, the Wright Propellers, and Aeroplanes and Motors) pp. 543–640 and 1183–1217, prepared by Fred S. Howard and followed by a bibliography, pp. 1221–1243, prepared by Arthur G. Renstrom.

Reviewed by Allan F. Bonnalie in *U.S. Air Services*, Feb. 1954, vol. 39, pp. 11–12; by Roy Fedden, *Journal of the Royal Aeronautical Society*, Jan. 1955, vol. 59, pp. 72–74 (reprinted *U.S. Air Services*, July 1955, vol. 40, pp. 18–20; by Brendan Gill, *New Yorker*, Feb. 13, 1954, vol. 29, pp. 109–110, 112–113; by N. J. Hoff, *Journal of the Royal Aeronautical Society*, Jan. 1955, vol. 59, pp. 70–71 (reprinted *Science*, Apr. 15, 1955, vol. 121, pp. 523–525 and in *U.S. Air Services*, June 1955, vol. 40, pp. 21–22); by Waldemar Kaempffert, *New York Times Book Review*, Dec. 20, p. 6; by James R. Newman, *Scientific American*, May 1954, vol. 190, pp. 88–93; by Alec Ogilvie, *Journal of the Royal Aeronautical Society*, Jan. 1955, vol. 59, pp. 66–68 (reprinted *U.S. Air Services*, Apr. 1955, vol. 40, pp. 16–19; by J. Laurence Pritchard, *Aeroplane*, June 18, 1954, vol. 86, pp. 803–806; by Ernest F. Relf, *Journal of the Royal Aeronautical Society*, Jan. 1955, vol. 59, pp. 68–70 (reprinted *U.S. Air Services*, May 1955, vol. 40, pp. 19–20; by Henry Ladd Smith, *Saturday Review of Literature*, Feb. 6, 1954, vol. 37, pp. 20; in *Army Aviation Digest*, Sept. 1956, vol. 2, pp. 23–24; in *Journal of the Royal Aeronautical Society*, Dec. 1953, vol. 57, pp. 825–826.

——— The Relations of Weight, Speed and Power of Flyers. In *Navigating the Air; a Scientific Statement of the Progress of Aeronautical Science Up to the Present Time*, by the Aero Club of America. New York: Doubleday, Page & Company, 1907, pp. 6–12.

Published also in Zahm, Albert F., *Aerial Navigation*, New York and London: D. Appleton and Company, 1911, pp. 478–480.

Gives comparative data for 1903, 1904, and 1905 Wright aeroplanes. Appended are letters to the Aero Club of America from four witnesses of flights made by the Wrights at Dayton in 1905.

Orville and Wilbur

Wright, Orville, and Wright, Wilbur. A Letter from Orville and

Wilbur Wright. *Aero* [New York], Mar. 23, 1912, vol. 3, p. 499.

Also *Scientific American*, Mar. 30, 1912, vol. 106 (n.s.), p. 287; *Flight*, Apr. 6, 1912, vol. 4, p. 305.

Letter to the editor setting forth grounds for the recent German Patent Office decision nullifying main claims of the Wright German patent.

——— Our Aeroplane Tests at Kitty Hawk. *Scientific American*, June 13, 1908, vol. 98 (n.s.), p. 423.

Partial translations, with titles, "Les derniers Essais des Wright en Amérique, racontés par eux-mêmes," *L'Aérophile*, June 15, 1908, vol. 16, pp. 222–223, and "Unsere neuen Flugversuche" [signed Mck, *i.e.*, Moedebeck], *Illustrierte Aeronautische Mitteilungen*, July 1, 1908, vol. 12, pp. 349–351.

Brief note on flights carried out in May 1908.

——— The Wright Brothers' Aeroplane. *The Century Magazine*, Sept. 1908, vol. 76, pp. 641–650, illus.

Abstract in *L'Illustration*, Sept. 5, 1908, vol. 66, p. 168; *Sport im Bild*, Oct. 1908, vol. 15, pp. 274–275; *La Conquête de l'air*, Nov. 15, 1908, vol. 5, p. 2; translation of selected excerpts with title, "Les Travaux des Wright exposés par euxmêmes," *L'Aérophile*, Nov. 1, 1908, vol. 16, pp. 426–428; translation in *Revue d'artillerie*, Jan. 1909, vol. 73, pp. 201–226; translation by L. Ferrus with title, "Notre Vie," *Je Sais Tout*, Jan. 15, 1909, vol. 4, pp. 713–724; translation in Peyrey, François, *Les Oiseaux artificiels*, Paris: H. Dunod et E. Pinat, 1909, pp. 636–655; translation with title, "Die Erfindung des Fliegens" in Adams, Heinrich, *Flug*, Leipzig; C. F. Amelang, 1909, pp. 30–44; slightly abridged Russian translation in Veigelin, K. E., *Zavoevanie vozdushnogo okeana*, S.-Peterburg: Knigoizd-vo P. P. Soikina, 1917, pp. 129–136; *Aeronautical Journal*, July/Sept. 1916, vol. 20, pp. 100–106; in *Orville Wright Dinner of the Society of Automotive Engineers, Inc., July [June] 17, 1918—Dayton, Ohio*, Dayton: Society of Automotive Engineers, 1918, pp. 1–13; in *The Early History of the Airplane*, Dayton: The Dayton-Wright Airplane Co. [1922], pp. 1–8; *Aviation*, Dec. 17, 1923, vol. 15, pp. 732–737; *U.S. Air Services*, Dec. 1923, vol. 8, no. 12, pp. 26–32; translation with brief introductory statement and tribute by the author in Ångström, Tord, *Bröderna Wright och Flygproblemets Lösning*, Stockholm: Nordisk Rotogravyr, 1928, pp. 7–20; *Aeronautics*, Jan. 1909, vol. 3, pp. 4–9.

First popular presentation by the Wrights of their aeronautical achievements. Though it appears under joint authorship, the article was entirely the work of Orville Wright.

——— Wright Flyer. A Report of Late Tests Is Given by Messrs. Wright, Inventors of the Machine. *Dayton Press*, Jan. 6, 1904.

Published also with title, "La Machine volante des frères Wright," *L'Aérophile*, Jan. 1904, vol. 12, pp. 16–18; *The Aeronautical Journal*, Apr. 1904, vol. 8, pp. 41–42; and in Freudenthal, Elsbeth, *Flight into History*, Norman, Okla.: University of Oklahoma Press, 1949, pp. 86–88.

Statement prepared for the Associated Press by the Wrights to correct printed information about their December 17, 1903 flights. This appeared in many of the Associated Press newspapers on January 6.

269-517—68——2

Interviews, Speeches, Statements

The Aeroplane. What Will it be Like in Five Years Time. Opinions of Prominent Aeroists. What Wilbur Wright Thinks. *Motor*, London, Nov. 17, 1908, vol. 14, pp. 457–458.

Predicts future of the aeroplane lies in use for military purposes.

Rouhier, Maurice. Wright professeur. *La Vie au grand air*, Feb. 27, 1909, pp. 134–136, illus.

Abridged in *La Conquête de L'Air*, Apr. 15, 1909, vol. 6, no. 8, p. 1.

Interview with Wilbur Wright on his training and instruction methods.

A Talk with Wilbur Wright. *Scientific American*, Oct. 23, 1909, vol. 101, p. 290.

Wilbur Wright states that future development of aviation will be in high altitude flying because of the more favorable atmospheric conditions provided by upper air strata.

Ohio in Aviation. Twenty-Fourth Annual Banquet of the Ohio Society of New York . . . January 10, 1910. In Ohio Society of New York, *Reports of Proceedings, 1910*, New York: 1910, pp. 93–138.

Includes brief remarks by Wilbur Wright on occasion of dinner given in Wrights' honor.

Wright's Statement Concerning Johnstone's Fatal Fall. *Mobile Era*, Dec. 1910, vol. 1, p. 16.

Wilbur Wright's statement as to probable cause of accident which killed Ralph Johnstone in Denver, November 17, 1910.

Remarks by Wilbur Wright on Presentation of Langley Medals to Wright Brothers. In *Annual Report of the Smithsonian Institution, 1910*, Washington: Government Printing Office, 1911, pp. 109–110.

In Honor of the Army and Aviation. Addresses of the Evening. *National Geographic Magazine*, Mar. 1911, vol. 32, pp. 279–281, illus.

Includes brief address by Wilbur Wright at the sixth annual banquet of the National Geographic Society, Washington, January 14, 1911, honoring the United States Army and the invention of the aeroplane by the Wright brothers.

Wright Considers High Speed too Dangerous. *Fly Magazine*, Aug. 1911, vol. 3, no. 11, p. 9.

Wilbur Wright's communication to Paris edition of an American newspaper explaining failure of Wright Company to enter a machine in the Gordon-Bennett race.

Wilbur Wright Favors Reliability Tests. *Aero*, St. Louis, Mar. 30, 1912, vol. 3, p. 514.

Statement made in Baltimore, March 24, that he favors cross-country reliability flight in preference to speed contest.

Wright Co. not Building Racer. *Aero and Hydro*, July 27, 1912, vol. 4, p. 374.

Includes Orville Wright's statement that company is building only regulation machines.

Orville Wright Talks on Automatic Stability. *Aircraft*, Nov. 1912, vol. 3, p. 275.

States that he has no faith in principle of the Sperry gyroscope.

Tenth Aniversary of Flight. *Aeronautics*, New York, Dec. 1913, vol. 13, pp. 208–209, 220, illus.

Includes brief statement by Orville Wright acknowledging honor done him at anniversary dinner given December 18 by the Aeronautical Society.

Wright Finds Ocean Crossing Risky Now. *Aero and Hydro*, Feb. 21, 1914, vol. 7, p. 261.

Reproduces Orville Wright's letter of February 13, 1914 to the editor.

Orville Wright Says his Health Would not Permit Him to Accept Commission to Rebuild British Air Fleet. *Aerial Age Weekly*, July 5, 1915, vol. 1, p. 367.

Kelly, Fred C. Flying Machines and the War; an Interview with Orville Wright. *Collier's*, July 31, 1915, vol. 55, pp. 24–25.

Published also in Simonds, Frank A., *History of the World War*, New York: Doubleday, Page & Co., 1917, vol. 1, p. 376.

Orville states that the aeroplane will prevent war by making its cost prohibitive.

The Annual Air Derby. *Aerial Age Weekly*, May 29, 1916, vol. 3, p. 334.

Includes brief comment by Orville Wright on proposed transcontinental air race for the Ralph Pulitzer trophy.

Dinner Given for Orville Wright. *Aerial Age Weekly*, Feb. 19, 1917, vol. 4, p. 652.

Dinner given at Delmonico's in New York by Grover Loening. Includes brief excerpts from Orville's speech on hardships and discouragements he and his brother experienced in their early experiments.

Hendrick, Burton J. The Safe and Useful Aeroplane. An Interview with Orville Wright. *Harper's Magazine*, Apr. 1917, vol. 134, pp. 609–619. illus.

Published also in *Aviation*, Apr. 1, 1917, vol. 2, pp. 224–226.

Extensive interview in which Orville Wright stresses peacetime uses of the aeroplane.

[Findley, Earl N.] Orville Wright Says 10,000 Aeroplanes Would Win the War Within Ten Weeks. *New York Times Magazine Section*, July 1, 1917, pp. 1–2.

Orville Wright's comments on the Aircraft Production Board and the government's proposed aircraft manufacturing program.

Brief Statement on Aircraft and War on Occasion of the Awarding of a Doctor of Science Degree by the University of Cincinnati. *Aerial Age Weekly*, July 2, 1917, vol. 5, p. 521.

Says Aircraft Will Win War. *Aerial Age Weekly*, July 9, 1917, vol. 5, p. 563.

Brief quotation from interview with Orville Wright.

The Work of Orville Wright. *Aerial Age Weekly*, Oct. 15, 1917, vol. 6, p. 195.

Includes Orville's statement on airplane as an instrument of peace.

Wright to Make Aeros for Commercial Use. *Aerial Age Weekly*, Oct. 29, 1917, vol. 6.

Includes quotations from interview with Orville Wright.

Orville Wright Calls Armored Plate Useless. *Aerial Age Weekly*, June 3, 1918, vol. 7, p. 579.

Orville's reported comment on occasion of death of Raoul Lufbery in a "flying tank."

Testimony of Orville Wright, October 3, 1918. In United States Department of Justice, Hughes Aircraft Investigation, *Testimony of Witnesses*, May to October 1918, vol. 22, pp. 175–193 (Typescript).

Interrogation by Charles Evans Hughes.

Orville Wright Disparages the Glider. *Literary Digest*, Jan. 6, 1923, vol. 76, pp. 59–60.

Crane, Carl J. Orville Wright; an Interview, *University of Dayton Opponent*, Apr. 1924, vol. 22, no. 4, pp. 7–9.

Orville Wright Forecasts Aircraft Expansion. *U.S. Air Services*, Nov. 1925, vol. 10, no. 11, pp. 20–22, illus.

Testimony before the President's Aircraft Board, October 12, 1925.

Statement of Mr. Orville Wright, Dayton, Ohio. In President's Aircraft Board, *Hearings, September 21–October 15, 1925*, Washington: United States Government Printing Office, 1925, vol. 3, pp. 1096–1100.

Kelly, Fred C. What's Going on Here? An Answer to Our Traveling Reporter. *Today*, Mar. 31, 1934, vol. 1, no. 23, pp. 8, 22, port.

Kelly's report on his interview with Orville Wright in Dayton.

Farber, James. Orville Wright Interviewed. *Popular Aviation*, Apr. 1934, vol. 14, no. 4, pp. 223–224, 261, illus.

Similar interview published in the *New York Times*, December 17, 1933, with title "Kitty Hawk Memories, Orville Wright Chats on the Brief History of Aviation."

Orville Wright Foresees Great Progress in Next Decade. *U.S. Air Services*, Jan. 1938, vol, 23, no. 1, p. 15.

Quotes from interview with Orville Wright, December 17 at Columbia University, reported in *New York Times.*

Orville Wright Favors All Aid to Britain. *U.S. Air Services*, May 1941, vol. 26, no. 5, p. 9.

Orville Wright's statement to the editor on a visit to Washington, April 24–25, 1941.

Orville Wright Takes a Look Back. Extension of Remarks of Hon. Herbert C. Bonner. *Congressional Record*, Nov. 10, 1943, vol. 89, appendix pp. A4774–A4775.

Interview at Dayton, November 6, by Fred C. Kelly, reprinted from St. Louis *Post-Dispatch*, Sunday, November 7, 1943, giving Orville Wright's views on the military aeroplane, and its use in World War II as contrasted with the Wrights' early conception of its use.

McSurely, Alexander. Wright Favors Free Competition on Postwar Foreign Air Routes. *Aviation News*, Dec. 11, 1943, vol. 1, no. 20, pp. 10–11.

An interview with Orville at his laboratory in Dayton.

Case, Leland D. Orville Wright—First Man to Fly. *Rotarian*, Apr. 1948, vol. 72, no. 4, pp. 8–10, 50–53, illus.

Press interview with the editor several weeks before Orville's death.

Biographical References—Wright Brothers

Books

Ångström, Tord. *Bröderna Wright och flygproblemets lösning. Minneskrift å den första motor-drivna flygningens 25-årsdag den 17 dec. 1928.* Stockholm: Nordisk Rotogravyr, 1928, 22 pp., illus.

A Swedish translation of the Wrights' *Century Magazine* article "The Wright Brothers Aeroplane" with a brief introductory statement and tribute by the author on the occasion of the 25th anniversary of the December 17, 1903, flights.

Abramowski, Wacław. Wilbur i Orwille Wright'owie [and] Latawiec braci Wright'ów. In his *Lotnictwo współczesne. Latawce (aeroplany)*, Warszawa: Drukarnia Artystyczna, 1910, pp. 32–39, 97–104.

Adams, Heinrich. *Flug . . .* Leipzig: C. F. Amelangs Verlag, 1909, 144 pp., illus.

Short history of aviation devoted largely to the Wright brothers with a detailed account of their 1908 and 1909 flights and including a German translation entitled "Unser Flieger. Die Erfindung des Fliegens" of their article originally published in the September 1908 issue of the *Century Magazine*, pp. 30–44.

L'Aéroplane des frères Wright. Historique - expériences - description. Avec une planche de dessins originaux. Paris: Berger-Levrault & Cie., 1908, 30 pp., illus.

Compilation based on three articles originally appearing in *Revue d'artillerie.* These comprise L. Ferrus' translations of the Wright letter of March 2, 1906, to the Aero Club of America, and the Signal Corps advertisement and specifications for a heavier-than-air flying machine, December 23, 1907, and Captain Lucas-Girardville's summary of the Wright French patents.

Albertson, Catherine. *Wings Over Kill Devil and Legends of the Dunes.* Elizabeth City, N.C. [1928], 37 pp., illus.

Privately printed in an edition of 25 copies.

Includes William J. Tate's account of his association with the Wright brothers at Kill Devil Hills in North Carolina.

Arrudão, Matias. *A questão Wright - Santos - Dumont.* Contribução ao Congresso Nacional de Aeronautica patrocinado pelo Aero Clube do Brasil. São Simão: Casa Minerva, 1946, 6 pp.

——— Os Wright. In his *Pequena história da aviacão*, São Paulo: Livraria Martins editora s.a. [1948], pp. 140–147.

Claims Santos-Dumont and not Wrights deserves honor of having first achieved powered flight.

Berget, Alphonse. L'Aéroplane des frères Wright. In his *La Route de L'Air*, Paris: Librairie Hachette et Cie, 1909, pp. 198–208.

Published also in translation in English edition entitled *The Conquest of the Air*, London: William Heinemann, New York: G. P. Putman, 1909, pp. 192–201, and in 1911 French edition, pp. 151–157.

Beringer, Sarah M. *The Beginning and Future of Aviation.* [Dayton, O., 1929], 59 pp. illus.

Account of Dayton's role in the development of the aircraft

industry emphasizing activities of the Wright brothers.

Besançon, Georges. L'École américaine. Les frères Wright. In his *Ballons et aéroplanes*, Paris: Garnier Frères, 1910, pp. 289–320, illus.

Bia, Georges. *Les frères Wright et leur oeuvre.* Rapport présenté à la Section Aéronautique de la Société Belge des Ingénieurs et des Industriels. Illustré par Fox. [Saint-Mihiel]: Imprimeries du journal *La Meuse* [1909], 56 pp., illus.

Published also in later edition, Paris: F. L. Vivien, 1910.

Account of the Wright brothers and their aeroplane by their Belgian representative. Based on French sources with section devoted to Wilbur Wright's flights in France and to the flights of his pupils Count de Lambert and Paul Tissandier. Includes an extensive account, entitled "Les négociations commerciales," of their negotiations for the sale of their aeroplane.

Black, Archibald. Mechanical Flight at Last! In his *The Story of Flying*, New York: Whittlesey House, 1940, pp. 53–72, illus.

Included also in revised edition, 1943.

Blériot, Louis, and Raymond Édouard. Les premiers hommes-oiseaux. Orville et Wilbur Wright. In their *La gloire des ailes; l'aviation de Clément Ader à Costes*, Paris: Les Éditions de France, 1928, pp. 37–52.

Bracke, Albert. *L'Aéroplane Wilbur Wright.* Mons: Dequesne-Masquillier & Fils, 1908, 16 pp., illus. (His [Monographies d'aviation] 1).

——— *Construction et manoeuvres de l'aéroplane Wright.* Paris: F. L. Vivien, 1909, 16 pp., illus. (His Monographies d'aviation. 5).

Brigole, Alexandre. Duas palavras aos Estados Unidos. In his *Santos-Dumont, o pioneiro do ar*, Rio de Janeiro: Aero Clube do Brasil, 1941, pp. 79–84, illus.

Published also in English edition 1943, pages 90–94.

Ascribes priority in flight to Santos-Dumont. Based on an article by Dr. Claudio Ganns in *Espelho*, October 1936.

Brown, Arch B. *Historic Sands of Eastern Carolina.* n. p., 1937, 40 pp.

Includes chapter on Wright brothers: pages 29–39.

Brown, Cecil L. M. Wilbur and Orville Wright. In his *The Conquest of the Air: an Historical Survey*, London: Oxford University Press, 1927, pp. 87–104, illus.

Carmer, Carl L., ed. From Flying Kites to Flying Machines (Wilbur and Orville Wright). In his *Cavalcade of America, the Deeds and Achievements of the Men and Women Who Made Our Country Great*, New York: Crown Publishers, 1956, pp. 236–239.

Chandler, Charles D., and Lahm, Frank P. *How Our Army Grew Wings, Airmen and Aircraft Before 1914.* New York: The Ronald Press Company, 1943, 333 pp., illus.

Includes two chapters devoted to the Wrights, "The Birth of Aviation" which recounts their early flying experiments and "The First Army Airplane" which is an account of their negotiations for the sale of their aeroplane to the Army and of their Fort Myer trials, 1908–1909.

Chanute, Octave. Fortschritte und neuere Erfahrungen im Kunstflug. In Moedebeck, Hermann W. L., *Taschenbuch zum praktischen Gebrauch für Flugtechniker und Luftschiffer*, Berlin: W. H. Kühl, 1904, pp. 322–340, illus.

English translation by W. Mansergh Varley, London: Whittaker & Co., 1907, pp. 301–307.

Includes section devoted to the Wrights: "5. Wright," pages 330–334.

Charnley, Mitchell V. Orville Wright and Wilbur Wright [Signed M. V. C.] In *The World Book Encyclopedia*, Chicago: Field Enterprises, Inc., 1952, vol. 18, p. 8932.

Clark, Ronald W. The Wright Brothers. In his *The Air*, London: Max Parrish [1966], pp. 55–83, illus.

A popular account of the early experiments of the Wrights.

Cobianchi, Mario. I voli di Wilbur Wright a Roma. In his *Pionieri dell' aviazione in Italia*, Rome: Editoriale Aeronautica, 1942, pp. 16–18.

Account of Wilbur Wright's flights at Centocelle, near Rome. in April 1909.

Conover, Charlotte R. The Birth of an Aeronautical Industry. In her *Dayton and Montgomery County, Resources and People*. New York: Lewis Historical Publishing Co., 1932, vol. 2, pp. 487–489.

Includes brief mention of early Wright activities in Dayton.

——— The Home of Aviation, 1896–1915. In her *The Story of Dayton*, Dayton, Ohio: The Otterbein Press, 1917, pp. 183–195, illus.

Discusses roles of Wrights in history of Dayton.

Coppens de Houthulst, Willy. Les Frères Wright. In his *L'Homme a Conquis le Ciel*, Paris: Hachette [1937], pp. 81–104.

An account of the Wright brothers' activities, 1899–1905.

Cottler, Joseph, and Jaffe, Haym. The Wright Brothers. In their *Heroes of Civilization*, Boston: Little, Brown, 1931, pp. 239–248.

Cox, James. The Wright Brothers. In his *Journey Through My Years*, New York: Simon and Schuster, 1946, pp. 81–84.

Reminiscences by long-standing friend of Orville Wright, a former governor of Ohio and owner of the Dayton *Daily News*.

Crowder, B. M. Wilbur and Orville Wright [signed B. M. C.] In *Chambers's Encyclopaedia*, New York: Oxford University Press, 1950, vol. 14, p. 758.

Derieux, Mary, ed. Orville and Wilbur Wright. In her *One Hundred Great Lives*, edited by John Allen [pseud.], New York: Greystone Press, 1948, pp. 674–680.

Dollfus, Charles, and Bouché, Henri. *Histoire de L'Aéronautique*. Paris: L'Illustration, 1942. 617 p., illus.

Includes sections dealing with the Wrights entitled "Le Premier Vol Humain," pp. 169–176; "Wilbur Wright en France," pp. 196–197, and "Les Premières Victimes de L'Aviation," p. 198.

Dollfus, Charles. Wilbur et Orville Wright, 1867–1912, 1871–1948. In *Les inventeurs célèbres*, Paris: Lucien Mazenod, 1951, pp. 246–248, illus.

Published also in a German translation by same publisher, with title, "Die Berühmte Erfinder," 1951, pp. 248–250, illus.

Donovan, Frank. *The Early Eagles.* New York: Dodd, Mead & Company, 1962, 312 p.

Chapter three, pp. 49–69, entitled "The First Winged Eagles," is a popular treatment of the Wright brothers.

Drury, Augustus W. Wilbur and Orville Wright. In his *History of the City of Dayton and Montgomery County, Ohio*, Chicago-Dayton: S. J. Clarke Publishing Co., 1909, vol. 2, pp. 871–876.

Egbert, Howard. *The Shop That Became a Shrine. A Recital of the Real Story of the First Flight in an Aeroplane by Wilbur and Orville Wright of Dayton, Ohio.* Dayton: The Dayton Chamber of Commerce, 1928, 8 pp.

Issued on the occasion of the twenty-fifth anniversary of the first successful flight.

Ferber, Ferdinand. *L'Aviation; ses débuts—son développement.* Paris: Berger-Levrault & Cie, 1908, 250 pp., illus.

Includes two chapters devoted to the Wright brothers, "Orville et Wilbur Wright," pages 49–55 and "Wright de 1903 à 1907 ou le soi-disant mystère des Wrights," pages 82–95. A German translation of these chapters was published in *Die Kunst zu Fliegen; ihre Anfänge—ihre Entwicklung*, Berlin: Richard Carl Schmidt & Co., 1910, pages 71–77, 105–117.

Fess, Simeon D. The Wright Brothers. In his *Ohio; a Four-Volume Reference Library on the History of a Great State*, Chicago and New York: The Lewis Publishing Co., 1937, vol. 4, pp. 396–399, ports.

Foltmann, John. Flygplanet blir verklighet. In his *Flykt över jorden*, Stockholm: Kooperativa Förbundets bokforlag, 1945, pp. 14–22, illus.

Fraser, Chelsea. The Wright Brothers. In his *Famous American Flyers*, New York: Thomas Y. Crowell Company, 1941, pp. 1–45.

Published also in 1942 edition.

——— The Wrights Enter the Field [and] The Wrights Invent the Airplane. In his *The Story of Aircraft*, New York: Thomas Y. Crowell Company, 1933, pp. 293–326, illus.

Freudenthal, Elsbeth E. *Flight into History; the Wright Brothers and the Air Age.* Norman, Okla.: University of Oklahoma Press, 1949, 281 pp., illus.

Pages 82–90 of chapter VI entitled "December 17, 1903—Climax and Beginning" reprinted with title "Flight Into History" in *Science Milestones*, New York: Windsor Press, 1954, pp. 270–275.

Biography emphasizing the business affairs of the Wrights and their relationship with Octave Chanute, with frequent quotation from the extensive Wright-Chanute correspondence, but minimizing and distorting their real contribution to the development of the aeroplane. Includes numerous footnotes and a bibliography, pages 253–261.

Galbreath, Charles B. The Wright Brothers. In his *History of Ohio*, Chicago and New York: The American Historical Society, Inc., 1925, vol. 2, pp. 792–796.

Garber, Paul E. The Wright Brothers. In his *The National Aeronautical Collections.* 9th ed.

Washington: The Smithsonian Institution, 1956, pp. 32–40, illus. (Smithsonian Institution. Publication 4255)

Included also in 10th ed., 1965.

Concise account of the Wright brothers by the Senior Curator and Historian, National Air and Space Museum.

Garcia de Souza, José. *A famosa controvérsia: irmãos Wright, Santos-Dumont*. Rio de Janeiro: Emprêsa Gráfica Ouvidor, 1948, 32 pp.

Presentation of evidence supporting Santos-Dumont and that supporting the Wrights in their claims to the honor of first achieving powered flight.

Gastambide, Robert. La joute France-Amérique. In his *L'Envol*, Paris: Librairie Gallimard, 1932, pp. 117–154.

Discussion of rivalry which prevailed in 1908 between the French flyers and the Wrights.

Gibbs-Smith, Charles H. *The Aeroplane; an Historical Survey of Its Origins and Development*. London: H. M. Stationery Off., 1960, 375 p., illus.

The Wright brothers and their contributions to aviation are discussed extensively in chapters entitled "The Wright Brothers and the Invention of the Practical Aeroplane: 1900–1905," pp. 35–44; "The Beginnings of Practical Aviation in Europe: 1900–1908," pp. 62–64; and in commentary on "Wright Brothers," pp. 224–234.

——— *The Invention of the Aeroplane (1799–1909)*. New York: Taplinger Publishing Co., Inc., 1966, 360 p., illus.

Originally published in Great Britain (London: Faber, 1966).

A comprehensive, well documented, and excellently illustrated technological history by an aeronautical historian associated for many years with the Victoria and Albert Museum, London, emphasizing the role of the Wright brothers in the development of the aeroplane. The experiments, achievements, flights, gliders, and aeroplanes of the Wrights are extensively covered in many chapters and sections, particularly sections 9–11, 13–14, 17–18, 22–23, 42–45, and 57. Eight appendices include data on Wright aeroplanes, engines, control systems, flights, and the Wrights' influence on the revival of European aviation, 1901–1903. Includes bibliography, pp. 353–355.

——— The Wright Brothers. In his *A History of Flying*, New York: Frederick A. Praeger, 1954, pp. 223–245. (Books That Matter).

Originally published in Great Britain (London: Batsford, 1953).

Chapter XI of this book entitled "The Invention of the Aeroplane" deals with the early Wright experiments and the technical development of their aeroplane, 1900–1908.

——— *The Wright Brothers: a Brief Account of Their Work, 1899–1911*. London: H. M. Stationery Off., 1963, 30p., illus.

Substance of a lecture delivered before the Royal Institution of Great Britain, May 3, 1963. Pages 1–13 originally published with title "Wright Brothers and Their Invention of the Practical Aeroplane" in *Nature*, June 1, 1963, vol. 198, pp. 824–826.

Concise and authentic survey of the Wright brothers' achievements, their early gliding experiments, 1900–1902, their aeroplanes and powered flights, 1903–1905, their patent and flight control systems, their flights in France and the U.S. in

1908–1909; Wright aeroplane modifications, 1909–1911, and their influence on aviation abroad during the period 1902–1909.

Goldstrom, John. The Wright Brothers. In his *A Narrative History of Aviation*, New York: MacMillan, 1930, pp. 24–45.

Goulder, Grace. Katharine Wright. In her *Ohio Scenes and Citizens*, Cleveland and New York: World Book Publishing Company, 1964, pp. 117–123.

Deals extensively with Katharine's brothers, Orville and Wilbur.

Grahame-White, Claude. Wright Brothers. In his *Heroes of the Air*, London: H. Frowde, Hodder and Stoughton, 1912, pp. 57–93.

Harrison, Michael. *Airborne at Kitty Hawk; the Story of the First Heavier-Than-Air Flight Made by the Wright Brothers, December 17, 1903.* With a Foreword by the Marquess of Donegall. London: Cassell and Company, Ltd., 1953, 118p.

Essentially a popular history of aeronautics with less than half, pp. 1–12, 86–114, devoted to the Wright brothers.

Hathaway, Esse V. The Wright Brothers. In her *Partners in Progress*, New York and London: McGraw-Hill Book Company, 1935, pp. 163–183, illus.

Hegener, Henri. *Overwinning op vleugels; Wilbur en Orville Wright leerden ons vliegen.* Haarlem; N. V. Drukkerij De Spaarnestad [1953], 160 p., illus.

Reviewed in *Avia Vliegwereld*, Dec. 10, 1953, vol. 2, p. 647 and by Marvin W. McFarland in *U.S. Air Services*, Nov. 1954, vol. 39, p. 17.

A popular general account of the Wright brothers. Includes tables of (1) Wrights' flights at Kitty Hawk, N.C., 1903–1905, p. 149; (2) Wrights' flights at Kitty Hawk, May 6–14, 1908, p. 150; and (3) Orville's flights at Fort Myer, Va., Sept. 3–17, 1908, p. 150.

Heinmuller, John P. V. Prologue. In his *Man's Fight to Fly*, New York and London: Funk & Wagnalls, 1944, pp. 1–6.

Account of Wright 1903 flights and their significance.

Hildebrandt, Alfred. *Die Brüder Wright; eine Studie über die Entwicklung der Flugmaschine von Lilienthal bis Wright* . . . Mit 44 Abildungen. Berlin: Otto Elsner Verlagsgesellschaft m. b. H., 1909, 64 pp., illus.

Based largely on materials on the Wrights sent the author by Octave Chanute and on an interview and materials obtained from Bishop Milton Wright on a visit to Dayton. Hildebrandt was the first European to do full justice to the achievements of the Wrights.

Hodgins, Eric, and Magoun, F. Alexander. The Immortal Wrights. In their *Sky High; the Story of Aviation.* Rev. ed., Boston: Little, Brown, and Company, 1935, pp. 178–191, illus.

Popular account of the Wrights through the year 1908.

Holland, Rupert S. The Wrights and the Airship. In his *Historic Inventions*, Philadelphia: George W. Jacobs & Company, 1911, pp. 273–295, illus.

Holst, Helge. Brødrene Wright og deres amerikanske Forgaengere. In his *Opfindernes Liv.* Vol. 1, Copenhagen: Gyldendal, 1914, pp. 262–297.

——— Flyveproblemets Løsning ved Brødrene Wright. In his *Luftens Erobring*, Copenhagen: Gyldendalske Boghandel, 1909, pp. 78–92, illus.

Hylander, Clarence J. Wilbur Wright and Orville Wright. In his *American Inventors*, New York: Macmillan, 1934, pp. 204–205.

Johnston, S. Paul. *Horizons Unlimited; a Graphic History of Aviation*. New York: Duell, Sloan and Pearce, 1941, 354 pp., illus.

Includes sections devoted to the Wright brothers in his chapters on "Gliders and Sailplanes," pages 190–194 and on "Airplanes," pages 230–248.

Jordanoff, Assen. Enter the Flying Machine . . . the Wrights Go Aeroplaning! (1902–1909). In his *Men and Wings*, Buffalo: Curtis-Wright Corporation, Airplane Division, 1942, pp. 23–29, illus.

Karlson, Paul. Die Brüder Wright. In his *Der Mensch Fliegt; Geschichte und Technik des Fliegens*, Berlin: Im Verlag Ullstein, 1937, pp. 109–140, illus.

Appears also in translation in Spanish, Portuguese, Swedish, and Italian editions.

Kelly, Fred C. *The Wright Brothers. A Biography Authorized by Orville Wright*. New York: Harcourt, Brace & Co., 1943, 340 pp., illus.

Published also in other editions, London: George G. Harrap and Co., Ltd., 1944, 276 pp.; New York: Farrar, Straus, and Young, Inc., 1951, 340 pp.; with introduction by Richard Tyre, New York: Ballantine Books, 1966, 224 pp.; Spanish translation by Mario dos Santos, with title *Los Hermanos Wright*, Buenos Aires: Plaza & Janes, 1964, 269 pp. and in German translation with title *Die Gebrüder Wright, die Erfinder des Motorfluges*, Stuttgart: I. Gnamm, 1947, 214 p., which does not include chapter XIX, "Why the Wright Plane Was Exiled," pages 300–333 in the English edition.

Popular non-technical biography based on original research in the Wright Papers and authenticated in manuscript by Orville Wright.

——— The Wright Brothers. In Dunaway, Philip and George de Kay, eds. *Turning Point; Fateful Moments That Revealed Men and Made History*, New York: Random House, 1958, pp. 245–249.

Klemin, Alexander. The Wright Brothers. In Lord, John, *Beacon Lights of History*, edited by George Spencer Hulbert, New York: Wm. H. Wise & Co., 1924, vol. 8, pp. 281–324.

Frequently cited by Orville as one of the best accounts of the Wright brothers to this date.

Larsen, Egon. Wilbur and Orville Wright. In his *Men Who Changed the World; Stories of Invention and Discovery*, London: Phoenix House, 1952, pp. 121–143.

Law, Frederick Houk. Wilbur and Orville Wright. In his *Civilization Builders*, New York: D. Appleton-Century, 1939, pp. 67–73.

——— Wilbur and Orville Wright: Inventors of the Aeroplane. In his *Modern Great Americans*, New York: Century, 1926, pp. 275–286.

Lelasseux, Louis, and Marque, René. L'Aéroplane Wright. In their *L'Aéroplane pour tous*. Paris: Société d'Éditions Aéronautiques, 1909, pp. 69–79, illus.

Included also in later editions.

Loening, Grover. *Our Wings Grow Faster.* Garden City, N. Y.: Doubleday, Doran & Co., 1935, 203 pp.

Includes account of Loening's association with the Wright Company, 1913–1914, pages 30–48.

McFee, Inez M. [The Wright Brothers]. In her *Stories of American Inventions*, New York: Crowell, 1921, pp. 236–251.

McMahon, John R. *The Wright Brothers, Fathers of Flight.* Boston: Little, Brown, and Company, 1930, 308 pp., illus.

Originally published with title, "The Real Fathers of Flight," as series of articles in *Popular Science Monthly*, Jan. 1929, vol. 114, no. 1, pp. 17–19, 142–144, Feb., no. 2, pp. 42–44, 152–158, Mar., no. 3, pp. 42–44, 142–147, Apr., no. 4, pp. 42–44, 156, 160, May, no. 5, pp. 48–58, 136–139, June, no. 6, pp. 52–53, 154; also published serially in *Dayton Sunday News*, Nov. 2–23, 1930, Jan. 4, 1931; also in another trade edition, New York: Grosset & Dunlap, 1930.

Romanticized biography in which interviews with the Wright family and accounts of the Wrights are presented in a highly dramatic and inaccurate form.

McSpadden, J. Walker. The Mechanics Who Taught Us How To Fly: Wilbur and Orville Wright. In his *How They Blazed the Way; Men Who Have Advanced Civilization*, New York: Dodd, Mead & Company, 1939, pp. 265–279.

Maitland, Lester J. *Knights of the Air.* Garden City, N.Y.: Doubleday, Doran & Company, Inc., 1929, 338 pp., illus.

Includes five chapters dealing with the Wrights, pages 10–24, 37–83, which were first published in *World's Work*, Aug.–Sept. 1927, vol. 56, pp. 374–387, 512–527.

Marchis, Lucien. Les vols de Wilbur Wright en France. In his *Vingt cinq ans d'aéronautique français*, Paris: Chambre Syndicale des Industries Aéronautiques, 1934, vol. 1, pp. 54–58, illus.

Marcosson, Isaac F. *Colonel Deeds, Industrial Builder.* New York: Dodd, Mead & Company, 1947, 374 pp.

Includes references to Deed's relationship and friendship with the Wrights.

Marquis, Raoul. *Les aéroplanes: historique, calcul et construction*, par H. de Graffigny [pseud.], 2. éd., Paris: Librairie Bernard Tignol, 1909, 140 pp.

Includes two chapters on the Wright brothers, "Historique de l'aviation: Aéroplanes Wright": pp. 22–24; "Construction des aéroplanes: Aéroplanes Chanute-Wright": pp. 60–69, illus.

Martin, Rudolf. *Wright und Zeppelin.* Berlin: Verlag von Mickisch, Segler & Co. [1909], 23 pp.

Author discusses the military significance for Germany of the development of the airship by Zeppelin and of the aeroplane by the Wrights.

Masters, David. Man's First Flight: the Wright Brothers. In his *On the Wing; the Pioneers of the Flying Age*, London: Eyre and Spottiswoode, 1934, pp. 3–22.

Meyer, Willy. Die Gebrüder Wright. In his *Von Wright bis Junkers; Das erste Vierteljahrhundert Menschenflug, 1903–1928*, Berlin: Deutsche Verlagsgesellschaft für Pölitik und Geschichte, M. B. H., 1928, pp. 5–11.

Meynell, Laurence W. *First Men to Fly*. London: W. Laurie, 1955, 158 p., illus.

A popular account of the Wright brothers.

Miller, Trevelyan. Birth of a New Age—Wrights in the Air. In his *The World in the Air*, New York: G. P. Putnam's Sons, 1930, vol. 2, pp. 96–107, illus.

Popular pictorial account.

Morris, Lloyd, and Smith, Kendall. *Ceiling Unlimited; the Story of American Aviation from Kitty Hawk to Supersonics*. New York: The Macmillan Company, 1953. 417 p., illus.

Part 1, "Dawn of the Aerial Age," pp. 1–59, is almost entirely devoted to the Wright brothers. Part 2, "Men Try Their Wings," pp. 61–126, also deals extensively with the Wrights.

Mortane, Jacques. Les frères Wilbur et Orville Wright. In his *La Vie des hommes illustres de l'aviation*, Paris: Éditions Roche d'Estrez, 1926, pp. 55–71.

Mowbray, Jay H. Early Experiments of the Wright Brothers. In his *Conquest of the Air by Airship and Other Flying Machines* . . . Philadelphia: National Publishing Co., 1910, pp. 156–175.

Naĭdenov, Vasiliĭ F. *Aėroplan brat'ev Raĭt. S 15 risunkami v tekstie.* [The Wright Brothers Aeroplane. With 15 Illustrations in the Text.] S.-Peterburg: Tip. V. A. Tikhanova, 1908, 46 pp., illus.

Originally published in *Vozdukhoplavatel'*, Sept.–Oct. 1908, vol. 3, pp. 349–390.

Popular account of the early Wright experiments with a description of their aeroplane, a report on the Wrights' 1908 flights in France and America, through October 11, and a discussion of their significance.

——— *Aėroplan brat'ev Raĭt. S. izlozheniem kratkoi teorii aeroplanov. Izd. 2., zannovo perer, i dop. S 34 risunkami v tekstie.* [The Wright Brothers Aeroplane. With 34 Illustrations in the Text. 2. ed., rev., and enl.] S.-Peterburg: Ind. zhurnala "Vozdukhoplavatel'," 1909, 86 pp., illus.

Revised edition of the above, including an account and chronological tables of the Wright flights through March 1909 and a discussion of the progress of aviation in Europe and of the possible applications of the aeroplane.

Nansontz, Max de. Biplan Wright. In his *Aérostation, aviation*, Paris: Boivin & Cie, 1911, pp. 677–688, illus.

Napoleão, Aluizio. Os irmãos Wright. In his *Santos Dumont e a conquista do ar*, Rio de Janeiro: Imprensa Nacional, 1941, pp. 115–129, 205–252.

This book and its sections devoted to the Wright brothers was published also in Spanish translation Rio de Janeiro: Imprensa Nacional, 1943, vol. 1, pp. 114–132, 205–251 and in English translation Rio de Janeiro: National Printing Office, 1945, vol. 1, pp. 130–155, 239–285. The sections on the Wrights are also included in the second edition (São Paulo: Companhia Editora Nacional, 1957), pp. 142–161, 253–312.

Extensive discussion of Wrights' flights and claims in sections entitled "The Flight with the Heavier-than-air Machine" and "Priority in Airplane Flying." Quotes extensively from accounts of the Wrights by Captain Ferber and John McMahon in his book

The Wright Brothers. Casts doubt on Wright claims and concludes that Santos-Dumont "was the first man to fly in a heavier-than-air machine."

News Front [periodical]. They Taught the World to Fly [The Wright Brothers]. In its *50 Great Pioneers of American Industry.* [Maplewood, N.J.: C. S. Hammond, 1964], pp. 144–147.

Orville Wright Dinner of the Society of Automotive Engineers, Inc., July [i.e. June], 1918, Dayton, Ohio. [New York: Society of Automotive Engineers, Inc., 1918], 32 pp., illus.

Commemorative brochure including reprints of "The Wright Brothers' Aeroplane" by Orville and Wilbur Wright, "How We Made the First Flight," by Orville Wright, and "Some Aeronautical Experiments," by Wilbur Wright.

Parkman, Mary R. The Wright Brothers. In her *Conquests of Invention*, New York: Century, 1921, pp. 330–343.

Patterson, John C. Wright Brothers; Self-Made Scientists. In his *America's Greatest Inventors*, New York: Thomas Y. Crowell, 1943, pp. 174–188, illus.

Peyrey, François. *Les premiers hommes-oiseaux; Wilbur et Orville Wright.* Paris: H. Guiton, 1908, 78 pp., illus.

First published monograph on the Wrights, describing their early experiments as reported in France, primarily in *L'Aérophile* and *L'Auto*, and reprinting many published letters and documents from these publications. Includes a Wright chronology, 1900-August 8, 1908.

——— *Les premiers hommes-oiseaux; Wilbur et Orville Wright.* Édition nouvelle, relatant toutes les expériences des frères Wright, en France et aux États-Unis d' Amérique. 50 photographies, dessins, croquis côtés & schémas. Paris: H. Guiton, 1909, 154 pp., illus.

Published also without chapter VII "L'Histoire résumée des frères Wright" and "Documents relatifs à diverses enquêtes," pages 127–154, in his *Les oiseaux artificiels*, Paris: H. Dunod et E. Pinat, 1909, pp. 121–211, 636–655.

Enlarged edition of the above with four additional chapters including an account of Wilbur's flights at Le Mans, Orville's flights at Fort Myer, extensive chronological tables of these flights, and a translation of the *Century Magazine* article by the Wrights, September 1908.

Polillo, Raoul. Santos-Dumont e os irmãos Wright. In his *Santos-Dumont gênio*, São Paulo: Companhia Editora Nacional, 1950, pp. 256–271.

Sets forth Brazilian viewpoint that Santos-Dumont was the first to achieve powered flight.

Pritchard, J. Laurence. The Wright Brothers and the Wright Machine. In his *The Book of the Aeroplane*, London, New York: Longmans, Green and Co., 1935, pp. 13–27.

Included also in the first and second editions of this work, 1926 and 1929, pp. 21–35.

A popular account of the Wrights and their activities through 1908.

Raleigh, Walter. The Wrights. In his *The War in the Air*, Oxford: Clarendon Press, 1922, vol. 1, pp. 56–73.

Santaló Sors, Luis. Los primeros aviones: los hermanos Wright. In his *Historia de la aeronáutica*, Buenos Aires: Espasa-Calpe Argentina, S.A., 1946, pp. 163–168.

Savorgnan di Brazzà, Francesco. *La navigazione aerea.* Milano: Fratelli Treves, 1910, 284 pp., illus.

Includes three chapters on the Wright brothers; "I fratelli Wright e la loro opera," pages 92–95, "La venuta dei fratelli Wright in Europa e el loro trionfo definitivo," pages 107–116, and "Il biplano Wright," pages 116–124.

[Schmidt, Georg.] *Die Flug-Maschine der Gebrüder Wright.* Westerland-Sylt: Druck von Fr. Rossberg [1909], 7 pp.

Sewell, W. Stuart, ed. Wilbur and Orville Wright. In *Brief Biographies of Famous Men and Women*, New York: Permabooks, 1949, pp. 207–209.

Sherman, Dallas B. *Street to the Sky; a Play in Three Acts.* San Francisco, Calif.: Dallas P. Sherman, 1953, 129 p.

Deals with the Wright brothers.

Smith, Henry Ladd. Kitty Hawk. In his *Airways: the History of Commercial Aviation in the United States*, New York: Alfred A. Knopf, 1942, pp. 3–18.

Popular version of the early Wright experiments.

Smith, Maurice H. Orville and Wilbur Wright [signed M. H. Sm.] In *Collier's Encyclopedia*, New York: P. F. Collier and Son, 1932, vol. 19, pp. 601–602, illus.

Stewart, Oliver. [Wright Brothers]. In his *First Flights*, New York: Pitman Publishing Corporation [1958], pp. 23–30.

Sullivan, Mark. Orville and Wilbur Wright. In his *Our Times, 1900–1925*, New York: Charles Scribner's Sons, 1935, vol. 2, pp. 568–613, illus.

Extensive and well documented account, based on interview and data supplied the author by Orville Wright.

Tate, William J. *Brochure of the Twenty-Fifth Anniversary of the First Successful Airplane Flight, 1903–1928; Kitty Hawk, N.C., December 17, 1928.* [Kitty Hawk, N.C.: The Author, 1928], 12 pp., illus.

"Compiled from photos, magazine articles, speech of Wilbur Wright before the Western Society of Engineers, Chicago and general data collected and kept by Wm. J. Tate including some extracts from personal letters from Orville Wright," p. 1.

Tatin, Victor. *Eléments d'aviation. Les expériences d'aviation de Wilbur et d'Orville Wright. Description de l'aéroplane Wright.* Paris: H. Dunod & E. Pinat, 1909, 71 pp., illus.

This second edition of Tatin's book includes several supplementary pages on the work of the Wrights, pages 61–65. The first edition 1908 included an "Appendice" of two pages on the Wrights, pp. 59–60.

Thomas, Henry, and Thomas, Dana L. The Wright Brothers. In their *50 Great Modern Lives*, Garden City, N.Y.: Hanover House, 1956, pp. 341–348.

Published also in their *Life Stories of the Great Inventors*, Garden City, N.Y.: Halcyon House, 1948, pp. 244–254, illus. and in their *50 Great Americans*, Garden City, N.Y.: Doubleday & Company, Inc., 1948, pp. 368–375.

——— Wright Brothers — Conquerors of the Air. In their *Living Adventures in Science*, Garden City, N.Y.: Hanover House, 1954, pp. 231–239.

Tillman, Stephen F. *Man Unafraid*. Washington: Army Times Publishing Company, 1958, 228 p.
Abridgements of these chapters originally published in *Army-Navy-Air Force Register*, June 1–August 17, 1957.
Chapters 1–10, pp. 1–79, concern the Wright brothers' negotiations with the War Department for the sale of their aeroplane, 1905–1908; the Fort Myer trials, 1908 and 1909; and the training of Lieutenants Frank P. Lahm and Benjamin D. Foulois by Wilbur.

A Tribute to the Wright Brothers, Who Accomplished the First Successful Powered Flight by Man on December 17, 1903. New York: Aerosphere, Inc., 1943, pp. ciii–cxlv, illus.
Preprint of a section from *Aerosphere*, 1943.
Includes brief fortieth year anniversary statement by Orville Wright, "The 1914 Tests of the Langley Aerodrome" by C. G. Abbot, "The Evolution of the Wright Airplane," by E. W. Robischon, and "Technical Descriptions of the Gliders and Airplanes Constructed by the Wright Brothers, Arranged in Chronological Order."

Turgan, L. Avions et aviateurs d'aujourd'hui. Les frères Wright. In his *Histoire de l'aviation*, Paris: Librairie des sciences et d'industrie, 1909, pp. 189–196, illus.

Untermeyer, Louis. Wilbur and Orville Wright. In his *Makers of the Modern World*, New York: Simon and Schuster, 1955, pp. 360–367.

Victorin, Harald. Bröderna Wright, de två som helt lyckades. In his *Flygbragder och bragdflygare* . . . Malmö: A.–B. Allhems Förlag, 1948, pp. 12–15, illus.

Vivian, E. Charles. The Wright Brothers. In his *A History of Aeronautics*, London: W. Collins Sons & Co., Ltd., 1921, pp. 145–175, illus.

Wead, Frank. *Wings for Men*. New York & London: The Century Co., 1931, 333 pp., illus.
Includes extensive reference to the Wright brothers, pages 126–148, 158–162.

Weiller, Lazare. L'aviation et l'aéroplane des frères Wright. In *De Montgolfier à Wilbur Wright; compte rendu de la 52e réunion de la Société archéologique Le Vieux Papier le 22 décembre 1908*. Paris: Chez P. Flobert, sécrétaire général de la Société "Le Vieux Papier," 1909, pp. 21–32, illus.
Reprinted from *Bulletin de la Société archéologique Le Vieux Papier*.
Address by the head of the French Wright company discussing his association and dealings with the Wrights.

Whitehouse, Arch. The Saga of the Wrights. In his *The Early Birds*, Garden City, N.Y.: Doubleday & Company, Inc., 1965, pp. 61–78.

Wilbur Wright (1867–1912), Orville Wright (b. 1871). In *The Encyclopaedia of Aviation*, London: Sir Isaac Pitman & Sons, Ltd., 1935, p. 642.

The Wright Brothers. Dayton, Ohio: Carillon Park [1949], [26 pp.], illus.
Wright Hall in Carillon Park houses the restored 1905 Wright aeroplane.

Wright Brothers Era. In *Flight; a Pictorial History of Aviation.* New York: Year, Inc., 1958, pp. 32–39, illus.

A pictorial record of the Wrights.

Wright Company. *The Beginnings of Human Flight.* New York: [1916], 4 pp.

Brochure prepared for distribution at the exhibition of the Wright 1903 aeroplane at the Massachusetts Institute of Technology, Boston, June 11, 12, and 13, 1916.

The Wrights (Orville and Wilbur). In *All the World's Airships . . . "1910–11."* London: Sampson Low, Marston & Co., Ltd., 1910, p. 440.

Zenkevich, Michael. *Brat'i͡a Raĭt.* [Wright Brothers.] Moskva: Zhurnal'no-gazetnoe ob'edinenie, 1933. [199 pp.], illus. (Zhizn' Zamechatel'-nykh li͡udeĭ, vyp. vii–viii).

Includes bibliography, page 198.

Periodical Articles

Allward, M. F. Some Practical Aspects of the Wrights' Work. *Aeronautics*, Dec. 1953, vol. 29, pp. 60, 63–64, illus.

Deals with and stresses the significance of the early Wright gliding experiments, 1900–1902.

Background of the Wrights. *Engineering*, Dec. 11, 1953, vol. 176, pp. 752–754, illus.

Deals primarily with Dayton, Ohio, and its influence on the Wright brothers.

Bassett, Preston R. 1903–1953: a Tribute to the Wright Brothers. *Sperryscope*, Dec. 1953, vol. 12, pp. 2–3, illus.

Bonnalie, Allan F. They Still Look to the Wrights. *Pegasus*, Dec. 1953, vol. 23, pp. 5–7, illus.

Stresses achievements and accomplishments of the Wright brothers.

Breyer, Victor, and Coquelle, Robert. La Vie et les inventions des frères Wright. *La Vie au grand air*, Mar. 20–May 29, 1909, pp. 195–196, 211–212, 227–228, 243–244, 259–260, 262–263, 275–276, 291–292, 307–308, 323–324, 339–340, 355–356, illus.

Series of eleven articles on the Wright brothers.

Brookins, Walter R. Early Days with the Wright Brothers. *Chirp*, June 1936, no. 16, p. 3.

Reminiscences of a neighbor of the Wrights in Dayton who learned to fly at Montgomery, Alabama under instruction of Orville Wright and was later put in charge of Wright Flying School.

Buist, H. Massac. The Human Side of Flying. Being an Attempt to Introduce the Reader to Messrs. Orville and Wilbur Wright at Pau. *Flight*, Mar. 6–13, 1909, vol. 1, pp. 128–129, 141–143, illus.

Casson, Herbert N. At Last We Can Fly. The Story of the Wright Brothers, Who, After Years of Experimenting, Have Made Flying Practicable. *American Magazine*, Apr. 1907, vol. 63, pp. 616–624, illus.

Published also in *Pearson's Magazine*, July 1907, vol. 24, pp. 94–999; French translation in *Le Revue de L'Aviation*, May 15, 1907, vol. 2, no. 10, pp. 2–5, and in *La Conquête de L'Air*, June 1, 1907, vol. 4, no. 11.

Coffyn, Frank T. Flying with the Wrights. *World's Work*, Dec. 1929, vol. 58, pp. 80–86, Jan. 1930, vol. 59, pp. 76–82, illus.

269–517—68——3

Author's reminiscences of his early flying days, including account of his associations with the Wrights, 1910–1912.

Coles, T. R. Orville and Wilbur Wright as a Schoolmate Knew Them. *Out West*, Jan. 1910, vol. 32, pp. 36–38.

Coppens de Houthulst, Willy. The Birth of Flying; the Wright Brothers. *Interavia; Review of World Aviation*, Dec. 1953, vol. 8, pp. 692–693, illus.

Popular account by a Belgian World War I air ace, based on *The Wright Brothers: Fathers of Flight*, by John R. McMahon.

Drury, Augustus W. The Wright Brothers and Their Aeroplane. *Religious Telescope*, Dec. 23, 1908, pp. 6–8, illus.

Published also in *Greater Dayton*, June 1909, vol. 2, pp. 214–218; *Herald of Gospel Liberty*, June 17, 1909, vol. 11, pp. 16–17.

Dryden, Hugh L. Our Heritage from Wilbur and Orville Wright. *Journal of the Aeronautical Sciences*, Dec. 1953, vol. 20, pp. 803–804.

Golden anniversary tribute by the Director, National Advisory Committee for Aeronautics.

Ewald, Gustav. 50 Jahre Menschenflug. *Flugwelt*, Dec. 1953, vol. 5, pp. 363–367, illus.

General review of the Wrights and their achievements on the occasion of the fiftieth anniversary of their first flights at Kitty Hawk, N.C.

Fifty Years of Aviation Progress; Background Information on Aviation's First 50 Years. Washington: National Committee to Observe the 50th Anniversary of Powered Flight, 1953, 59p.

Chapter 2, pp. 5–8, is entitled "A New Dimension for Travel—the Wrights."

Findley, Earl N. The Wrights and the Reporter. *Beehive*, Spring 1953, vol. 28, no. 2, pp. 25–29, illus.

Author's reminiscences of his long acquaintance and association with the Wrights, beginning in 1908 when he was a reporter on the New York *Tribune* and continuing until Orville's death, January 30, 1948.

Flying Men of America. *Current Literature*, Dec. 1910, vol. 49, pp. 615–616, illus.

Includes brief sketch of the Wright brothers.

Foltmann, John. 17. December 1903. Da Orville og Wilbur Wright løste flyveproblemet for 50 år siden. *Flyv*, Dec. 1953, vol. 26, pp. 243–244, illus.

Wright brothers' fiftieth anniversary article by the editor of *Flyv*.

Giacomelli, Raffaele. In Memoria di Wilbur e Orville Wright. *L'Aerotecnica*, Feb. 15–Apr. 15, 1949, vol. 29, pp. 34–45, 95–107, (English abstract pp. 64, 126–128).

Abridged *Scienza e tecnica*, Nov.–Dec. 1948.

Communciation commemorating the life and work of the Wright brothers, submitted to the Seventh Meeting of the Associazione Italiana di Aerotecnica, September 23–25, 1948. Extensive study of the Wrights with an account of their early experiments and flights, their negotiations for the sale of their aeroplane, the Wright-Smithsonian controversy, and an examination of their writings. Includes a discussion of their early laboratory experiments, their importance, and the question of their authenticity with inclusion of author's correspondence with English scientist, F. W. Lanchester, regarding these experiments.

Gibbs-Smith, Charles H. The Seal of Half a Century. *Aeronautics*, Dec. 1953, vol. 29, pp. 28–35, illus.
An anniversary article reviewing the achievements, early experiments, and flights of the Wright brothers through the year 1908. Includes a general arrangement drawing of the original Wright 1903 "Flyer" and a facsimile of the patent drawing of their flying machine as found in their patent application filed March 23, 1903, which was granted May 22, 1906.

Hegener, Henri. Belangrijke data uit het leven der gebroeders Wright. *Het Vliegveld*, Dec. 1928, vol. 12, pp. 369–371.
Chronology.

Hegener, Henri, and Reyneker, F. H. Het werk der gebroeders Wright. *Het Vliegveld*, Jan. 1924, vol. 8, pp. 3–9, illus.
First article in a series entitled "De Baanbrekers der Dynamische Luchtvaart."

Hildebrandt, Alfred. Fliegende Menschen. *Gartenlaube*, Sept. 2, 1909, vol. 57, pp. 720–722, illus.

Impressions of American Inventors. II. The Wright Brothers and Their Achievements. *Scientific American*, June 12, 1909, vol. 114, p. 443.

Ingells, Douglas J. Wilbur and Orville—Student Pilots. *Flying*, Apr. 1954, vol. 54, pp. 32–33, 54–56.
Primarily an account of the early experiments of the Wright brothers prior to their first successful flight on December 17, 1903.

Kelly, Fred C. At Home with the Wrights. *New York Times*, Oct. 11, 1953, Sec. 10, p. 4, illus.

Kettering, Charles F. [Tribute to the Wright Brothers.] *Aviation and Yachting*, Dec. 1943, vol. 11, no. 7, pp. 7, 48.
Guest editorial by Orville Wright's friend, vice-president and general manager of General Motors Corporation.

Kinzler, Alice E. A Pass at the Infinite. *USA 1; Monthly News and History*, July 1962, vol. 1, pp. 32–37, illus.
Popular summary of Wright brothers' achievements.

Langewiesche, Wolfgang. What the Wrights Really Invented. *Harper's Magazine*, June 1950, vol. 200, pp. 102–105.
Reprinted: *U.S. Air Services*, Aug. 1950, vol. 35, no. 8, pp. 13–17, illus.

List of Firsts for Wrights. *Air Force Times*, April 5, 1958, vol. 18, p. 37.

McFarland, Marvin W. The Gentlemen and the Press. *Boeing Magazine*, Dec. 1953, vol. 23, pp. 8–11.
Deals with the relations of the Wright brothers with the press, 1903–1908, and with their press policy.

——— A Look at Aviation Fifty-Three Years After. *U.S. Air Services*, Dec. 1956, vol. 41, pp. 5–6.
An anniversary editorial contrasting piloting as practiced by the Wrights with increasingly mechanized techniques in the jet age.

——— When the Airplane Was a Military Secret: a Study of National Attitudes Before 1914. *U.S. Air Services*, Sept. 1954, vol. 39, pp. 11, 14, 16; Oct. 1954, vol. 39, pp. 18, 20–22.

Published also in *Air Power Historian*, Oct. 1955, vol. 2, pp. 70–82, and adapted in Emme, Eugene M., *The Impact of Air Power; National Security and World Politics* (Princeton, N.J.: D. Van Nostrand Company, 1959), pp. 20–26.

Lecture delivered before the Annual History Conference at the State University of Iowa, on April 10, 1954, dealing especially with the long and unsuccessful negotiations for the sale of their aeroplane to the governments of England, France, Germany, and the United States prior to their American contract of February 10, 1908.

McMahon, John R. How a Twisted Paper Gave Us Aviation. *Popular Science Monthly*, Sept. 1925, vol. 107, no. 9, pp. 28–29, 128–131, illus.

Popular presentation of early Wright experiments, 1899–1903.

Mayer, Robert. Wright Brothers, 1903–1943. *Scott's Monthly Journal*, Dec. 1943, vol. 24, pp. 324–329, illus.

Mingos, Howard. Thus Man Learned to Fly; the Story of the Wright Brothers and the Airplane. *Saturday Evening Post*, July 7–14, 1928, vol. 201, no. 1, pp. 10–11, 105–106, 109–110; no. 2, pp. 18–19, 121–122, 124–126, illus.

Mosquitoes Almost Drove Wright Brothers From Kitty Hawk. *Army-Navy-Air Force Register*, Dec. 22, 1956, vol. 77, p. 5.

Brief account of Kitty Hawk and the Wright brothers' difficulties with mosquitoes there in 1901.

Naĭdenov, Vasliĭ F. Pervonachal'nyi͡a raboty br. Raĭt v Amerikie͡. [The Pioneer Work of the Wright Brothers in America.] *Vozdukhoplavatel'*, Jan. 1909, vol. 4, pp. 1–17.

——— Aėroplan v svoem istoricheskom razvitii i ego elementarnai͡a teorii͡a. [The Elementary Theory and Historical Development of the Aeroplane.] *Vozdukhoplavatel'*, Feb.–Mar. 1909, vol. 4, pp. 85–106, 171–236.

Includes a section on the Wright brothers, pages 193–211.

O'Malley, Frank W. When the Wrights Joined the Flying Shows. *U.S. Air Services*, Dec. 1923, vol. 8, pp. 19–25, illus.

Newspaper reporter's story of his first aeroplane ride with Arch Hoxsey in Wright aeroplane at Asbury Park, N.J., August 20, 1910, and his impressions of the Wrights during the meets at Asbury Park, Boston, and Belmont Park in 1910.

Our Tribute to Dayton's Own. *Dayton Motor News*, Dec. 1928, vol. 6, no. 12, pp. 1–15, illus.

Special issue devoted to the Wright brothers.

Page, Arthur W. How the Wrights Discovered Flight. *World's Work*, Aug. 1910, vol. 20, pp. 13303–13318, illus.

Author's recollections of the Wrights. Includes facsimile of document signed by W. S. Dough, A. D. Etheridge, and John Moore, witnesses of first flight, December 17, 1903, certifying location of the start of the flight.

Perreault, William D. Wright Brothers Fly Without Balloons. *American Aviation*, Dec. 7, 1953, vol. 17, pp. 13–14, illus.

Anniversary article dealing with the December 17, 1903 flights at Kitty Hawk, N.C.

Peugler, Hanns. Die Brüder Wilbur und Orville Wright—Pioniere des Motorfluges. *Ausbau*, 1952, vol. 5, pp. 467–474.

Pritchard, J. Laurence. The Work of the Wright Brothers for Aviation. *Journal of the Royal Society of Arts*, Jan. 8, 1954, vol. 102, pp. 112–124, illus. Discussion, pp. 124–128. With comments by Colonel Alexander Ogilvie, Sir Roy Fedden, E. Gordon England, and Peter Masefield.

Paper read to the Royal Society of Arts, December 16, 1953. A fiftieth anniversary tribute to the Wright brothers by the Secretary, Royal Aeronautical Society.

——— The Wright Brothers and the Royal Aeronautical Society; a Survey and Tribute. *Royal Aeronautical Society Journal*, Dec. 1953, vol. 57, pp. 739–818.

Contents: The Years Before, 1896–1902; The Gliding Years, 1900–1902; The Year of Destiny, 1903; Years of Recognition, 1904–1913; Years of Disparagement, 1914–1942; The Year of Recantation, 1942; Years of Honor, 1928–1948; Wilbur and Orville Wright; the Memorial Years, 1913–1953 (with list of and extracts from Wilbur Wright Memorial Lectures). Includes references (32), p. 812.

Renstrom, Arthur G. Wright Chronology. *Aero Digest*, July 1953, vol. 67, pp. 152–197.

Extensive chronology of the Wright brothers' activities from the birth of Wilbur Wright, April 16, 1867, to the year 1953, golden anniversary of the Wright brothers' first power flight at Kitty Hawk, N.C.

Rozendaal, John. De Allereersten. *Avia-Vliegwereld*, Dec. 10, 1953, vol. 2, pp. 648–650, illus.

A commemorative account of the Wright brothers by a Dutch pioneer engineer who flew with Wilbur in 1908.

Saunders, William O. Then We Quit Laughing. *Collier's*, Sept. 17, 1927, vol. 80, no. 12, pp. 24, 56.

Reminiscences of John T. Daniels, one of the witnesses of the December 17, 1903 flights, as set forth in an interview with the author.

Sherman, Dallas. The Bishop's Boys. *Flying*, Dec. 1959, vol. 65, pp. 36–39, 86–93.

A popular account of the Wright brothers.

Shepherd, William G. They Lifted the World with a Toy. *Collier's*, Aug. 20, 1927, vol. 80, no. 8, pp. 8–9, 38–39, illus.

Popular account of the Wright brothers.

The Story of the Wrights. *The Wright Engine Builder*, Aug. 1922, vol. 2, no. 2, pp. 6–7, Sept., pp. 5, 10, Nov., pp. 10–11. Dec., pp. 9–10, illus.

Based on the account of the Wrights in E. Charles Vivian's *A History of Aeronautics.*

Tate, William J. I Was Host to Wright Brothers at Kitty Hawk. *U.S. Air Services*, Dec. 1943, vol. 28, no. 12, pp. 29–30, illus.

Statement on attitude of the Kitty Hawk community toward Wrights, 1900–1903.

——— With the Wrights at Kitty Hawk. Anniversary of the First Flight Twenty-Five Years Ago. *Aeronautic Review*, Dec. 1928, vol. 6, no. 12, pp. 189–192, illus.

Taylor, Charles E. My Story of the Wright Brothers, as told to Robert S. Ball. *Collier's*, Dec. 25, 1948, vol. 122, no. 26, pp. 27, 68, 70, illus.

Tweney, George H. The Wright Brothers. *American Book Collector*, Oct. 1958, pp. 5–13, illus.
A general account. Includes 16 references.

The Victorious Wrights. *Current Literature*, June 1909, vol. 46, pp. 608–610, illus.

Het Werk der Wrights, door anderen en door henzelf verteld. *De Luchtvaart*, June 5, July 3, 1909, vol. 1, pp. 19–25, 68–70, illus.

Werthner, William. Personal Recollections of the Wrights. *Aero Club of America Bulletin*, July 1912, vol. 1, p. 13.
Orville Wright's high school teacher relates his impressions of the Wright brothers and their flights at Huffman Prairie.

When the Wright Brothers Were Boys. *American Magazine*, June 1909, vol. 68, pp. 206–207.
Published also in *Greater Dayton*, June 1909, vol. 2, pp. 210–211.

When Wings Were Young. *Collier's*, Sept. 24, 1927, vol. 80, pp. 18–19, illus.
Pictorial history of the Wright brothers.

The Wrights—A Personal Impression, by "The Fly." *Flight*, May 8, 1909, vol. 1, pp. 262–263, port.
Based on observation of and conversations with Wrights at Aero Club dinner, May 4, at Ritz Hotel, London.

Biographical References—Wilbur Wright

Wilbur Wright. In *Who's Who in America . . . 1908–1909*, Chicago: A. N. Marquis & Company, 1908, vol. 5, p. 2119.
Continued in volumes 6–7, 1910 through 1913.

The King of the Air. An Insight into the Life of Wilbur Wright at Le Mans. *Motor*, London, Oct. 20, 1908, vol. 14, pp. 317–318.

Anderson, Frederick I. The French Think Wilbur is a Bird. *Harper's Weekly*, Oct. 24, 1908, vol. 52, p. 30.

M. Wright à l' "Aéro-Club de la Sarthe." *L'Ouest-Touriste et Sportif*, vol. 2, no. 6, 1908, pp. 44–46.
Account of dinner given in honor of Wilbur Wright at Le Mans, September 24, 1908.

Palmer, Frederick. Veelbure Reet—American. *Collier's*, May 15, 1909, vol. 43, no. 8, pp. 18, 31–32 illus.
Account of Wilbur Wright's activities in France and of adulation by the French.

Beck, J. M., Jr. Impressions of Wilbur Wright. *The Wissahickon*, Oct. 1909, pp. 4–12, illus.

Wilbur Wright. In *Les Rois de l'air. 1re année*, Paris [Georges Berg, 1910], pp. 40–41, port.

Wilbur Wright. In *The National Cyclopædia of American Biography*, New York: James T. White & Company, 1910, vol. 14, pp. 56–57.
Published also in 1917 edition.

Sketch of Wilbur Wright. *American Magazine*, Feb. 1910, vol. 69, pp. 451–452.

Big Men of the Movement: Wilbur Wright. *Aircraft*, June 1910, vol. 1, p. 141.

U.S. Congress. House. *Resolution Expressing the Profound Regret of the House on Hearing of the Death of Wilbur Wright, of Dayton, Ohio.* Washington: United States Government Printing Office, 1912, 2 pp. (62d Congress, 2d Session. H. Res. 560).

Submitted by Mr. Timothy T. Ansberry, of Ohio, May 31, 1912.

Death of Wilbur Wright. *Aeronautics*, New York, May–June 1912, vol. 10, p. 176.

Everstag, R. W. d'. Wilbur Wright. [Signed R. W. d'E.] *Schweizer. Aero-Club Bulletin*, June 1912, vol. 6, pp. 146–148, port.

Wilbur Wright. *Aeronautics*, London, June 1912, vol. 5, p. 157, illus.

The Flags are at Half-Mast Today as a Token of Respect to the Memory of Wilbur Wright. *The NCR* [National Cash Register] *Weekly*, June 1, 1912, vol. 6, no. 28, 4 pp., illus.

Includes numerous tributes to Wilbur Wright and a sketch of his life authorized by the family and read at the funeral by Rev. Maurice E. Wilson.

Wilbur Wright, 1867–1912. *Flight*, June 1, 1912, vol. 4, pp. 488–489, illus.

The Passing of Wilbur Wright. *The Car*, June 5, 1912, vol. 41, pp. 125–126, illus.

Wilbur Wright. *Flugsport*, June 5, 1912, vol. 4, pp. 453–457, port.

Whittaker, W. E. de B. Wilbur Wright. 1867–1912. [Signed *W. E. de B. W.*] *Aeroplane*, June 6, 1912, vol. 2, p. 548.

Wilbur Wright. *Independent*, June 6, 1912, vol. 72, pp. 1280–1281.

Aviation History and Wilbur Wright. *Flight*, June 8, 1912. vol. 4, p. 519.

Reference to the first British newspaper report on Wrights' flights. Includes letter from Wilbur Wright to Sidney Hollands, dated July 16, 1905.

Buist, H. Massac. Death of the First Flying Man. *The Motor News*, June 8, 1912, pp. 1180–1186.

Conqueror of the Air. *Outlook*, June 8, 1912, vol. 101, pp. 280–281.

Estimate of Wilbur Wright. *Literary Digest*, June 8, 1912, vol. 44, pp. 1192–1193.

Nations Honor Wilbur Wright's Memory. *Aero*, June 8, 1912, vol. 4, no. 10, p. 235, port.

Passing of a Great Inventor. *Scientific American*, June 8, 1912, vol. 106, p. 518, illus.

Prade, Georges. W. Wright est mort! *La Vie au grand air*, June 8, 1912, vol. 15, p. 401, illus.

Wilbur Wright. *Harper's Weekly*, June 8, 1912, vol. 56, p. 5.

Wilbur Wright. *L'Illustration*, June 8, 1912, vol. 139, p. 493, illus.

Wilbur Wright. *Fachzeitung für Automobilismus und Flugtechnik*, June 9, 1912, vol. 6, pp. 17–19, illus.

Henry-Coüannier, André. L'Aviation en deuil. *La Revue aérienne*, June 10, 1912, vol. 5, pp. 301–304, illus.

Wilbur Wright. *Der Motorwagen*, June 10, 1912, vol. 15, pp. 403–404.

Wilbur Wright. *Deutsche Luftfahrer-Zeitschrift*, June 12, 1912, vol. 16, p. 289.

Death of Wilbur Wright, the Bird Man. *The Watchword*, June 15, 1912, pp. 7–8, illus.

Un Grand disparu; Wilbur Wright est mort. *L'Aérophile*, June 15, 1912, vol. 20, pp. 282–284, illus.

Popper, Stefan. Wilbur Wright. *Österreichische Flug-Zeitschrift*, June 15, 1912, vol. 6, pp. 283–284.
Obituary.

Vorreiter, Ansbert. Wilbur Wright. *Zeitschrift für Flugtechnik und Motorluftschiffart*, June 15, 1912, vol. 3, p. 152, port.

Wilbur Wright. *Avia*, June 15, 1912, vol. 2, pp. 39–42.

Wilbur Wright. *Technique aéronautique*, June 15, 1912, vol. 5, pp. 375–376.

Wilbur Wright. *Wiener Luftschiffer-Zeitung*, June 15, 1912, vol. 11, pp. 214–216.

Woodhouse, Henry. Wilbur Wright, the Man Who Made Flying Possible. *Collier's*, June 15, 1912, vol. 49, p. 13, illus.

Notre Maître Wilbur. [Signed *C. Cam. Sat.*] *Le Mois automobile*, June 25, 1912, pp. 9–11, illus.

The Faith that Sees. *Youth's Companion*, June 27, 1912, vol. 86, p. 338, port.
Tribute to Wilbur Wright.

Brewer, Griffith. Wilbur Wright, Gold Medalist of the Society. *The Aeronautical Journal*, July 1912, vol. 16, pp. 148–153, port.
Reprinted in *The Aeronautical Journal*, July–Sept. 1916, vol. 20, pp. 128–135.
Tribute to Wilbur Wright with extensive reference to author's association with him in 1908 and 1909.

Cablegrams and Messages Received by the Aero Club of America from Abroad on the Death of Wilbur Wright. *Aero Club of America Bulletin*, July 1912, vol. 1, no. 6, p. 6.

Death of the Dean of Birdmen. *Hearst's Magazine*, July 1912, vol. 22, pp. 141, 143 illus.

Eberhardt, J. C. The Death of Wilbur Wright. *Aero Club of America Bulletin*, July 1912, vol. 1, no. 6, pp. 4–5.
Brief note on funeral ceremonies.

Entire World Mourns the Loss of Wilbur Wright. *Fly*, July 1912, vol. 4, no. 9, pp. 8–10.

Inventor Who Solved the Most Difficult of All Mechanical Problems. *Current Literature*, July 1912, vol. 53, pp. 57–59. port.

The Late Wilbur Wright. *Aero*, London, July 1912, vol. 6, no. 112, pp. 194–195, illus.

Tributes to Wilbur Wright from Representative American Men. *Aero Club of America Bulletin*, July 1912, vol. 1, no. 6, pp. 6–7.

Wilbur Wright. *Aeronautics*, July 1912, vol. 11, pp. 1–3, ports.

Wilbur Wright. *Review of Reviews*, July 1912, vol. 36, p. 44, port.

Wilbur Wright Gone. *Aircraft*, July 1912, vol. 3, p. 146, port.

Wood, Henry A. Wise. Wilbur Wright. *Aero Club of America Bulletin*, July 1912, vol. 1, no. 6, pp. 2–3, port.

Woodhouse, Henry. The World's Tribute to Wilbur Wright. *Aero Club of America Bulletin*, July 1912, vol. 1, no. 6, pp. 9–12.

Wilbur Wright, *L'Aérostation*, July 1, 1912, vol. 9, pp. 12–13, illus.

Wilbur Wright. In *The New International Encyclopædia*, New York: Dodd, Mead and Company, 1916, vol. 23, p. 283.

Continued in later editions, 1917 and 1930.

Brewer, Griffith. The Life and Work of Wilbur Wright. *The Aeronautical Journal*, July–Sept. 1916, vol. 20, pp. 68–84, illus.

Abstract with title, "In Memory of Wilbur Wright," in *Aeroplane*, June 14, 1916, vol. 10, pp. 940–942, 944, illus.

The Fourth Wilbur Wright Memorial Lecture delivered before the Royal Society of Arts, June 16, 1916. In a group of eleven accompanying appendices, pages 84–135, the author reprints articles by the Wrights and materials from *The Aeronautical Journal* relating to them.

Drury, Marion R. The Conversion of Wilbur Wright. *The Watchword*, Mar. 31, 1918, pp. 4–5, illus.

Marbury, Elizabeth. The Triumph of Wilbur Wright at Le Mans. *U.S. Air Services*, Dec. 1923, vol. 8, no. 12, p. 18.

Reprinted from one of a series of articles in the *Saturday Evening Post*, Oct. 13, 1923, vol. 196, no. 14, pages 129–130 which were later published in book form with title *My Crystal Ball*, New York: Boni and Liveright, 1923, pp. 179–180.

Martin, Hans. Herinnerungen aan de gebroeders Wright. *Het Vliegveld*, Nov. 1928, vol. 12, pp. 317–319, illus.

Author's recollections of Wilbur teaching Calderara to fly at Centocelle, Italy, in April 1909.

Essais de Wilbur Wright Le Mans — 1908. Wilbur Wright's Trial. La Conquête de L'Air. The Conquest of the Air. [Le Mans] Usines Léon Bollée [1929?] [28 pp.]

Album of 24 postal card photographs issued as tribute to Wilbur Wright. Includes foreword in English and French and facsimile of telegram sent to Léon Bollée by Orville Wright on May 30, 1912, announcing Wilbur's death.

Wright, Orville. Wilbur Wright [Signed O. W.]. In *The Encyclopædia Britannica*, 14th ed., London, New York: Encyclopædia Britannica, Inc., 1929, vol. 23, pp. 808–809.

Continued in later editions.

Wilbur Wright. In *Blue Book of Aviation*, Los Angeles: Hoagland Company, 1932, p. 232, port.

Wilbur Wright. In *National Encyclopædia*, New York: P. F. Collier & Son, 1932, vol. 10, p. 526.

Published also in later editions, 1934–1947; revised 1948–1949.

[Findley, Earl N.] Wilbur Wright's Hudson River Flight. *U.S. Air Services*, Oct. 1934, vol. 19, no. 10, p. 11.

Editorial on twenty-fifth anniversary of flight of October 4, 1909, from Governors Island to Grant's Tomb and return.

Beck, James M. Wilbur Wright's Last Flight. *U.S. Air Services*, Nov. 1934, vol. 19, no. 11, pp. 22–23. Supplementary note, Dec. 1934, vol. 19, no. 12, p. 33.

Another account by the Chairman of the Committee on Aeronautics of the Hudson-Fulton Commission who arranged contract with Wilbur Wright for the flight.

Lambert, *marquise*, Charles M. de My Memories of Wilbur Wright. *U.S. Air Services*, Mar. 1935, vol. 20, no. 3, pp. 13–15, illus.

Account of her flight as a passenger with Wilbur Wright at Pau in February 1909.

Klemin, Alexander. Wilbur Wright [Signed *A. K.*] *Dictionary of American Biography*, New York: Charles Scribner's Sons, 1936, vol. 20, pp. 568–570.

Mee, Arthur. *The Broken Dream of Wilbur Wright.* London: Hodder and Stoughton, 1938, 32 pp. (Arthur Mee's Rainbow Books).

Title based on Wilbur Wright's hope that the aeroplane would become an instrument of peace.

[Findley, Earl N.] Wilbur Wright Pays Grant's Tomb a Flying Visit. The Story of a Great Achievement of Thirty Years Ago. *U.S. Air Services*, Oct. 1939, vol. 24, no. 10, pp. 10–12, 36, illus.

Rewrite of an account originally published in the *New York Herald Tribune*, October 5, 1909.

Wilbur Wright's flight up the Hudson River from Governors Island to Grant's Tomb and return, October 4, 1909.

Cass Gilbert and Wilbur Wright; Record of an Interview, October 5, 1909. *Minnesota History*, Sept. 1941, vol. 22, pp. 302–305.

Impressions of the architect, Cass Gilbert, published here for the first time from documents in the Minnesota Historical Society.

Kelly, Fred C. When Wilbur Wright Won France. *Harper's Magazine*, Dec. 1941, vol. 184, pp. 84–90.

Account of Wilbur Wright's stay and flights at Le Mans and Pau, 1908 and 1909.

Williams, Al. Wilbur Wright is an Everlasting Inspiration to me. *U.S. Air Services*, Dec. 1943, vol. 28, no. 12, pp. 27–28, illus.

Excerpts from articles published by the author in Scripps-Howard newspapers.

Stein, Gertrude. Wilbur Wright. In her *Four in America.* Introduction by Thornton Wilder, New Haven: Yale University Press, 1947, pp. 83–117.

When Wilbur Wright First Met Marconi. *U.S. Air Services*, May 1953, vol. 38, no. 5, p. 7.

Reference to meeting with Marconi, September 23, 1909, on Governors Island.

Harper, Harry. Wilbur Wright as I Remember Him. *Flight*, Dec. 11, 1953, vol. 64, pp. 796–797, illus.

The author's recollections of a dinner conversation with Wilbur Wright at Le Mans, France at the end of 1908.

Wilbur Wright's Political Prophecy. *U.S. Air Services*, Sept. 1954, vol. 39, p. 7.

Wilbur predicted, speaking before the Ohio Society of New York in January 1910, that an Ohioan would be the next president.

McFarland, Marvin W. The Fame of Wilbur Wright. *U.S. Air Services*, Dec. 1955, vol. 40, pp. 4–6.

A tribute to Wilbur written subsequent to his election to the Hall of Fame for Great Americans on October 31, 1955.

Wilbur Wright et les débuts de l'aviation. Exposition du cinquantenaire, Le Mans, 6 juillet—15 septembre 1958. [Le Mans]: Musée de Tessé, 1958, 40 pp., illus.

Brochure prepared on the occasion of the fiftieth anniversary celebration of Wilbur's flights at Le Mans in 1908. Lists documents, pictures, models, and memorabilia exhibited.

Wilbur Wright. In Lassalle, Eugène J. *Les 100 premiers aviateurs brevetés au monde et la naissance de l'aviation.* [Paris]: Nauticaero, [1962], pp. 51–53.

Wilbur was granted pilot's license no. 15 by Aéro-Club of France in 1909.

Wilbur Wright. In *Encyclopedia of American History.* Updated and rev. Edited by Richard B. Morris. New York: Harper and Row, 1965, p. 807.

Garber, Paul E. The Rightness of the Wright Name. *AOPA Pilot,* Dec. 1966, vol. 9, pp. 74–75, illus.

Tribute to Wilbur on the occasion of the upcoming 100th anniversary of his birth, April 16.

Biographical References—Orville Wright

Orville Wright. In *Who's Who in America . . . 1908–1909,* Chicago: A. N. Marquis & Company, 1908, vol. 5, p. 2119.

Continued from 1910 through 1949, in volumes 6–25.

Big Men of the Movement: Orville Wright. *Aircraft,* June 1910, vol. 1, p. 140, port.

Orville Wright. In *The National Cyclopædia of American Biography,* New York: James T. White & Company, 1910, vol. 14, pp. 56–57, illus.

Published also in 1917 edition.

Orville Wright. In *Les Rois de l'air. 1re année,* Paris: [Georges Berg, 1910], p. 42, port.

Devoted to activities of years 1908 and 1909.

Wright Flies Single Propeller Plane. *Aero and Hydro,* Sept. 27, 1913, vol. 6, p. 483.

Experimental flights at Dayton with Model E machine.

The Reception to Orville Wright. *Flying,* New York, Jan. 1914, vol. 2, no. 12, pp. 24–25, illus.

Account of tenth anniversary dinner and reception sponsored by Aero Club of America, December 17, 1913, in New York. Accompanied by photograph of the first meeting of Orville and Thomas A. Edison.

Dunham, Samuel R. Orville Wright. In Webb, Mary Griffin, and Webb, Edna Lenore, *Famous Living Americans,* Greencastle, Ind.: Charles Webb & Company, 1915, pp. 570–580, port.

Accompanying portrait is of Glenn H. Curtiss and not Orville Wright.

Testimonial to Orville Wright. *Technology Review,* July 1916, vol. 18, pp. 566–568.

Account of dinner given by Massachusetts Institute of Technology at the Engineers' Club, Boston, June 12, 1916. Published also with two illustrations, one of the Wright 1903 aeroplane exhibited at the Massachusetts Institute of Technology, in *Aerial Age,* July 3, 1916, vol. 3, pp. 475, 488.

Orville Wright Proposed for Nobel Prize. *Aerial Age*, Aug. 28, 1916, vol. 3, p. 718.
Favorable editorial comment on suggestion that a petition be drawn up endorsing Orville Wright as a candidate for the Nobel physics prize.

Orville Wright is Flying Again. *Aviation*, Nov. 1, 1916, vol. 1, p. 233.
Announces that Orville has resumed daily flying.

Orville Wright. In *The New International Encyclopædia*, New York: Dodd, Mead and Company, 1916, vol. 23, p. 822, port.
Continued in 1917 and 1930 editions.

The Work of Orville Wright. *Aerial Age*, Oct. 15, 1917, vol. 6, p. 195, illus.
Quotes Orville Wright's views on uses of the aeroplane in war.

Orville Wright Dinner an Ovation. *Automotive Industries*, June 20, 1918, vol. 38, pp. 1165–1166, port.
Report on dinner held at Triangle Park, Dayton, June 17, 1918, in connection with meeting of the Society of Automotive Engineers.

Orville Wright Dinner. *Journal of the Society of Automotive Engineers*, July 1918, vol. 3, pp. 8–14, illus.
Lengthy account of dinner with abstracts of addresses by Colonels Deeds and Vincent, Lieutenant Miozzi, Messrs Coffin, Stratton, Diffin, and Manly.

The Orville Wright Banquet. *Aviation*, July 1, 1918, vol. 4, pp. 765–771, illus.
Another extensive account of June 17 testimonial dinner.

Schmidt, J. R. Visiting Orville Wright. *The Guide to Nature*, Aug. 1918, vol. 9, pp. 68–69, illus.
Reprinted from *Every Week*, with editorial comment.

Orville Wright. In *Who's Who 1921*, London: Adam and Charles Black, 1921, p. 2911.
Biography continued in later editions, 1922–1948. Listed in *Who Was Who, 1941–1950*, London: 1952, pp. 1267–1268.

Who's Who in American Aeronautics: Orville Wright. *Aviation*, Mar. 21, 1921, vol. 10, p. 365.

Who's Who in Aeronautics: Orville Wright. *Aerial Age Weekly*, Mar. 28, 1921, vol. 13, p. 61, port.

Dr. Orville Wright. In *American Men of Science*, 3rd ed., Garrison, N.Y.: Science Press, 1921, p. 672.
Also included in 4th–7th editions, 1927, 1933, 1938, 1944.

Orville Wright. In *Who's Who in American Aeronautics*, New York: Gardner, Moffat Co., 1922, p. 108, port.
Also included in 2nd edition, 1925, pages 118–119 and 3rd edition, 1928, page 130.

[Wright, Katharine.] Orville Wright. In *The John Fritz Medal*, New York: John Fritz Medal Board of Award [1922], pp. 111–116, illus.
One of a series of biographical notices on the John Fritz medalists. Presumptive authorship of this article is established by the correspondence between Orville Wright and the secretary of the John Fritz Medal Fund, May 12 and June 4, 1921.

Orville Wright Succeeds Col. F. P. Lahm as Chairman, N. A. A. Contest Committee. *National Aeronautic Association Review*, Aug. 1, 1924, vol. 2, no. 8, p. 1, port.

Cesare, Oscar. With Orville Wright in his Workshop. *New York Times Magazine*, Feb. 1, 1925, p. 8, illus.

Orville Wright and His Brother Built the First Successful Aeroplane. *National Magazine*, Jan. 1926, vol. 54, p. 242.

First Man to Fly Works on. *New York Times Magazine*, July 10, 1927, pp. 1–2, illus.
Also published with title, "The First Man to Fly," in *U.S. Air Services*, Sept. 1927, vol. 12, no. 9, pp. 22–25.

Orville Wright. In *Who's Who in Aviation*, London: Airways Publications, Limited, 1928, pp. 124–125.

Lent, L. B. Orville Wright the Flight Bringer; a Picture of a Quiet Man After Twenty-Five Years of Fame. *Liberty*, Dec. 22, 1928, vol. 5, no. 51, pp. 16–18, 20, illus.

Life Stories of Famous Living Inventors. Chapter 101. Orville Wright. *Patent News*, May 1929, vol. 19, no. 4, pp. 2, 4.

Orville Wright. In *Encyclopædia Britannica*, New York: Encyclopædia Britannica, Inc., 1929, vol. 3, p. 808.
Continued in later editions.

Gage, Nevin I. Exchange Honors Orville Wright. *The Exchangeite*, Mar. 1930, vol. 9, no. 3, pp. 1, 28–29, illus.

Hodgins, Eric. Profiles; Heavier than Air. Orville Wright. *New Yorker*, Dec. 13, 1930, vol. 6, pp. 29–32, illus.

Henderson, Archibald. Orville Wright. In his *Contemporary Immortals*, New York, London: D. Appleton, 1930, pp. 134–148, port.

Rutledge, Paul. Glorious Pioneers of Aviation. *Our Hobbies*, Feb.–Mar. 1931, vol. 3, no. 1, pp. 12–13.

Orville Wright's 60th Birthday Celebration. [New York: Vacuum Oil Company, 1931.] [10 pp.]
Collection of congratulatory messages broadcast August 19, 1931.

Orville Wright. In *Blue Book of Aviation*, Los Angeles: Hoagland Company, 1932, p. 231, port.

Orville Wright. In the Daniel Guggenheim Medal Fund, Inc., *The Daniel Guggenheim Medal for Achievement in Aeronautics. Biographies* . . . New York: 1932, pp. 2–9, port.
Reprinted in revised 1936 edition, and brought up to date in 1953 edition entitled, *Pioneers in Aeronautics; Recipients of the Daniel Guggenheim Medal, 1929–1932*, pages 1–7. One of a series of sketches of the Daniel Guggenheim medalists. Correspondence between Orville Wright and the secretary of the Daniel Guggenheim Medal Fund in 1932 establishes Orville Wright as the author.

Orville Wright. In *The National Encyclopædia*, New York: P. F. Collier & Son, 1932, vol. 10, p. 526.
Published also in later editions, 1934–1946; revised 1947–1949.

New Member. *Time*, May 11, 1936, vol. 27, no. 19, p. 44.
Comment on election of Orville Wright as a member of the National Academy of Sciences.

Prophet of the New World. *National Aeronautics*, Dec. 1937, vol. 15, no. 12, p. 7, port.

Cesare, Oscar. Orville Wright Looks Back to Aviation's Birthday. *New York Times Magazine*, Dec. 11, 1938, pp. 6–7, 23.

[Findley, Earl N.] Orville Wright Goes Again to Kitty Hawk. *U.S. Air Services*, May 1939, vol. 24, no. 5, pp. 12–15, 40, illus.

Account of Orville Wright's automobile trip from Dayton to Kitty Hawk in April, 1939.

Ellis, Carlyle. Flying as It Was—The Birth of American DH's. *Sportsman Pilot*, Oct. 15, 1939, vol. 22, no. 4, pp. 16–17, 30, illus.

Includes interview with Orville Wright and account of his flight at Dayton in 1918 with an early Wright aeroplane.

[Findley, Earl N.] Orville Wright Visits Washington. *U.S. Air Services*, Nov. 1941, vol. 26, no. 11, p. 11.

Visit of October 23, 1941.

Ingells, Douglas J. Orville Wright Today. *Air Trails*, June 1942, vol. 18, no. 3, pp. 42, 44, illus.

[Findley, Earl N.] The Orville Wright Suite. *U.S. Air Services*, Nov. 1942, vol. 27, no. 11, p. 44.

Reference to three-room suite in the Raleigh Hotel, Washington, D.C., where Orville Wright usually stayed when visiting the National Capital.

Cuneo, John R. Orville Wright Reminds a German General of a Circus. In his *Winged Mars*, Harrisburg, Pa.: Military Service Publishing Company, 1942, pp. 79–87, illus.

Origins of military aviation in Germany with quotation from the diary of Lieutenant General Walter von Eberhardt who witnessed flights of Orville Wright at Tempelhof Field, Berlin, in 1909.

Orville Wright. In *Who's Who in Aviation . . . 1942–43*, Chicago & New York: Ziff-Davis Publishing Company, 1942, p. 477.

Orville Wright Studies Gliders. *Aviation News*, Aug. 30, 1943, vol. 1, no. 5, p. 9.

Report on a device to aid towed gliders being developed by Orville Wright.

[Findley, Earl N.] On the Eve of the 40th Anniversary. *U.S. Air Services*, Nov. 1943, vol. 28, no. 11, p. 10.

Editor's comments on Orville Wright's visit to Washington, October 21, 1943.

Wright Honor Guest at Anniversary Fete. *Aviation News*, Nov. 22, 1943, vol. 1, no. 17, p. 15.

Announcement of fortieth anniversary dinner to be held in Washington, December 17.

[Findley, Earl N.] Orville Wright Without an Equal in Several Different Fields. *U.S. Air Services*, Dec. 1943, vol. 28, no. 12, pp. 9–10.

Author's reminiscences of Orville Wright.

Loening, Grover. First Flyer in More Ways than One. *U.S. Air Services*, Dec. 1943, vol. 28, no. 12, p. 20.

Early manager of the Wright Company comments on Orville Wright's skill as a pilot.

Honoring Mr. Orville Wright on the Fortieth Anniversary of the First Flights of the Wright Brothers at Kitty Hawk, North Carolina, 17 December 1903. [Washington: 1943]. 8p.

Official dinner program issued on the occasion of the dinner honoring Orville and attended by him, December 17, 1943, in Washington. Includes "Contributions of Wilbur and Orville Wright to Aeronautical Science," by George W. Lewis, pp. 6–7.

Brewer, Griffith. The Wright Trilogy. *Journal of the Royal Aeronautical Society*, Apr. 1944, vol. 40, pp. 92–94.
Letter to the editor, March 15, commenting on Fred C. Kelly's interview with Orville Wright as reported in *New York Herald Tribune*, November 12, 1943.

Orville Wright Flies Constellation. *Aviation News*, May 1, 1944, vol. 1, no. 40, p. 15.
Report on 50 minute flight at Wright Field, Dayton.

Orville Wright Honored. *Aeronautical Engineering Review*, June 1944, vol. 3, no. 6, p. 203.
Announces his election to an honorary life membership in the Aeronautical Chamber of Commerce of America, Inc.

Ingells, Douglas J. and Lawrence Lader. Orville Wright: First to Fly. *Coronet*, Aug. 1946, vol. 20, no. 4, pp. 120–127.

Orville Wright. *Current Biography*, Oct. 1946, vol. 7, pp. 54–57.
Revised *Current Biography 1946*, New York: The H. W. Wilson Company, 1947, pp. 662–665, port.

[Findley, Earl N.] Orville Wright. *U.S. Air Services*, Feb. 1948, vol. 33, no. 2, pp. 5–8, port.
Obituary article by a personal friend of forty years' standing.

Orville Wright, Co-Inventor of the Airplane, Dies at Dayton, 44 Years After First Flight. *National Aeronautics*, Feb. 1948, vol. 27, no. 2, pp. 3–4.

The Late Orville Wright. Extension of Remarks of Hon. Chester E. Merroa. *Congressional Record*, Feb. 4, 1948, vol. 94, appendix p. A678.
Reprints editorial from New Hampshire *Morning Union*, February 2, 1948.

Grey, C. G. The First To Fly [signed C. G. G.]. *Aeroplane*, Feb. 6, 1948, vol. 74, p. 148, illus.
Obituary note.

Obituary. Orville Wright. *Engineer*, Feb. 6, 1948, vol. 185, pp. 139–140, port.

Orville Wright. *Engineering*, Feb. 6, 1948, vol. 165, pp. 133–134.

Begetter of an Age. *Time*, Feb. 9, 1948, vol. 51, p. 22.
Obituary article.

Died: Orville Wright. *Newsweek*, Feb. 9, 1948, vol. 31, no. 6, p. 55.

Death of Albert Medalist. *Royal Society of Arts Journal*, Feb. 13, 1948, vol. 96, p. 185.

Davy, M. J. B. Mr. Orville Wright. *Nature*, Feb. 21, 1948, vol. 161, p. 269–270.

In Memoriam. Orville Wright. *Aeronautical Engineering Review*, Mar. 1948, vol. 7, p. 15, illus.

On the Death of Orville Wright. *Interavia*, Mar. 1948, vol. 3, pp. 129–130, illus.

Orville Wright. *Chirp*, Mar. 1948, no. 37, pp. 7–8.

Dorman, Geoffrey. Orville Wright—an Appreciation. *The Light Plane*, Apr. 1948, vol. 2, p. 30.

Kelly, Fred C. Orville Wright at Work. *Technology Review*, Apr. 1948, vol. 50, p. 309.
Brief account of Orville's habits and activities at his Dayton laboratory.

We Knew Orville Wright. *Rotarian*, Apr. 1948, vol. 72, no. 4, p. 53.
Account of meeting of the Rotarians of Dayton in memory of Orville Wright with a tribute by Frank D. Slutz.

Obituaries: Orville Wright. *Isis*, May 1948, vol. 39, p. 69.

Durand, William F. Orville Wright. *Mechanical Engineering*, July 1948, vol. 70, pp. 581–585.

Horan, Joseph C. Orville Wright—Philatelic Memorial. *Stamps*, Oct. 23, 1948, vol. 65, pp. 150–160, illus.
Popular account of the Wrights with note on commemorative covers flown on the fortieth anniversary of their first flights in 1903 and on Orville's flight aboard a Constellation in 1944.

Durand, William F. *Biographical Memoir of Orville Wright, 1871–1948*. Presented to the Academy at the Autumn Meeting, 1948. Washington: National Academy of Sciences, 1948, 3 p.l., pp. 257–273, port. (Biographical Memoirs, Volume XXV, Eleventh Memoir).

King, Ernest J. Some Remembrances of Orville Wright. *U.S. Air Services*, Feb. 1949, vol. 34, no. 2, pp. 13–14.
World War II Chief of Naval Operations writes an account of his three visits to Dayton on the December 17 anniversary, 1933, 1934, and 1935.

Abelin, Rudolf. Orville Wright—Motorflyningens Fader. *Ett År i Luften, 1949*, pp. 116–127, illus.

Obituaries: Orville Wright. In *1949 Britannica Book of the Year*, Chicago, Toronto, London: Encyclopædia Britannica, Inc., 1949, p. 537.

Obituary. *Current Biography 1948*, New York: H. W. Wilson Company, 1949, p. 696.

Orville Wright. In *The Americana Annual . . . 1949*, New York: Americana Corporation, 1949, p. 738.

When Orville Wright Lived at the Cosmos Club. *Cosmos Club Bulletin*, May 1950, vol. 3, no. 7, p. 2.
Note on Orville's stay at the Club in May 1908.

Orville Wright. In *Who Was Who in America.* Vol. 2. Chicago: A. N. Marquis Company, 1950, p. 595.

Hanuschke, Wilhelm. I Flew with Orville Wright. *U.S. Air Services*, Dec. 1952, vol. 37, no. 12, pp. 7–9, illus.
Account of the author's meeting and flight with Orville Wright at Tempelhof Field, Berlin, in 1909.

McFarland, Marvin W. Orville Wright and Friend. *U.S. Air Services*, Aug. 1956, vol. 51, pp. 5–7.
An account of the association of Orville Wright and Earl N. Findley, deceased July 11, 1956, with excerpts from their correspondence.

Kelly, Fred C. A Psychic Mystery of Aviation. *Michigan Alumnus Quarterly Review*, Aug. 9, 1958, vol. 64, pp. 352–353.
An account of a practical joke played by Orville on his friend Griffith Brewer involving the source of the quotation "so easy it seemed, once found, which, yet unfound, most would have

thought impossible" from Milton's *Paradise Lost.*

Orville Wright. In Lassalle, Eugène J. *Les 100 premiers aviateurs brevetés au monde et la naissance de l'aviation.* [Paris] Nauticaero, [1962], pp. 50–51.

Orville was granted pilot's license no. 14 by L'Aéro-Club of France in 1909.

Orville Wright. In *The Guggenheim Medalists: Architects of the Age of Flight*, New York: The Guggenheim Medal Board of Award, 1964, pp. 56–57, port.

Much abridged and rewritten version of biography originally published by the Daniel Guggenheim Medal Fund in 1932, 1936, and 1953.

Wind Tunnel

Baker, M. P. The Wright Brothers as Aeronautical Engineers. *SAE Quarterly Transactions*, Jan. 1951, vol. 5, pp. 1–17, illus.

Originally issued with slightly varying text as SAE Preprint 459, New York: Society of Automotive Engineers, 1950, 23 pp.; reprinted with exception of appendices and discussion, pages 12–17, in *Annual Report of the Smithsonian Institution, 1950*, Washington: United States Government Printing Office, 1951, pp. 209–223; as Smithsonian Publication 4030, Washington: United States Government Printing Office, 1951, 2 p. 1., pp. 209–223; in *Smithsonian Treasury of Science*, vol. III, edited by Webster P. True, New York: Simon and Schuster, Inc., 1960, pp. 1075–1104; and abridged with title, "Wright Brothers; World's First Aeronautical Engineers," in *Aero Digest*, July 1953, vol. 67, pp. 18–24.

Paper given before the National Aeronautic Meeting of the Society of Automotive Engineers, New York, April 17, 1950, by the Assistant Technical Advisor to the Orville Wright Estate. Presents technical details of Wrights' 1901 wind tunnel experiments. Also included are discussions: "Wright Brothers and Aerodynamics," by Francis H. Clauser; "Design, Structural Features of Wright Brothers Airplane," by Alexander Kartvelli; "Powerplants Built by Wright Brothers," by Opie Chenoweth.

——— *The Wright Brothers' Wind Tunnel Experiments.* [Dayton: The Author, 1949], 20 pp., illus., processed.

Lecture delivered at Oberlin College, May 26, 1949.

Brewer, Griffith. Original Wind Tunnel of the Wright Brothers. *U.S. Air Services*, Nov. 1938, vol. 23, no. 11, pp. 17–18.

Published also in *Proceedings of the Fifth International Congress for Applied Mechanics, Cambridge, Mass., Sept. 12–16, 1938*, New York: John Wiley & Sons, 1939, pp. 741–743; Brewer, Griffith, *Fifty Years of Flying*, London: Air League of the British Empire, 1946, pp. 96–101.

Address delivered at the dedication of the Wright Brothers Memorial Wind Tunnel at the Massachusetts Institute of Technology, September 12, 1938.

Gerhardt, W. F. *Wright and Prandtl; Some Early Wind Tunnel Tests Interpreted in the Light of Prandtl's Induction Theory.* [Detroit: The Author, 1938], 18 pp. (typescript) and diagrs., 5 pp.

260-517—68——4

Paper presented at the Sixth Annual Meeting of the Institute of the Aeronautical Sciences, January 26, 1938. Author deals briefly with 1901 wind-tunnel experiments and attempts modern interpretation of Wright data.

Lewis, George W. The Wright Brothers as Researchers. *Aviation*, Aug. 1939, vol. 38, no. 7, pp. 20–21, 81, illus.

Advance publication with special title of the section, "Research in the Wright Brothers' Wind Tunnel" in his 27th Wilbur Wright Memorial Lecture "Some Modern Methods of Research in Problems of Flight," delivered before the Royal Aeronautical Society, London, May 25, 1939, and published in *The Journal of the Royal Aeronautical Society*, Oct. 1939, vol. 53, pp. 773–778.

Based on data supplied the author by Orville Wright.

McClarren, Ralph H. The Wright Brothers' Aeronautical Engineering Collection at the Franklin Institute, Philadelphia, Pa. *Journal of the Franklin Institute*, Aug. 1951, vol. 252, pp. 175–196, illus.

Includes listing of Wrights' 1901 and 1917 wind-tunnel apparatus and drawings and descriptions of data sheets and notes of the 1901 and 1917 wind-tunnel tests bequeathed to the Franklin Institute by Orville Wright.

Randers-Pehrson, Nils H. Wright Brothers. In his *Pioneer Wind Tunnels*, Washington: Smithsonian Institution, 1935, pp. 11–13, illus. (Smithsonian Publication 3294 and Smithsonian Miscellaneous Collections, vol. 93, no. 4).

Shaw, Herbert. Orville Wright Finds Historic Relic, Long Lost. Mechanism Which Made First Flight Possible Comes to Light in Laboratory Attic. *U.S. Air Services*, Jan. 1947, vol. 32, no. 1, pp. 17–18, illus.

Reprinted from *Dayton Daily News.*

The balances used in the Wrights' 1901 wind tunnel and lost December 6, 1916 were found in the attic of Orville's laboratory, December 9, 1946.

Warner, Edward P., and Norton, Fredrick H. Wind Tunnel Balances. *National Advisory Committee for Aeronautics Report No. 72*, 1920, 40 pp.

Preprinted from *Fifth Annual Report of the National Advisory Committee for Aeronautics, 1919*, Washington: Government Printing Office, 1920, pp. 647–648.

Includes "Brief Notes on Balances of Other Types. (4) Wright," pages 39–40. This was the balance used by Orville Wright in the wind tunnel at his Dayton laboratory, 1917–1922.

Wright Brothers' Studies. *Science News Letter*, June 4, 1949, vol. 55, p. 355, port.

Brief note on Wright wind-tunnel instruments on the occasion of presentation of reproductions to Oberlin College.

The Wright Brothers' Wind Tunnel. *U.S. Air Services*, July 1939, vol. 24, no. 7, p. 7.

Editorial comment on Dr. George W. Lewis' 1939 Wilbur Wright Memorial Lecture before the Royal Aeronautical Society.

Aeroplanes and Flights

1903

Chanute, Octave. Gliding Machines. The Latest Aeronautical Experiments. *Illustrated Scientific News*, Feb. 1903, vol. 23, p. 73, illus.

Brief account of 1902 Wright glider and gliding experiments illustrated by three photographs of glider in flight.

Die Brüder Wright. *Wiener Luftschiffer-Zeitung*, Mar. 1903, vol. 2, pp. 56–57.

Brief mention of Wrights' 1902 glider experiments.

Nimführ, Raimund. Die Neuesten Fortschritte in der praktischen Fliegekunst. *Illustrirte Zeitung*, Mar. 5, 1903, vol. 120, p. 351, illus.

Brief reference to Wright gliding experiments, 1900–1902, illustrated by five photographs of their 1902 glider. This was one of a number of contemporary articles later cited by the courts as including disclosures which invalidated the Wright patent claims.

Le Beschu, F. Locomotion aérienne en Amérique. *Le Monde illustré*, Mar. 28, 1903, vol. 47, p. 299, illus.

Includes details of the Wright glider supplied by Octave Chanute.

Diner-Conférence du 2 avril 1903. M. Chanute à l'Aéro-Club. *L'Aérophile*, Apr. 1903, vol. 11, pp. 81–86, illus.

Chanute's address before the Aéro Club of France detailing Wright experiments of 1900, 1901, and 1902 illustrated with photographs from *La Locomotion* below.

Archdeacon, Ernest. M. Chanute à Paris. *La Locomotion*, Apr. 11, 1903, vol. 3, pp. 225–227, illus.

This report of Chanute's speech of April 2, before the Aéro Club of France, Paris, aroused tremendous French interest in heavier-than-air flight and led to experiments which marked the beginning of European aviation. Has reference to the Wright experiments but photographs of several of the Wright gliders are erroneously labeled as those of Chanute. This is one of the articles later cited by the courts in the Wright patent suits.

Séance du 23 avril 1903, Société Français de Navigation Aérienne. *L'Aéronaute*, May 1903, vol. 36, pp. 93–106.

Includes Mr. Paul Bordé's report on Chanute's address to the Aéro Club of France.

Contains reference to the Wrights' method of warping the wings to effect lateral balance and to their use of warping in conjunction with the vertical tail. French and German courts later held that these disclosures invalidated their patent claims.

Villethiou, Jean de. L'Aéronautique. *La Revue technique*, May 25, 1903, p. 311.

Includes brief mention of the Wright brothers.

André, Henri. Les aviateurs américains et l'aviation. *Revue générale des transports*, June 1903, pp. 395–396, illus.

Based on account of Wright brothers by Ernest Archdeacon in *La Locomotion* above.

Includes photographic illustrations, scale drawings, and structural details of the Chanute multiple-wing and two-surface gliders and of the Wright 1902 glider.

Chanute, Octave. La Navigation aérienne aux Etats-Unis. *L'Aérophile*, Aug. 1903, vol. 11, pp. 171–183, illus.
English translation in *The Papers of Wilbur and Orville Wright* (New York: McGraw-Hill, 1953), vol. 1, pp. 659–673.
Includes plans for and illustrations of the Wright 1902 glider.

Learning to Fly. *Automotor Journal*, Oct. 3, 1903, vol. 8, pp. 1032–1033.
Editorial comment on the Wright 1902 gliding experiments.

Chanute, Octave. L'Aviation en Amérique. *Revue générale des sciences pures et appliquées*, Nov. 30, 1903, vol. 14, pp. 1133–1142, illus.
Extensive account of Chanute's early gliding experiments and those of the Wright brothers, 1900–1902, with description and numerous illustrations and drawings of the Chanute and Wright 1902 gliders.

L'Aviation en Amérique. *L'Aérophile*, Dec. 1903, vol. 11, p. 282.
Brief report on Wright December 17 flights.

The Empire of the Air. An Important Step Forward. *Automotor Journal*, Dec. 30, 1903, vol. 8, p. 1385.
Editorial comment on reported motor flights by the Wright brothers, December 17.

1904

La machine volante des frères Wright. *L'Aérophile*, Jan. 1904, vol. 12, pp. 16–18.
French translation of Wrights' January 6 statement to the Associated Press describing their 1903 flights.

The Wright Flyer. *Gas Power*, Jan. 1904, vol. 1, no. 8, p. 39.
Brief report on flights of Wright brothers, December 17, 1903.

Le Beschu, F. L'Aéroplane des États-Unis. *Le Monde illustré*, Jan. 2, 1904, vol. 48, p. 17, illus.
Reports flight of 5 kilometers accomplished with a powered machine, illustrated by photograph of the Wright 1902 glider.

Clayton, Henry H. Wilbur Wright's Successful Flight in a Motor-Driven Aeroplane. *Science*, Jan. 8, 1904, vol. 19 (n. s.), p. 76.
Statement on significance of Wrights' December 17, 1903 flights.

The Machine That Flies; Performance of the Wright Brothers Aerostat Gives Promise of Success, Details of Machine (by W. H. S.). *New York Herald Magazine Section*, Jan. 17, 1904, p. 3.

A Flying Machine That Actually Flies. *Collier's*, Jan. 23, 1904, vol. 32, no. 17, p. 12, illus.
Highly inaccurate account of Wrights' Kitty Hawk experiments. Photographs erroneously labeled "The flying machine made by the Wrights" comprise three views of the Chanute glider and one of the Wright 1902 glider.

The Problem of Flight. *Harper's Weekly*, Jan. 30, 1904, vol. 48, p. 180.
Brief statement on Wright 1903 flights.

A Motor Aeroplane; Successful Trials with a Man-Carrying Machine. *Knowledge & Scientific News*, Feb. 1904, vol. 1, pp. 3–4, illus.

Based on Wrights' statement to the Associated Press, January 6.

The Flight of the Wrights. *Automotor Journal*, Feb. 6, 1904, vol. 9, pp. 148–150, illus.
Based on the Wrights' January 6 statement to the Associated Press which was reported in *L'Auto*.

Dienstbach [Carl] Die Erfindung der Flugmaschine. *Illustrierte Aeronautische Mitteilungen*, Mar. 1904, vol. 8, pp. 97–98.
Report on the Wrights' December 17, 1903 flights by the American correspondent of the journal.

——— Der Motorflug der Gebrüder Wright. *Illustrierte Aeronautische Mitteilungen*, Mar. 1904, vol. 8, pp. 98–100, illus.
Supplements foregoing report by the author with inclusion of sketches of the Wright machine from the *New York Herald*, January 17, 1904.

Chanute, Octave. Aerial Navigation. *Popular Science Monthly*, Mar. 1904, vol. 64, pp. 385–393.
Published also in *Annual Report of the Smithsonian Institution, 1903*, Washington: Government Printing Office, 1904, pp. 173–181.
Paper presented before section D, American Association for the Advancement of Science, December 30, 1903. Includes reference to the successful flights of the Wright brothers, December 17, 1903.

Ferber, Ferdinand. Les progrès de l'aviation depuis 1891 par le vol plané. *Revue d'artillerie*, Mar. 1904, vol. 63, pp. 397–443, illus.
Abstract in *Scientific American*, Apr. 1, 1905, vol. 92, pp. 260, 262, illus.

Includes brief résumé of the gliding experiments of the Wrights and of their December 17, 1903 flights.

Gleitflug in Amerika und in Frankreich. *Wiener Luftschiffer-Zeitung*, Mar. 1904, vol. 3, pp. 66–68.
Includes German translation of Wrights' statement published in *L'Aérophile*, January 1904.

Root, A. I. [Wright Brothers Flying Machine.] *Gleanings in Bee Culture*, Mar. 1, 1904, vol. 32, pp. 240–241.
Author's mention to his Sunday school class of the Wright 1903 flights.

The Experiments of the Wright Brothers. *Aeronautical Journal*, Apr. 1904, vol. 8, pp. 37–42, illus.
Published also in *Esso Air World*, Nov./Dec. 1953, vol. 6, pp. 63–67, illus.
Summarizes Wilbur Wright's lecture, "Experiments and Observations in Soaring Flight," and reprints Associated Press statement of January 6 communicated to the Aeronautical Society of Great Britain by Orville Wright.

Crocco, Arturo. La prima macchina volante. *Bollettino della Società Aeronautica Italiana*, July 1904, vol. 1, pp. 3–4.

Nouveaux essais de l'aéroplane automobile Wright. *L'Aérophile*, Sept. 1904, vol. 12, p. 216.
Brief mention of Wright flights, May 26, 1904 and December 17, 1903.

Dominik, Hans. Neuere Versuche mit Motor-Drachenfliegern. *Der Motorwagen*, Nov. 20, 1904, vol. 7, pp. 507–511, illus.
Includes reference to Wright experiments, 1900–1902, and to their powered flights of December 17, 1903.

1905

[Root, A. I.] My Flying-Machine Story. *Gleanings in Bee Culture*, Jan. 1, 1905, vol. 33, pp. 36–39, 48.

Pages 36–39 reprinted with title "The First Eye-witness Account of a Powered Aeroplane Flight (1904)" in *The Aeroplane; an Historical Survey of Its Origins and Development*, by Charles H. Gibbs-Smith (London: H. M. Stat. Off., 1960), pp. 234–239.

His report on the Wrights' 1904 flights at Huffman Prairie near Dayton, previously unpublished because he had been sworn to secrecy by the Wrights, is contained in a regular feature section, with moral lesson included, of the magazine entitled "Our Homes," pp. 36–39, with preceding biblical quotation "What hath God wrought?—Num. 23:23."

[———] The Wright Brothers' Flying Machine. *Gleanings in Bee Culture*, Jan. 15, 1905, vol. 33, pp. 86–87, illus.

Author attempts description of 1903 aeroplane.

Dienstbach, [Carl] Das erste Lebensjahr der praktischen Flugmaschine. *Illustrierte Aeronautische Mitteilungen*, Mar. 1905, vol. 9, pp. 91–93, illus.

Includes German translation of statement by the Wrights on their 1904 flights with accompanying drawing based on author's conception of their machine.

Esnault-Pelterie, Robert. Expériences d'aviation exécutées en 1904, en vérification de celles des frères Wright. *L'Aérophile*, June 1905, vol. 13, pp. 132–138, illus.

Report of experiments conducted with a Wright-type glider built from available published data on it.

Zur Wrightschen Flugmaschine. [Signed *m.*] *Illustrierte Aeronautische Mitteilungen*, June 1905, vol. 9, pp. 183–184.

Anonymous author casts doubt on Dienstbach's report in the March issue of this journal.

Verifica delle esperienze di aviazione dei fratelli Wright. *Bollettino della Società Aeronautica Italiana*, July-Sept. 1905, vol. 2, pp. 147–148.

Based on Esnault-Pelterie's account in *L'Aérophile*, June 1905, above.

[Root, A. I.] The Wright Brothers Flying Machine to Date: Flying 24 Miles in 38 Minutes. *Gleanings in Bee Culture*, Dec. 1, 1905, vol. 33, p. 1258.

Report on 1905 flights.

Brothers Wright Rumours. *Automotor Journal*, Dec. 9, 1905, vol. 10, p. 1542.

Brief note expressing skepticism about Wright 1905 flights as reported in *L'Auto*. The source of *L'Auto's* information was the Wright brothers' letter of October 9 to Captain Ferber.

Le plus lourd que l'air. *La Conquête de l'air*, Dec. 15, 1905. vol. 2, pp. 1-2.

The Wright Brothers Experiments. *Automotor Journal*, Dec. 23, 1905, vol. 10, p. 1601.

Reports Harvey M. Weaver's letter of December 3 to Frank S. Lahm and Robert Coquelle's article in *L'Auto* in confirmation of rumors of Wrights' successes.

Breyer, Victor. L'Aéroplane des frères Wright. *La Vie au grand air*, Dec. 29, 1905, pp. 1099–1100, illus.

Based on article in *L'Auto*.

Les Frères Wright et leur aéroplane à moteur. *L'Aérophile*, Dec. 1905, vol. 13, pp. 265–272, ports.

Extensive discussion of the merits of the Wright aeroplane and the evidence supporting the claims of flights by the Wrights. Introduces pertinent letters and materials including French translations of letters of Wilbur and Orville Wright to Georges Besançon, the editor, November 17, 1905, and to Captain Ferber, October 9 and November 4, 1905, Octave Chanute's letter of November 9 to Ferber, and quotes from articles by Ernest Archdeacon in *Les Sports* and Robert Coquelle in *L'Auto*.

Gardner, Gilson. When Men Wear Wings. *Technical World Magazine*, Dec. 1905, vol. 4, pp. 447–454.

Includes reference to the Wright brothers' aeroplane, pages 449–450.

More Wright Rumours. *Automotor Journal*, Dec. 30, 1905, vol. 10, pp. 1621–1622.

Expressing confidence in the reports of the Wrights' 1903 and 1905 flights as stated by Orville Wright in his letter of November 17, 1905 to Mr. Patrick Y. Alexander of the Aeronautical Society of Great Britain and by Octave Chanute in a letter to Captain Ferber which was published in *Revue d'Artillerie*, Aug. 1905, editors state they have reversed their skeptical attitude expressed in December 9 issue of this journal above.

The Conquest of the Air. *Automotor Journal*, Dec. 30, 1905, vol. 10, p. 1611.

Editorial comment on the above report.

1906

L'Aéroplane Wright. *L'Aérophile*, Jan. 1906, vol. 14, pp. 18–23, illus.

Presentation of further statements on the Wright flights in continuation of the discussion in the December 1905 issue of this journal. Publishes letter of the Wrights to the editor, December 13, 1905, two letters of Henry M. Weaver to Frank S. Lahm, December 6, 1905, and January 3, 1906, and reports originally appearing in the *New York Herald*, January 4, 1906, and by Robert Coquelle in *L'Auto*.

Cléry, A. Derniers perfectionnements connus des machines volantes Wright. *L'Aérophile*, Jan. 1906, vol. 14, pp. 23–26, illus.

Lacking details on the Wright machine author reprints specifications of the Wright French patent, published September 1, 1904.

Recent Experiments of the Brothers Wright. *The Aeronautical Journal*, Jan. 1906, vol. 10, pp. 14–15.

Includes letter from Orville Wright dated November 17, 1905, read by Mr. Alexander before Aeronautical Society of Great Britain, giving brief account of their 1905 experiments at Huffman Field near Dayton.

The "White Flyer"—the Motor Driven Aeroplane for the Brothers Wright. *Automotor Journal*, Jan. 6, 1906, vol. 11, pp. 17–20, illus.

The Wright Aeroplane and Its Fabled Performances. *Scientific American*, Jan. 13, 1906, vol. 108, p. 40.

Based on a report in a French automobile publication which published a letter from the Wrights to Captain Ferber, November 4, 1905, describing their 1905 flights.

Ancora intorno alle esperienze dei fratelli Wright. *Bollettino della Società Aeronautica Italiana*, Jan./Feb. 1906, vol. 3, pp. 19–21.

Report on recent available information on the Wrights, including their letters of November 4, 1905, to Captain Ferber, November 17, 1905, to Patrick Alexander, and January 3, 1906, to Frank S. Lahm.

Dienstbach, [Carl] Das Zweite Lebensjahr der praktische Flugmaschine. *Illustrierte Aeronautische Mitteilungen*, Feb. 1906, vol. 10, pp. 50–54.

A report on the 1905 Wright flights, with a German translation of their letter of November 17, 1905, to the author and a translation of selected extracts from articles originally published in *Gleanings in Bee Culture* above.

Die Versuche der Gebrüder Wright im Jahre 1905. *Illustrierte Aeronautische Mitteilungen*, Feb. 1906, vol. 10, pp. 48–50.

Editor expresses great doubt of reported Wright flights. Includes Wrights' letter of November 4, 1905, to Captain Ferber.

Die Wright-Frage. *Wiener Luftschiffer-Zeitung*, Feb. 1906, vol. 5, pp. 30–34.

Based on reports on Wrights' flights originally published in *L'Auto* in December and January issues. Includes German translation of Henry Weaver's letter of December 6, 1905, to Frank S. Lahm confirming Wright flights, as well as their letter of January 3, 1906, to Lahm.

The Conquest of the Air. *The Car*, Feb. 21, 1906, vol. 16, p. 8.

Reprints Chanute's letter of February 6 to the editor giving details of the Wrights' 1903–1905 experiments.

Mauni, Baron de. À propos de la performance des frères Wright. *La Vie automobile*, Feb. 24, 1906, vol. 6, pp. 114–115.

Fly Fast in the Air. Wright Brothers of Dayton Make Public Results of Recent Tests of Aeroplane. *Motor Age*, Mar. 8, 1906, vol. 9, no. 10, pp. 8–9.

Partially based on letter of Wrights to the editor, Charles R. Root, February 7, 1906. Includes comments by Orville Wright on Walter Wellman's proposed trip to the North Pole by balloon.

The Experiments of the Brothers Wright. *The Aeronautical Journal*, Apr. 1906, vol. 12, pp. 25–26.

Few details on Wright machine based on data derived from *L'Aérophile*, January 1906 above.

The Wright Aeroplane and Its Performances. *Scientific American*, Apr. 7, 1906, vol. 94, pp. 291–292, illus.

Reports Wright brothers' statement to the Aero Club of America, March 12, 1906, and presents summaries of answers to a series of eleven questions submitted by the editor to the 17 persons listed by the Wrights in this statement as having witnessed their flights. Reprints in full reply of Charles Webbert, March 21, 1906.

Chanute, Octave. Chanute on the Wright Brothers' Achievement in Aerial Navigation. *Scientific American*, Apr. 14, 1906, vol. 94, p. 307.

Chanute's letter of reply, March 31, to the editor's letter of March 19, requesting verification of statement by Chanute published in *Illustrierte Aeronautische Mitteilungen*.

The Wright Brothers' Aeroplane. *Pathfinder*, Apr. 14, 1906, vol. 13, no. 641, p. 2.

Based on report in *Scientific American*, April 7.

The Wright Brothers' Flying Machine and What It has Accomplished. *Scientific American Supplement*, Apr. 17, 1906, vol. 61, p. 25303.

Wright brothers' statement submitted to the Aero Club of America, March 12, 1906, reporting on their flights to date.

The Wright Flyer, 1905. *The Aeronautical News*, May 1906, vol. 1, no. 1, pp. 14–15, illus.

Grimes, E. B. Man May Now Fly at Will. *The Technical World Magazine*, June 1906, vol. 5, pp. 330–338, illus.

Article on the Wright brothers based largely on, and incorporating, their statement of March 12, 1906 to the Aero Club of America.

Von den Gebrüdern Wright. *Wiener Luftschiffer-Zeitung*, July 1906, vol. 5, pp. 139–141, ports.

Translation by W. E. von Lössl of Wright brothers' letter of May 19, 1906, to the Weiner Luftschiffer Verein and their enclosed communication to the Aero Club of America, March 12, 1906, with added note by the editor, Victor Silberer, that he is not convinced by the testimony of the witnesses of the 1905 flights.

Maxim, Hiram S. The Recent Experiments Conducted by the Wright Brothers. *The Aeronautical Journal*, July 1906, vol. 10, pp. 37–39.

Reprinted in the *Aeronautical Journal*, July–Sept. 1916, vol. 20, pp. 126–128.

General statement on significance of flights with accompanying discussion by S. F. Cody, J. T. C. Moore-Brabazon and others.

La Costruzione di un aeroplano Wright. *Il Secolo XX*, 1906, vol. VIII, pp. 419–424.

Genesis of the First Successful Aeroplane. Editorial on the Work of the Wright Brothers of Dayton, Ohio. *Scientific American*, Dec. 15, 1906, vol. 95, p. 442.

1907

Bell, Alexander G. Aerial Locomotion. *National Geographic Magazine*, Jan. 1907, vol. 18, pp. 1–34, illus.

Reprinted Washington, D.C.: Press of Judd & Detweiler, Inc., 1907, 34 pp., and published also in the *Proceedings of the Washington Academy of Sciences*, 1907, vol. 8, pp. 407–408; *Scientific American Supplement*, May 25, 1907, vol. 63, pp. 26244–26246.

An address read before the Washington Academy of Sciences, December 13, 1906. Includes an account of the Wrights entitled, "The First Practical Flying Machine," pages 7–8.

Wieder die Brüder Wright! Sensationelle Nachrichten! Ein Flug von 38 Kilometer Lange?! Die Flugmaschine von den Vereinigten Staaten Gekauft? *Wiener Luftschiffer-Zeitung*, Jan. 1907, vol. 6, pp. 7–9.

Report on current rumors about the Wrights. Includes German translation of their letter to Georges Besançon of *L'Aérophile*.

The Wright Aeroplane. *Ballooning and Aeronautics*, Jan. 1907, vol. 1, pp. 9–11, illus.

Attempt to explain working

principles of the Wright aeroplane with two accompanying photographs of a model of their aeroplane constructed by the engineering staff of King's College.

Berty. Le secret des frères Wright. *La revue d'aviation*, Jan. 15, 1907, vol. 2, pp. 8–10, illus.

Based on reports about the Wrights originally published in the *Scientific American*.

Chanute, Octave. Uspekhi i novyi͡a usovershenstovanii͡a v iskusstvennom polete. [Successes and new accomplishments in artificial flight.] *Vozdukhoplavatel'*, Jan–Feb. 1907, vol. 2, pp. 40–46, 84–96.

Includes reference to Wright brothers, pages 84–86. Article translated by N. Kamen'shchikov.

Masfrand, Albert de. The Mysterious Wright Brothers. What Have They Really Accomplished in Flight? *Fry's Magazine*, Mar. 1907, pp. 530–536, illus.

The Brothers Wright. *Ballooning and Aeronautics*, Apr. 1907, vol. 1, p. 152.

Extract from a letter to the editor from C. S. Rolls, who visited the Wrights in America and who states he is convinced that they have achieved powered flight.

Elias, Hermann. Das Rätsel der Gebrüder Wright. [Signed *E.*] *Illustrierte Aeronautische Mitteilungen*, May 1907, vol. 11, pp. 173–174.

Gives a German translation of the account in *Ballooning and Aeronautics*, above, but expresses doubt about the Wright flights.

Wilbur Wright à Paris. *L'Aérophile*. June 1907, vol. 15, pp. 167–168.

Capt. Ferber's letter to Georges Besançon, with added details from an article in *L'Auto*, June 14.

Chanute, Octave. History of the Wright Flying Experiments. *Scientific American Supplement*, June 1, 1907, vol. 63, p. 26262.

Reprinted from *New York Herald*.

Masfrand, Albert de. Les frères Wright à Paris. [Signed *A. de M.*] *L'Aérophile*, July 1907, vol. 15, p. 175.

Progress in Aeronautics. *American Magazine of Aeronautics*, July 1907, vol. 1, pp. 23–24.

Report on Wright flights of 1905, based on their statement to the Aero Club of America, March 12, 1906.

A propos des frères Wright. *La Conquête de l'air*, July 15, 1907, vol. 4, no. 14, p. 3.

Reproduces Chanute's letter to the editor, dated June 27, 1907, telling of Wrights' flights, 1903–1906.

Hildebrandt, [Alfred]. La Machine volante des frères Wright. *La Conquête de l'air*, Dec. 15, 1907, vol. 4, no. 24, p. 3.

French translation of an article published in the *Lokal Anzeiger*, Berlin.

Chanute, Octave. The Wright Brothers' Motor Flyer. In Aero Club of America, *Navigating the Air*, New York: Doubleday, Page & Company, 1907, pp. 3–5, illus.

Brief statement on 1903, 1904, and 1905 flights.

1908

Dienstbach, Carl. The Perfect Flying Machine. First Description of the Marvelous Invention Which Has Given Wilbur Wright and Orville Wright Mastery of Man's Flight. How They Fly and How They Learned the Secret. *American Aeronaut*, Jan. 1908, vol. 1, no. 3, pp. 3–11, illus.

Most extensive account to date on the Wright machine. "Referential Data on the Wright Flyer," page 11, cites source of much of data.

Hildebrandt, Alfred. The Wright Brothers Flying Machine. *American Magazine of Aeronautics*, Jan. 1908, vol. 2, no. 1, pp. 13–16.

Translation from an article originally published in October in the *Lokal Anzeiger*, Berlin.

Turner, George Kibbe. The Men Who Learned to Fly . . . *McClure's Magazine*, Feb. 1908, vol. 30, pp. 443–452, illus.

Based on interview with Wright brothers in January 1907. Includes many incorrect statements and uses direct quotations which were not mentioned nor a part of their conversations.

Les premiers aéroplanes militaires. *L'Aérophile*, Mar. 1908, vol. 16, pp. 115–116.

Announces signing of contract by the Wrights for delivery of an aeroplane to the U.S. Army to meet certain specified conditions.

Espitallier, Georges. L'Etat actual de l'aviation. *Le Génie civil*. Apr. 4, 1908, vol. 53, pp. 398–401, illus.

Includes discussion of the Wright brothers in sections entitled "Les aviateurs américains" and "Appareil Wright à moteur," pp. 400–401.

Ruhl, Arthur. History at Kill Devil Hill. *Collier's*, May 30, 1908, vol. 41, no. 10, pp. 18–19, 26, illus.

Report on Wright May flights at Kitty Hawk by one of a group of reporters witnessing flights from a distance of about a mile away.

American Aeronaut's Disclosure of Wright Brothers' Secret. *American Aeronaut*, June 1908, vol. 1, no. 6, p. 208.

Editorial comment on Carl Dienstbach's article on the Wrights in the January issue of the journal.

Dienstbach, Carl. The Recent Flights of the Wright Brothers in North Carolina. *American Aeronaut*, June 1908, vol. 1, pp. 209–211, illus.

Author's comparison of his version of the Wright aeroplane published in the January issue of the journal with that in the newspaper reports of the Wright May 1908 flights, particularly as reported by Byron Newton of the *New York Herald*.

Newton, Byron R. Watching the Wright Brothers Fly. *Aeronautics*, New York, June 1908, vol. 2, pp. 6–10.

Correspondent of the *New York Herald* reports on the Wright May 1908 flights.

Verney, L. L'Aéroplane Wright. *L'Ouest-Touriste et Sportif*, no. 6, 1908, vol. 2, pp. 41–44, illus.

Von den Brüdern Wright. Erstaunliche Berichte! Rekords von 8–12 Kilometer! Eine Herausforderung Farmans! *Wiener Luftschiffer-Zeitung*, June 1908, vol. 7, pp. 125–126.

Quotations and summary of newspaper accounts of the Wrights in Kitty Hawk appearing May 2, 3, 7, 9, 14, and Farman's open letter of May 17, which appeared in a number of newspapers.

Chanute, Octave. Wright Brothers' Flights. *Independent*, June 4, 1908, vol. 64, pp. 1287–1288.

Report on Wright May flights at Kitty Hawk, North Carolina.

Secret of the Wright Air-ship. *Literary Digest*, June 13, 1908, vol. 36, pp. 861–862, illus.

Description of the Wright aeroplane based on the account of the May 1908 Wright flights reported in the *New York Herald*, May 29 and 31.

Wright's Secret of Flying Revealed at Last: Photographs of the Mysterious Aeroplane. *Illustrated London News*, June 13, 1908, vol. 132, p. 849.

Reproduces photographs originally published in the *Scientific American* and the *New York Herald*.

Philos. Les Frères Wright en Amérique et en France. *L'Aérophile*, June 15, 1908, vol. 16, pp. 222–223.

Includes the Wrights' letter of June 3, 1908, giving details on their May 1908 flights at Kitty Hawk, announcement of the arrival of Wilbur Wright in France, and a statement about his plane as given in an interview with François Peyrey in *L'Auto*.

Sauvage. Adjudication d'aéroplanes militaires aux États Unis. *La Nature*, June 27, 1908, vol. 36, p. 54.

Dominik, H. A. Tollaire über die Wright. *Der Motorwagen*, June 30, 1908, vol. 11, pp. 480–481.

Reprinted from *La France Automobile*.

Chanute, Octave. Recent Aeronautical Progress in the United States. *Aeronautical Journal*, July 1908, vol. 12, pp. 52–55.

Includes reference to Wright 1908 flights and the Wright contract with the United States Government.

——— Bevorstehende Flugversuche in Amerika. (Uebersetzt von Mathilde v. Buttlar) *Illustrierte Aeronautische Mitteilungen*, July 1, 1908, vol. 12, pp. 345–349.

C[lery], A. Les préparatifs de Wilbur Wright. *L'Aérophile*, July 1, 1908, vol. 16, pp. 250–251, illus.

Further statement on Wilbur Wright's plans based on an interview with Léon Bollée as reported in *L'Auto*. Gives details on the Wright machine and conditions of the Wright contract with the Weiller syndicate in France.

Philos. Les préparatifs de Wilbur Wright. *L'Aérophile*, July 15, 1908, vol. 16, p. 279.

Reports Wilbur Wright's early July activities.

Selfridge, Thomas. A Brief Sketch of the Art of Aviation. *Bulletin of the Aerial Experiment Association*, July 20, 1908, no. II, pp. 3–44.

Includes discussion of the early Wright flying experiments, pp. 25–28.

Bain, George G. The Man Bird and His Flight. *Broadway Magazine*, Aug. 1908, vol. 21, pp. 170–181, illus.

Includes reference to the Wright brothers and their machine.

" 'Disclosure' of Wright Brothers' Secret." *Aeronautics*, Aug. 1908, vol. 3, no. 2, p. 42.

Editorial comment on recent stories about the Wrights.

Newton, Byron R. On the Wings of the Wind. *Van Norden Maga-*

zine, Aug. 1908, vol 3, no. 5, pp. 49–57, illus.

Abridged with title, "The Wright Airship," *Literary Digest*, Aug. 29, 1908, vol. 37, pp. 269–270.

Article dealing with the forthcoming Fort Myer Wright tests, with a discussion of the Wright aeroplane and earlier Wright experiments.

Les expériences de Wilbur Wright. Un accident. *L'Aérophile*, Aug. 15, 1908, vol. 16, p. 328.

Mention of accident August 13, in which one wing was slightly damaged.

Voisin, Charles, and Voisin, Gabriel. La solution américaine. [Signed Les Frères Voisin] *La Revue de l'aviation*, Aug. 15, 1908, vol. 3, No. 21, pp. 1–2.

Authors take François Peyrey to task, disputing his statement about the Wright aeroplane in *L'Auto*, contending that the necessary calculations for the building of this type aeroplane were published in an article by Commander Renard in *La Revue de L'Aviation*, in 1888.

Wilbur Wright s'envole! *La Vie au grand air*, Aug. 15, 1908, vol. 14, pp. 127–130, illus.

How Wilbur Wright Flies. *Motor*, London, Aug. 18, 1908, vol. 14, pp. 64–65, illus.

Reports his flights, August 8–13.

The "Mystery" of the Wrights. *Automotor Journal*, Aug. 22, 1908, vol. 13, pp. 1120–1122, illus.

Peyrey, François. Wilbur Wright s'entraîne. *La Vie au grand air*, Aug. 22, 1908, vol. 14, pp. 132–133, 138–139, illus.

Wilbur Wright Has an Accident. *Automotor Journal*, Aug. 22, 1908, vol. 13, p. 1122.

Reports his accident, August 13, when he damaged a wing on landing.

Neue Flugversuche. [Signed kr.] *Illustrierte Aeronautische Mitteilungen*, Aug. 26, 1908, vol. 12, pp. 510–512, illus.

Summarizes Wilbur Wright's flights, August 8, 10, 11, 12, and 13 at Le Mans.

Vorreiter, Ansbert. Erstes Debüt des Drachenfliegers der Gebrüder Wright in Europa. *Prometheus*, Aug. 26, 1908, vol. 19, pp. 765–766.

Reports Wilbur Wright's flight of August 8 at Le Mans.

Peyrey, François. Wilbur Wright au Camp d'Auvours. *La Vie au grand air*, Aug. 29, 1908, vol. 14, pp. 152–153, illus.

The Wright Aeroplane in France. *Collier's*, Aug. 29, 1908, vol. 41, no. 23, p. 4, illus.

The Wright Brothers Aeroplane in France and the United States. *Scientific American*, Aug. 29, 1908, vol. 99, pp. 140–141.

Presents brief general description of their aeroplane, quoting in part from the Wrights' *Century Magazine* article, September 1908.

Wilbur Wright Makes Successful Flight. *Motor*, London, Aug. 11, 1908, vol. 14, p. 42.

Reports Wilbur's flight of August 8, at Les Hunaudières Race Course, near Le Mans.

Recent Aeroplane Experiments. *Engineering Magazine*. Aug. 14, 1908, vol. 86, p. 216, illus.

Brief mention of August flights of Wilbur Wright.

L'Aéroplane Wright. *La Revue de l'aviation*, Aug. 15, 1908, vol. 3, no. 21, pp. 9–11 and 1 p. supplement.

Reports Wilbur's flights, August 8–13.

L'Appareil des frères Wright a franchi trois kilomètres avec une parfaite aisance. *La Conquête de l'air*, Aug. 15, 1908, vol. 5, p. 2, port.

Report on flights of Wilbur Wright, August 8, 10, 11, 12, and quotation from tribute to him by Franz Reichel in *Figaro*.

Degoul, M. Les premiers vols de Wilbur Wright en France. *L'Aérophile*, Aug. 15, 1908, vol. 16, pp. 324–328, illus.

Details on Wilbur Wright's flights of August 8, 10, 11, and 12.

Delagrange, Léon. Impressions sur l'aéroplane Wright. *L'Illustration*, Aug. 15, 1908, vol. 132, pp. 105, 108, illus.

Neue Flugversuche. [signed kr.] *Illustrierte Aeronautische Mitteilungen*, Sept. 1908, vol. 12, pp. 537–538.

Compares Wright machine with French machines.

Orville Wright Breaks All Records—62 Minutes in the Air. *Aeronautics*, New York, Sept. 1908, vol. 3, no. 3, pp. 4–5.

Account of his flight September 9 at Fort Myer.

Wilbur Wright fliegt. *Wiener Luftschiffer-Zeitung*, Sept. 1908, vol. 7, pp. 218–220.

Summary of press reports on August flights at Camp d'Auvours.

Wilbur Wright's Flights in France. *Aeronautics*, New York, Sept. 1908, vol. 3, no. 3, pp. 5–7, illus.

Description of Wright machine and August flights at Le Mans.

Wilbur Wright's Trial Flights in France. *Aeronautics*, London, Sept. 1908, vol. 1, pp. 66–67, illus.

Mention of his flights August 8, 10, and 12, with few details on the Wright aeroplane.

Degoul, M. Wilbur Wright au Mans. *L'Aérophile*, Sept. 1, 1908, vol. 16, pp. 338-339, illus.

Reports transfer of the Wright aeroplane from Les Hunaudières to Camp d'Auvours August 19, and flights there August 21.

L'Entraînement de Wilbur Wright. *La Vie au grand air*, Sept. 5, 1908, vol. 14, pp. 170–171, illus.

Sauvage L'Aéroplane des frères Wright. *La Nature*, Sept. 5, 1908, vol. 36, pp. 214–218, illus.

The First Flight of the Wright Aeroplane at Fort Myer. By our Washington Correspondent. *Scientific American*, Sept. 12, 1908, vol. 99, p. 169, illus.

Report on Orville Wright's September 3 flights and some details on the Wright machine.

Perry, Frank L. The Wright Aeroplane and Wireless Communication. *Western Electrician*, Sept. 12–Oct. 3, 1908, vol. 43, pp. 187–189, 212–213, 226–227, 230, 250–251, illus.

Description of Orville Wright's Fort Myer flights, September 3 and 4, details on the construction of the Wright machine, its operation and performance, and discussion of its possible uses as a base for wireless telegraphy.

L'Aéroplane Wright. *La Revue de l'aviation*, Sept. 15, 1908, vol. 3, pp. 9–11.

Summary of flights August 21–September 6.

La Machine volante est née. *La Revue de l'aviation*, Sept. 15, 1908, vol. 3, no. 22, p. 4 of supplement following p. 10.

Washington Times account of Orville Wright's flight of September 9.

Masfrand, Albert de. Les Wright en France et en Amérique. *L'Aérophile*, Sept. 15, 1908, vol. 16, pp. 354, 356, illus.

Reports Wilbur Wright's flights of September 3, 4, and 5, and Orville Wright's flights, August 29, September 3, and 9.

Orville Wright. *La Conquête de l'air*, Sept. 15, 1908, vol. 5, no. 18, p. 21.

Details on Orville Wright's record flights September 9 and 11 at Fort Myer.

Que penser de l'appareil Wright? *La Revue de l'aviation*, Sept. 15, 1908, vol. 3, pp. 4–7.

Comments on the Wright plane by Ernest Archdeacon, Captain Ferber, Gabriel Voisin, Henri Farman, Léon Delagrange, Armengaud, Jr., General Bouttieaux, Henry Kapférer, Calderara, and Surcouf.

Witzig, Aug. Quelques réflexions sur l'aéroplane Wright. *L'Aérophile*, Sept. 15, 1908, vol. 16, pp. 358–360, illus.

Comparison of the Wright aeroplane with some French machines, including one built by the author.

Noel, E. Percy. How Orville Wright Made His Flights. *Automobile*, Sept. 17, 1908, vol. 19, pp. 408–409, illus.

The Wright Brothers. *Independent*, Sept. 17, 1908, vol. 65, pp. 669–670.

Editorial tribute on recent successful flights.

Babin, Gustave. "Comme un oiseau." Une matinée au Camp d'Auvours. *L'Illustration*, Sept. 19, 1908, vol. 132, pp. 188–189, illus.

Peyrey, François. Les records tombent! *La Vie au grand air*, Sept. 19, 1908, vol. 14, pp. 196–197, illus.

Extracts from Letters from Members, Sept. 7, 1908, Curtiss to Bell. (About Orville Wright's Machine.) *Bulletin of the Aerial Experiment Association*, Sept. 21, 1908, no. XI, pp. 9–11, illus.

Curtiss' report on Orville Wright's September Fort Myer flights.

The Wright Brothers Flying Machine. *American Machinist*, Sept. 24, 1908, vol. 31, p. 466.

Editorial comment on story in *Engineering Magazine*, August 14.

Construction of the Wright Aeroplane. *Scientific American*, Sept. 26, 1908, vol. 99, pp. 208–210, illus.

Presents detailed photographs and description of machine in elaboration of previous account in August 29 issue of the magazine.

Fall of the Wright Aeroplane. *Literary Digest*, Sept. 26, 1908, vol. 37, p. 411, illus.

Summary of press opinion on the September 17, 1908, Fort Myer accident.

The Fatal Fall of the Wright Aeroplane. *Harper's Weekly*, Sept. 26, 1908, vol. 52, no. 2701, p. 7, illus.

Pictorial account of accident and the principals involved.

Le record de Wilbur Wright. *La vie au grand air*, Sept. 26, 1908, vol. 14, pp. 229–230, illus.

Pictorial account of his record-breaking flight of September 21.

Skyscraping at Fort Myer. Photographs by James H. Hare. *Collier's*, Sept. 26, 1908, vol. 42, p. 11, illus.

Brief note on September flights.

Wilbur Wright's Great Flight. *Automotor Journal*, Sept. 26, 1908, vol. 13, p. 1271.

Reports his flight of September 21.

L'Aeroplane dei fratelli Wright. *L'Illustrazione italiana*, Sept. 27, 1908, vol. 2, p. 303, illus.

Wilbur Wright's Record Flight. *Motor*, Sept. 29, 1908, vol. 14, p. 252, illus.

Naĭdenov, Vasilii. Aėroplan brat'ev Raĭt. [The Wright Brothers Aeroplane]. *Vozdukhoplavatel'*, Sept.-Oct. 1908, pp. 349–390.

1½-chasovoĭ polët na aėroplanie. [1½ hour flight in an aeroplane]. *Vozdukhoplavatel'*, Sept. - Oct. 1908, vol. 3, pp. 338–339.

Brown, Harold H. Some Construction Details of the Wright Aeroplane. *Aeronautics*, New York, Oct. 1908, vol. 3, no. 4, pp. 14–15, 44, illus.

The Brothers Wright. *Aeronautics*, London, Oct. 1908, vol. 1, pp. 74–75.

Brief summary of their September flights.

First Official Flights of the Wrights. *Popular Mechanics*, Oct. 1908, vol. 10, pp. 642–643, illus.

Reports Wilbur Wright's August flights in France.

Fullerton, J. D. The Wright Bros.' Flying Machine. *The Aeronautical Journal*, Oct. 1908, vol. 12, pp. 114–119, illus.

Orville Wright in Fort Myers. *Wiener Luftschiffer-Zeitung*, Oct. 1908, vol. 7, pp. 229–233.

Reports his flights, September 3–17.

Successes of Mr. Wilbur Wright. *The Aeronautical Journal*, Oct. 1908, vol. 12, p. 121.

Reprinted from the *London Times*, September 29, 1908.

Todd, Frederick. The Man in the Air. Personal Experiences of Messrs. Wright, Farman, Curtiss, Baldwin, and Others and Explanations of the Different Kinds of Aircraft—Unsolved Problems of the Air. *World's Work*, Oct. 1908, vol. 16, pp. 10802–10819, illus.

Includes section "The Work of the Wrights," pp. 10807–10810, based on an interview with Orville Wright.

W. Wright fliegt 1½ Stunden ! ! *Wiener Luftschiffer-Zeitung*, Oct. 1908, vol. 7, pp. 225–226.

Summary of press reports on his flights to date.

Weltrekord Wilbur Wrights: 1:31:25. *Wiener Luftschiffer-Zeitung*, Oct. 1908, vol. 7, pp. 227–228.

Reports his flight of September 21.

The Wright Aeroplane Triumphs. *Current Literature*, Oct. 1908, vol. 45, pp. 366–368, illus.

Report on September Fort Myer flights, with quotations from an interview with Orville Wright as reported in the *New York Herald*.

L'Accident d'Orville Wright. *La Conquête de l'air*, Oct. 1, 1908, vol. 5, no. 19, p. 4.

Summary of recent reports on accident, September 17.

Alford, Leon P. Wright Aeroplane—a Note-worthy Invention. *American Machinist*, Oct. 1, 1908, vol. 31, pp. 473–478, illus.

Similar account published also in the *Scientific American Supplement*, Oct. 31, 1908, vol. 66, pp. 280–282, illus.

Degoul, M. Post-scriptum. Suite des essais de Wilbur Wright. *L'Aérophile*, Oct. 1, 1908, vol. 16, p. 385.

Reports his flight of September 25.

Hildebrandt, Alfred. Die Flugmaschine der Gebrüder Wright. *Die Welt der Technik*, Oct. 1, 1908, vol. 70, pp. 361–366, illus.

La Navigation aérienne. *La Conquête de l'air*, Oct. 1, 1908, vol. 5, no. 19, p. 5.

Reports on August and September flights of the Wright brothers.

Orville Wright à Fort Myer. *L'Aérophile*, Oct. 1, 1908, vol. 16, pp. 383–385, ports.

Reports his flights of September 9, 10, 11, 12, and 17.

Wilbur Wright. *La Conquête de l'air*, Oct. 1, 1908, vol. 5, pp. 4–5.

Summary of September flights.

Wilbur Wright au camp d'Auvours. *L'Aérophile*, Oct. 1, 1908, vol. 16, pp. 379–383, illus.

Reports his flights of September 12, 16, 17, 21, 22, 23, and 24 in which he established new distance and duration records and won the Michelin Cup and the Aero-Club of France Prize.

Hildebrandt, Alfred. Die Flugmaschine der Gebr. Wright. *Die Umschau*, Oct. 3, 1908, vol. 12, pp. 796–798, illus.

Some details on the construction of the machine.

Peyrey, François. Wilbur Wright recordman du monde. *La Vie au grand air*, Oct. 3, 1908, vol. 14, pp. 231–233, illus.

The Tragic Flight at Fort Myer. Photographs by James H. Hare. *Collier's*, Oct. 3, 1908, vol. 42, no. 2, p. 11, illus.

Vorreiter, Ansbert. Neue Rekordflüge mit Drachenfliegern. *Prometheus*, Oct. 7, 1908, vol. 20, pp. 12–13, illus.

La chute d'Orville Wright. *L'Illustration*, Oct. 10, 1908, vol. 66, p. 224, illus.

More Wonders by Wright. *Motor*, London, Oct. 13, 1908, vol. 14, pp. 302–303, illus.

Summary of Wilbur Wright's flights, October 5, 7, and 8.

L'Accident d'Orville Wright. La première victime de l'aviation. *La Revue de l'aviation*, Oct. 15, 1908, vol. 3, pp. 10–11, port.

Ancelle, Paul. Les prouesses de Wilbur Wright. *L'Aérophile*, Oct. 15, 1908, vol. 16, pp. 398–400, illus.

Reports his flights of September 28, 30, October 3, 5, 6, 7, 8, and 9.

Mousset, Émile. L'Aéroplane Wright. *La Revue aérienne*, Oct. 15, Nov. 10–25, 1908, vol. 1, pp. 7–11, 37–41, 73–76; Jan. 25, Feb. 10–25, 1909, vol. 2, pp. 33–35, 77–79, 111–113, illus.

Les vols de Wilbur Wright. *La Conquête de l'air*, Oct. 15, 1908, vol. 5, no. 20, pp. 5–6, illus.

Reports Wilbur Wright's

269-517—68——5

flights, October 5, 6, 7, 8, and 10, and reproduces part of Franz Reichel's description of a flight with Wilbur originally published in *Figaro.*

Wilbur Wright recordman. *La Revue de l'aviation*, Oct. 15, 1908, vol. 3, pp. 4–8
Flights, September 12–October 5.

Rolls. Charles S. A Flight in the Wright Aeroplane. *Automotor Journal*, Oct. 17, 1908, vol. 13, pp. 1354–1355.
Translation in *La Conquête de l'air*, Nov. 15, 1908, vol. 5, no. 22, p. 2. Reprinted with title *An Aeroplane Flight with Wilbur Wright* (Esher (Sy.): Tabard Press, 1964, 12p.)
Author describes sensations of a flight with Wilbur Wright at Le Mans, October 8, 1908.

Wilbur Wright Opens Out a Little. *Automotor Journal*, Oct. 24, 1908, vol. 13, p. 1382.
Quotes from interview with him originally published in *L'Auto.*

Wilbur Wright au Mans. Liste des vols au Mans. *L'Étoile sportive*, Oct. 25–Dec. 25, 1908, vol. 17, pp. 1568–1569, 1575–1576, 1586–1587.

The Triumph of Genius in the Air. *The Watchword*, Oct. 31, 1908, pp. 4–5, illus.

The Wright Brothers' Successful Flying Machine. *The Watchword*, Oct. 31, 1908, p. 4, illus.

Martin, Rudolf. Zeppelin und Wright. *Die Gegenwart*, Oct. 31–Nov. 7, 1908, vol. 74, pp. 273–274, 289–290.
Discussion of the relative merits of the aeroplane and the airship for military purposes.

The Aeroplane of the Wright Brothers. *Woodcraft*, Nov. 1908, vol. 10, pp. 33–35, illus.

Bache, René. Wright Brothers Make Good. *The Technical World*, Nov. 1908, vol. 10, pp. 268–275, illus.

September a Memorable Month in Aerial Navigation. *Popular Mechanics*, Nov. 1908, vol. 10, 717–722, illus.
Report on Wilbur Wright's flights in France and Orville Wright's flights at Fort Myer.

Von Wilbur Wright. Neue Rekords zu Zeit. *Wiener Luftschiffer-Zeitung*, Nov. 1908, vol. 7, pp. 276–280, illus.
Reports his flights, September 25–October 24.

Degoul, M. Les vols de Wilbur Wright. *L'Aérophile*, Nov. 1, 1908, vol. 16, pp. 428–429, illus.
Reports his flights of October 12 and 15 and gives summary statistics on his flights to date as well as a list of passengers carried, with dates, through October 15, 1908.

Wilbur Wright. *La Conquête de l'air*, Nov. 1, 1908, vol. 5, p. 1, illus.
Mention of his October flights.

Ravigneaux, Pol. L'Aéroplane Wright. *La Vie automobile*, Nov. 14–21, 1908, vol. 8, pp. 721–722, 742–744, illus.
Extensive account by the editor.

Degoul, M. Wilbur Wright forme des élèves. *L'Aérophile*, Nov. 15, 1908, vol. 16, pp. 461–462.
Reports his flights of October 24, 28, 29, 30, 31, November 10 and 11, and includes an account of his lessons to French officers

as pupils, the first lesson being given on October 28.

Wright au Mans. *La Revue de l'aviation*, Nov. 15, 1908, vol. 3, pp. 18–19.

[Thoughts Suggested by Disaster in Which Our Secretary, Lieut. Selfridge, Met his Death]. *Bulletin of the Aerial Experiment Association*, Nov. 16, 1908, no. XIX, pp. 1–34, illus.

Special issue with contributions by Alexander G. Bell, pp. 4–22, Glenn H. Curtiss, p. 23, F. W. Baldwin, pp. 24–27, W. S. Clime, pp. 28–32, and Gardiner S. Bell, pp. 33–34.

Wellner, Georg. Theoretische Betrachtungen über den Wrightschen Flieger. *Illustrierte Aeronautische Mitteilungen*, Nov. 18, 1908, vol. 12, pp. 705–710, illus.

Espitallier, Georges, Les expériences de MM. Wright, Farman, et Blériot. *Le Génie civil*, Nov. 21, 1908, vol. 54, pp. 33–37, 61–63, illus.

Hoernes, Hermann. Über die Wrightschen Flugmaschinen. *Rundschau für Technik und Wirtschaft*, Nov. 21, 1908, vol. 1, pp. 433, 435.

Wilbur Wright's Record for Height. *Scientific American*, Nov. 21, 1908, vol. 99, p. 350.

Reports his flight of November 13, when he flew to a height of 196 feet.

Curtiss, Glenn H. Lesson of the Wright Disaster. *Bulletin of the Aerial Experiment Association*, Nov. 23, 1908, no. XX, p. 13.

Author's letter of November 18.

McCurdy, John A. D. Lessons of the Wright Disaster. *Bulletin of the Aerial Experiment Association*, Nov. 23, 1908, no. XX, pp. 14–16.

His letter of November 11.

Orville Wright. [Signed M.W.] *La Vie au grand air*, Nov. 28, 1908, vol. 14, p. 372, port.

Baden-Powell, B. F. S. A Trip with Wilbur Wright. *Aeronautics*, London, Dec. 1908, vol. 1, pp. 89–91, illus.

Baudry de Saunier, Louis. L'Aéroplane Wright. *Omnia; revue pratique de locomotion*, Dec. 1908, pp. 2–5, illus.

Cronaca scientifica. L'Aeroplano Wright. *Bollettino della Società Aeronautica Italiana*, Dec. 1908, vol. 5, pp. 410–415, illus.

Espitallier, Georges. Les aéroplanes Wright et Farman. *La Technique moderne*, Dec. 1908, vol. 1, pp. 5–9, illus.

Hunter, Chadwick. "Control" of Soaring Bird's Wings and the Planes of the Wright Machine. *Fly Magazine*, Dec. 1908, vol. 1, no. 2, p. 5.

Translation *L'Aviation illustrée*, Mar. 20, 1909, vol. 1, no. 9, p. 2, and *La Conquête de l'air*, Apr. 1, 1909, vol. 6, no. 7, pp. 3–4; comment by Jehan Donet in *L'Aviation illustrée*, Apr. 3, 1909, vol. 1, no. 11, p. 5.

Rozendaal, John. En tocht met Wilbur Wright in diens vliegtoestel. *De Weer*, Dec. 1908, pp. 504–506.

Rozentsveig, L. Teoreticheskie soobrazhenii͡a po povodu apparata brat'ev Raĭt. [Theoretical considerations in regard to the Wright Brothers' machine]. *Vozdukhoplavatel'*, Dec. 1908, vol. 3, pp. 469–477.

Structural Features of the Wright Flyer. *Automobilia*, Dec. 1908, vol. 5, no. 41, p. 10, illus.
Illustrations reproduced from *Omnia*.

Degoul, M. L'Aviation en France. Les expériences de Wright. *L'Aérophile*, Dec. 1, 1908, vol. 16, pp. 476–477.
Reports Wilbur Wright's flights of November 12, 14, 16, 17, and 18.

Gasnier, René. L'Aéroplane Wright décrit par un de ses passagers. Comment il est fait—comment il vole. *L'Aérophile*, Dec. 1, 1908, vol. 16, pp. 470–476, illus.

Another Remarkable Aeroplane Flight. *Nature*, Dec. 24, 1908, vol. 79, p. 227.
Reports Wilbur Wright's flight of December 18, and gives table of heavier-than-air flights, 1905–1908, from the *London Daily Mail.*

Wilbur Wright's New Record. *Scientific American*, Dec. 26, 1908, vol. 99, p. 468.
Reports his flight of December 18.

Wright's High Flight. *Motor*, Dec. 29, 1908, vol. 14, p. 730.

Baudry de Saunier, Louis. L'Aéroplane Wright. In *Rapport sur le premier salon de l'aéronautique, Grand Palais, Paris, Décembre 1908*, Paris: Librairie des Sciences Aéronautiques, 1908, p. 37–44, illus.

Bracke, Albert. *L'Aéroplane Wilbur Wright.* Mons: Dequesne-Masquillier & Fils, 1908, 16 p., illus. ([Monographies d'aviation]1)
Based on patent drawings and specifications.

1909

Aeroplano Wright riassunto voli principali. *Bollettino della Società Aeronautica Italiana*, No. 1, 1909, vol. 6, pp. 17–18.
Chronology of Wright flights, September 5 – December 31, 1908.

Baden - Powell, B. Experiences with the Wright Machine. *Aeronautical Journal*, Jan. 1909, vol. 13, pp. 12–15.
Account of Wilbur Wright's flights at Le Mans. Includes prints from moving pictures of flights taken by the Charles Urban Trading Company.

Foster, Maximilian, The Highway of the Air. *Everybody's Magazine*, Jan. 1909, vol. 20, pp. 104–105, illus.
Popular account of current developments in aviation emphasizing the achievements of the Wright brothers.

The History of Flight from Ader to Wright. *Automobilia*, Jan. 1909, vol. 6, pp. 20–22, illus.
Includes tabular list of Wilbur Wright's flights, August 8–December 18, 1908, and flights of Orville Wright, September 9–17, 1908.

Lanchester, F. W. The Wright and Voisin Types of Flying Machine; a Comparison. *Aeronautical Journal*, Jan. 1909, vol 13, pp. 4–12, illus.
Published also in *Flight*, Jan. 2–9, 1909, vol. 1, pp. 14–16, 29–30; *Engineering Review*, Feb. 1909, vol. 20, pp. 116–122; *La Revue de l'aviation*, Feb. 1, 1909, vol. 4, pp. 11–13; *Allgemeine Automobil - Zeitung*, no. 1, 1909, pp. 33–41; *Pegasus*, Aug. 1955, vol. 24, pp. 14–15.
Paper read before the Aeronautical Society of Great Britain, December 8, 1908.

Rozendaal, John. Der Drachenflieger der Gebrüder Wright. *Illustrierte Aeronautische Mitteilungen*, Jan. 1909, vol. 13, pp. 6–14, illus.

Published also with title, "Der Motorflieger der Gebrüder Wright. Bauart und Steuerung," *Die Luftflotte*, Jan. 1909, vol. 1, pp. 3–7.

——— Ein Flug mit Wright. *Illustrierte Aeronautische Mitteilungen*, Jan. 1909, vol. 13, pp. 21–22.

Merveilleuses performances de Wilbur Wright. *L'Aérophile*, Jan. 1, 1909, vol. 17, pp. 12–13, 38–39, illus.

Reports his flights in preparation for contesting the Michelin Cup, December 16, 18, 19.

Nouveaux exploits de Wilbur Wright. Il fait 100 kilomètres sur son aéroplane puis il gagne le prix de hauteur. *La Conquête de l'air*, Jan. 1, 1909, vol. 6, no. 1, p. 4.

Wilbur Wright Definitely Secures the Michelin Prize by Flying 76.5 Miles. *Motor*, London, Jan. 5, 1909, vol. 14, pp. 762–763, illus.

La Coupe Michelin à Wilbur Wright. *L'Industrie vélocipèdique et automobile*, Jan. 9, 1909, vol. 28, pp. 27–28, port.

Brewer, Griffith. The Wright Flying Machine. *The Field*, Jan. 9–16, 1909, vol. 113, pp. 78, 114, illus.

Details on the construction and operation of the machine.

123 kilometer in 2:18. Wilbur Wright gewinnt den Michelin-Preis. *Allgemeine Automobil-Zeitung*, Jan. 10, 1909, vol. 1, pp. 34–35, illus.

Voisin oder Wright? Was Sir Hiram Maxim sagt. *Allgemeine Automobil-Zeitung*, Jan. 10, 1909, vol. 1, pp. 36–37.

Quotation from Maxim's introductory note to R. P. Hearne's book *Aerial Warfare*.

Elias, Hermann. Der Sieger im Michelinpreis. [Signed Elias] *Illustrierte Aeronautische Mitteilungen*, Jan. 13, 1909, vol. 13, pp. 1–5.

Description of Wilbur Wright's record-breaking flights December 18 and 30, with a chronological summary of his 1908 flights in France.

Foerster, August. Ein verkanntes Brüderpaar. Ein Beitrag zur Geschichte der Flugmaschine. *Illustrierte Aeronautische Mitteilungen*, Jan. 13, 1909, vol. 13, pp. 66–72, illus.

À Wilbur Wright, la Coupe Michelin, 1908. *L'Aérophile*, Jan. 15, 1909, vol. 17, p. 38–40, illus.

Reports that Wilbur had won the Michelin Trophy on December 31, 1908, with a spectacular world record flight of 2 hours 20 minutes 23⅕ seconds in the air. Includes a facsimile of Wilbur's contest entry letter of December 28 to the Aero-Club of the Sarthe.

Breyer, Victor. Orville Wright à Paris. *La Vie au grand air*, Jan. 16, 1909, vol. 15, p. 57, illus.

The Car in the Air. By Engineer. *Motor*, London, Jan. 19, 1909, vol. 14, pp. 809–810, illus.

Description of Wright aeroplane exhibited at the Paris Automobile show.

Claudy to Bell About Enlargements of his Photographs of the Flights of Orville Wright at Fort Meyer. *Bulletin of the Aerial Ex-*

periment Association, Jan. 25, 1909, no. XXIX, pp. 7-8.

His letter of January 4, 1909, stating that enlargements were made by the Eastman Kodak Company. They were later presented to the Smithsonian Institution.

De Lafaurie. Les frères Wright à Pau. *L'Aviation illustrée*, Jan. 30, 1909, vol, 1, no. 2, p. 4, illus.

Wheel, F. A. Les frères Wright à Pau. *La Vie au grand air*, Jan. 30, 1909, vol. 15, p. 72, illus.

Lefort, H. L'Aéroplane Wright et les aéroplanes français. *L'Aérophile*, Feb. 1, 1909, vol. 17, pp. 51–54.

Wilbur Wright détient les records du monde. *La Revue de l'aviation*, Feb. 1, 1909, vol. 4, p. 11.

Les Wright à Pau. *L'Aérophile*, Feb. 1, 1909, vol. 17, p. 55.

Wright hat in Pau seine Vorbereitungen beendet. *Flugsport*, Feb. 5, 1909, vol. 1, pp. 119–120, illus.

Short account of Wilbur Wright's flights with his pupil Count Lambert.

Compton, A. H. Comparison of the Wright and Voisin Aeroplanes. *Scientific American*, Feb. 13, 1909, vol. 100, p. 135.

Based on Lanchester's article in the *Aeronautical Journal*, January 1909.

Wilbur Wrights erste Flug in Pau. *Allgemeine Automobil-Zeitung*, Feb. 14, 1909, vol. 1, pp. 29–32, illus.

McCurdy, John A. D. Lanchester's Comparison of the Wright Machine with the Voisin Machine. *Bulletin of the Aerial Experiment Association*, Feb. 18, 1909, no. XXXI, pp. 18–22.

Résumé of Lanchester's article above.

Zur Verbesserung des Höhensteuers. *Fachzeitung für Automobilismus*, Feb. 21, 1909, vol. 3, pp. 17–18, illus.

Alphonse XIII et l'aviation. *L'Illustration*, Feb. 27, 1909, vol. 69, pp. 139–140, illus.

King Alfonso and the Wrights. *Flight*, Feb. 27, 1909, vol. 1, pp. 116–118, illus.

Account of Wrights' meeting with King Alfonso of Spain and Wilbur's exhibition flight for him February 20, at Pau.

Rouhier, Maurice, Wright professeur. *La Vie au grand air*, Feb. 27, 1909, pp. 134–136, vol. 15, illus.

German translation, *Allgemeine Automobil-Zeitung*, Mar. 7, 1909, vol. 1, p. 36.

Based on interview with Wilbur Wright. Includes account of visit of King Alfonso of Spain to Pau.

König Alfons von Spanien in Pau. *Allgemeine Automobil-Zeitung*, Feb. 28, 1909, vol. 1, pp. 39–42, illus.

Les aéroplanes en France et l'Étranger. Les Wright et leurs élèves à Pau . . . *L'Aérophile*, Mar. 1909, vol. 17, pp. 133–135 illus.

Reports flights of February 24 and 25.

Bell, Alexander G. The Orville Wright Disaster. *Aeronautics*, New York, Mar. 1909, vol. 4, p. 108.

Originally published in the *Bulletin of the Aerial Experi-*

ment Association, November 16, 1908, no. XIX, pp. 4–22.

Clime, W. S. The Orville Wright Disaster. *Aeronautics*, New York, Mar. 1909, vol. 4, p. 108.
Originally published in the *Bulletin of the Aerial Experiment Association*, November 16, 1908, no. XIX, pp. 28–32. Eyewitness account of Orville's accident at Ft. Myer. September 17.

Garnier, G. L'Aéroplane Wright et les aéroplanes français. Réponses diverses à l'article de M. Lefort paru sous ce titre dans l'"Aérophile." *L'Aérophile*, Mar. 1909, vol. 17, pp. 99–100.

Von den Brüdern Wright. Ein kleiner Unfall. *Wiener Luftschiffer-Zeitung*, Mar. 1909, vol. 8, pp. 101–102.
Reports on accident to Wilbur Wright, March 1.

Les Wright à Pau. *L'Aérophile*, Mar. 1, 1909, vol. 17, pp. 107–108, illus.
Reports flights, February 9, 11, 15, 17–19.

Vorreiter, Ansbert. Ein Besuch in Wrightville, Le Mans. Wie Wright Fliegt. *Prometheus*, Mar. 3, 1909, vol. 20, pp. 344–347, illus.

Rouhier, Maurice. Les premiers élèves de l'homme-oiseau. *La Vie au grand air*, Mar. 13, 1909, vol. 15, pp. 166–167, illus.
Includes quotations from interviews with three of Wilbur Wright's pupils, Count de Lambert, Paul Tissandier, and Captain Lucas-Girardville.

Ursinus, Oskar. Die Konstruktion des Wright'schen Fliegers. *Flugsport*, Mar. 19, 1909, vol. 1, pp. 188–192, illus.

Buist, H. Massac. How Wilbur Wright Rides the Wind. *Flight*, Mar. 20, 1909, vol. 1, pp. 157–161, illus.

Rozendaal, John. Konstruktion und Betriebsergebnisse des Wrightschen Döppeldeckers. *Der Motorwagen*, Mar. 20, 31, Aug. 20, 31, Sept. 20, Oct. 20, Nov. 10, 1909, vol. 12, pp. 177–182, 214–217, 632–634, 658–661, 702–704, 767–769, 816–818; Aug. 31, Nov. 30, 1910, vol. 13, pp. 582–586, 866–869, illus.

The Flights of Wright—a Pretty Sight to Set Before the King. *The Bystander*, Mar. 24, 1909, vol. 21, p. 576.

König Eduard bei den Wrights. *Allgemeine Automobil-Zeitung*, Mar. 28, 1909, vol. 1, pp. 38–40, illus.

Ein Verbesserung an dem Wright-Aëroplan. *Allgemeine Automobil-Zeitung*, Mar. 28, 1909, vol. 10, p. 46.
From *Autocar*.

King Alphonso of Spain Regretted his Royalty. *Automobilia*, Apr. 1909, vol. 6, no. 45, pp. 6–7, illus.

Cei, Umberto. Il secreto dei fratelli Wright. *Oceanus novus*, No. 4, 1909, vol. 2, pp. 97–99.

Le mois de Wright. *La Revue de l'aviation*, Apr. 1, 1909, vol. 4, pp. 54–55.

W. Wright termine ses expériences en France. *L'Aérophile*, Apr. 1, 1909, vol. 17, pp. 157–158, illus.
Reports Wilbur's flights February 27, March 1, 11–13, 16–20, and 24.

Wright et ses élèves. *La Conquête de l'air*, Apr. 1, 1909, vol. 5, p. 4.
Summary of March flights.

Broca, A. de. Une Journée avec Wright. *L'Aérophile*, Apr. 15, 1909, vol. 17, pp. 171–173, illus.

Heumann, S. Wilbur Wright auf dem Centocelle in Rom. *Illustrierte Aeronautische Mitteilungen*, Apr. 21, 1909, vol. 13, pp. 377–378.

Rouhier, Maurice. Les premiers élèves de Wright. *La Vie au grand air*, Apr. 24, 1909, vol. 15, pp. 262–263, illus.

Impressions of their training flights given by Count de Lambert and Paul Tissandier. Includes chronologies of their training flights.

Rozendaal, John. Die Erste Luftschiffahrtschule der Welt. *Die Woche*, Apr. 24, 1909, vol. 11, pp. 716–720, illus.

I voli di Wilbur Wright a Centocelle. *L'Illustrazione*, Apr. 25, 1909, vol. 36, p. 433, illus.

La costruzione di un aeroplano Wright. *Il Secolo XX*, May 1909, pp. 419–424.

Wilbur Wright à Rome. *L'Aérophile*. May 1, 1909, vol. 17, p. 205.

Reports flights of April 16, 17, 19, 21, and 22.

Aero Club Banquet to the Wright Brothers. *Flight*, May 8, 1909, vol. 1, p. 260.

Details of dinner held May 4 at Ritz Hotel, London.

Aeronautics. *Field*, May 8, 1909, vol. 113, p. 771.

Reports visit of Wrights to England.

What the Wrights Think of the Aero Club's Flying Ground. *Flight*, May 8, 1909, vol. 1, p. 259.

Les aéroplanes. Les appareils Wright en Italie et en France . . . *L'Aérophile*, May 15, 1909, vol. 17, p. 224–227, illus.

Lefort H. L'Aéroplane Wright et les aéroplanes français. (À propos de l'article de M. Garnier publié dans l'Aérophile du 1er mars.) *L'Aérophile*, May 15, 1909, vol. 17, pp. 221–222, illus.

Reports flights of April 24 and 25.

Peyrey, François. Wilbur Wright et ses élèves. *La Vie automobile*, May 15, 1909, vol. 9, pp. 312–313.

Banquet offert au Mans aux Frères Wright. *L'Étoile sportive*, May 25, 1909, vol. 18, pp. 1624–1628.

Account of banquet in honor of the Wrights at Le Mans, May 1, 1909.

Return of the Wright Brothers. *Scientific American*, May 15, 1909, vol. 100, p. 366.

Wright Brothers' Home Celebration Number. *Greater Dayton*, June 1909, vol. 2, pp. 201–248, illus.

Includes editorial on the Wright brothers, program of the Dayton celebration, June 17–18, articles on the Wright brothers, report by the Wrights to the Aero Club of America, March 12, 1906, and other materials relating to the occasion.

Official Program of the Wright Brothers Celebration, Dayton, Ohio, June 17 and 18, 1909. [Dayton, 1909], 3 pp.

America's Reception to the Wrights. *Aeronautics*, New York, July 1909, vol. 5, pp. 26–27.

Account of welcome given in New York, May 11–12, and in Dayton, May 13.

The Crest of Fame. *Fly Magazine*, July 1909, vol. 1, no. 9, p. 18.

Dayton Wright Brothers Celebration. *Greater Dayton*, July 1909, vol. 3, no. 1, pp. 8–28, illus.
Account of elaborate celebration honoring the Wrights in Dayton, June 17–18.

Two Prophets Not Without Honor. *Harper's Weekly*, July 3, 1909, vol. 53, p. 7, illus.
Pictorial account of Dayton homecoming celebration.

Die Flugversuche Wrights in Rom. *Der Motorwagen*, July 10, 1909, vol. 12, p. 525, illus.

The Senate Studies the Problem of Flight. *Harper's Weekly*, July 10, 1909, vol. 53, p. 7, illus.
Series of photographs of congressmen visiting Fort Myer to witness the Wright flights.

Vorreiter, Ansbert. Kritik der Drachenflieger: Wright. *Zeitschrift des Vereins Deutscher Ingenieure*, July 10, 1909, vol. 53, pp. 1093–1102, illus.

The Wrights at Fort Myer. Photographs by James H. Hare. *Collier's*, July 17, 1909, vol. 43, p. 21, illus.

Hildebrandt, Alfred. Die Wrightsche Flugmaschine and ihre Verwendungsmöglichkeit. *Sport im Bild*, July 23, 1909, vol. 15, pp. 823-826, illus.

Aeronautics: Orville Wright. *Scientific American*, July 24, 1909, vol. 101, p. 55.
Comments on unsuccessful flights at Fort Myer, June and July.

Orville Wright's Flights at Fort Myer. *Scientific American* July 31, 1909, vol. 101, p. 73.
Brief mention of flights, July 17, 19, 20, and 21.

Brown, Harold A. On Wright's Trials at Fort Myer. *Aeronautics*, New York, Aug. 1909, vol. 5, pp. 44–45, illus.
Author points out changes made in the Wright machine since the September 1908 flights and reports on flights through July 2.

Lahm, Frank S. Flying with Wilbur Wright. *American Aeronaut*, Aug. 1909, vol. 1, no. 1, pp. 19-22, illus.
Account of Wilbur Wright's flight at Auvours, France in 1908.

Wright Celebration at Dayton. *Aeronautics*, New York, Aug. 1909, vol. 5, pp. 43, 79, illus.
Brief note on ceremonies, June 17–18.

Wrights and Their Biplane at Fort Myer. *Fly*, Aug. 1909, vol. 1, no. 10, pp. 18–19, illus.
Pictorial account.

Orville Wright's Record Flights at Fort Myer. *Scientific American*, Aug. 7, 1909, vol. 101, pp. 88, 99, illus.
Description of flights, July 24, July 26, before President Taft, July 27 with Lieut. Lahm as passenger, and July 30 ten-mile flight with Lieut. Foulois as passenger.

Hildebrandt, Alfred. Orville Wright Flight in Berlin. *Sport im Bild*, Aug. 8, 1909, vol. 15, pp. 923–925, illus.

Completion of the Government Contract by Orville Wright at Fort Myer. *Scientific American*, Aug. 14, 1909, vol. 101, pp. 111–112.

Good-by to the Wrights. *Collier's*, Aug. 14, 1909, vol. 43, pp. 22–23, illus.

Brief comment on July Wright flight tests at Fort Myer.

Inglis, William. How the Wrights "Made Good." *Harper's Weekly*, Aug. 14, 1909, vol. 53, p. 7–8, illus.

Account of Fort Myer flights.

Wright Bros. Next Visit to Europe. *Flight*, Aug. 14, 1909, vol. 1, p. 488.

Reports departure of Orville Wright and Katharine Wright for Europe aboard "Kronprinzessin Cecile."

Le biplan Wright. *Le Génie civile*, Aug. 28, 1909, vol. 55, pp. 341–342, illus.

Claudy, Carl H. With the Wright Brothers at Fort Myer. *World Today*, Sept. 1909, vol. 17, pp. 929–936, illus.

Foerster, August. Orville Wrights Flug über das Tempelhofer Feld. [Signed A.F.] *Illustrierte Aeronautische Mitteilungen*, Sept. 8, 1909, vol. 13, pp. 814–816, illus.

Dienstbach, Carl. The Revelations at Fort Myer. *American Aeronaut*, Sept. 1909, vol. 1, pp. 80–86, illus.

Description of Wrights' 1909 machine at Fort Myer and flights.

Orville Wright in Berlin. *Die Luftflotte*, Sept. 1909, vol. 1, no. 12, p. 11.

Orville Wright Makes New Two Man Record. *Aeronautics*, New York, Sept. 1909, vol. 5, no. 3, p. 92.

Account of record flights, July 27 and 30, when he fulfilled endurance and distance tests before the Aeronautical Board of the Signal Corps.

Young, Edward H. Ft. Myer and the Wrights. *Fly*, Sept. 1909, vol. 1, no. 11, pp. 8–9, illus.

Description of the Fort Myer flying field, comparison of the 1908 and 1909 aeroplanes, and account of the record flights, July 27 and 30.

Die Premier der Berliner Wright-Flüge. *Sport im Bild*, Sept. 10, 1909, vol. 15, pp. 1000–1001, illus.

I fratelli Wright giudicali dai loro compatrioti. *L'Aviatore italiano*, Sept. 11, 1909, vol. 1, no. 1, p. 51, illus.

Wright in Berlin. *Wiener Luftschiffer-Zeitung*, Sept. 15, 1909, vol. 8, pp. 321–322.

Account of Orville Wright's flights, September 4 and 7.

Freund, Alfred. Wright-Flüge in Berlin. *Flugsport*, Sept. 17, 1909, vol. 1, pp. 555–556, illus.

Reports Orville's flights, September 4–8.

The Wright Glider as Made by Clarke. *Flight*, Sept. 18–25, 1909, vol. 1, pp. 568–571, 585–588, illus.

Der Berliner Flüge Orville Wrights. [Signed R. E.] *Der Motorwagen*, Sept. 20, 1909, vol. 12, p. 708.

Report of first public flights in Germany and record-breaking altitude flight of September 18.

Dienstbach, [Carl.]. Der glänzende Erfolg Orville Wrights zu Fort Myer, Washington. *Illustrierte Aeronautische Mitteilungen*, Sept. 22, 1909, vol. 13, pp. 841–847, illus.

Wrights Flugvorführungen. *Militär-Wochenblatt*, Sept. 23, 1909, vol. 94, pp. 2763–2764.

Résumé of Orville's flights of September 4, 7, 8, 9, 10, 11, 13, 17, and 18, at Tempelhof Field from accounts in the *Lokal-Anzeiger*, Berlin.

Claudy, Carl H. Our First Army Flying Machine. *Technical World*, Oct. 1909, vol. 12, pp. 222–223.

Schematic Drawing of the Wright Bros. Aeroplane. *Automobilia and Flight*, Oct. 1909, vol. 6, p. 33.

Some Curious Views of Wilbur Wright in Flight in Rome Last Spring. *Automobilia and Flight*, Oct. 1909, vol. 6, p. 25, illus.

Photographs taken from a captive balloon by Hart O. Berg.

I voli di Orville Wright in America. *L'Aviatore italiano*, Oct. 1, 1909, vol. 1, no. 2, p. 24, illus.

Wright Brothers and Their Flyer. *Flight*, Oct. 2, 1909, vol. 1, p. 613.

Wilbur Wright Makes a Marvelous Flight. *Automobile Topics*, Oct. 9, 1909, vol. 19, pp. 12, 18–20, illus.

Account of preparations for and flight of October 4, from Governors Island to Grant's Tomb and return, in connection with the Hudson-Fulton celebration.

Wright Will Give no More Exhibitions. *Automobile Topics*, Oct. 9, 1909, vol. 19, p. 17.

Wilbur Wright's future plans as reported in an interview with him.

Inaugurating the Hudson's Aerial Highway. *Harper's Weekly*, Oct. 16, 1909, vol. 53, p. 7, illus.

Photographs of Wilbur Wright's flight over the Hudson from Governors Island to Grant's Tomb.

The Spectator. Wilbur [Wright and his Aeroplane at New York]. *Outlook*, Oct. 16, 1909, vol. 93, p. 332–334.

Wilbur Wright's Amazing Flight. *Harper's Weekly*, Oct. 16, 1909, vol. 53, pp. 3, 7, illus.

Photos of flight of October 4 between Battery and Grant's Tomb.

Wright and Curtiss Fly in Hudson-Fulton Celebration. *Aeronautics*, New York, Nov. 1909, vol. 5, pp. 178–182.

Wright's New York Flight. *Review of Reviews*, Nov. 1909, vol. 40, p. 518–519, illus.

Ruzer, L. Aėroplan brat'ev Raĭt (s chertezhami i snimkami). *Vi͡estnik vozdukhoplavanii͡a*, Nov. 1909, no. 1, pp. 51–56, illus.

Garinei, R. Un'interessante applicazione all'aeroplano Wright. *L'Aviatore italiano*, Nov. 1, 1909, vol. 1, no. 3, p. 54, illus.

Isendahl, W. Wie ein Wrightfliege entsteht. [*Signed W. I.*] *Illustrierte Aeronautische Mitteilungen*, Nov. 17, 1909, vol. 13, pp. 1077–1080, illus.

Baudry de Saunier, Louis. Le biplan des frères Wright. In his *Éléments de locomotion aérienne*, Paris: Bibliothèque "Omnia," 1909, pp. 163–176, illus.

Included in book is an incorrectly labeled photograph of Archdeacon glider rather than Wright glider of 1900.

Bracke, Albert. *Construction et manœuvres de l'aéroplane Wright*. Paris: F.-L. Vivien, Liège:

Librarie Nierstrasz, 1909, 16 pp., illus. (His Monographies d'aviation.5).

Brewer, Robert W. A. The Wright and Voisin Machines Compared. In his *The Art of Aviation*, London: Crosby Lockwood and Son, 1910, pp. 154–167.

Dumas, Alexandre. *Stud book de l'aviation; ceux qui ont volé et leurs appareils*, Paris: Édition du journal L'Aéro, 1909, 185 pp.

Includes "Wright (Type 1903)": pp. 14–15; "Wright (Type 1908)": pp. 53–54; "Wright (Type d'Auvours)": pp. 64–70; "Wright (Fort-Myers 1908)": pp. 73–74; "Wright (Type d'Italie)": pp. 110–111; "Wright (Type 1909) Fort-Myers": pp. 127–128; "Expériences d'Orville Wright à Berlin (1909)": p. 156.

Each aeroplane type is accompanied by brief descriptive note and chronological list of flights made with it.

Häntzschel, Walter. *Modell eines Aëroplans der Brüder Wright. Ein zerlegbares Modell zum Zwecke der Selbstbelehrung und für den Unterricht an gewerblichen Fachschulen, mit beschreibendem Text.* Fürth i. B.: Druck und Verlag von G. Löwensohn [190–] 8p.

Painlevé, Paul. Impressions d'un passager. In Lelasseux, Louis and Marque, René. *L'Aéroplane pour tous*, Paris: Société d'Editions aéronautiques, 1909, pp. 99–100.

Reprinted from *Le Matin*, October 11, 1908.

Account of flight with Wilbur Wright at Camp d'Auvours, October 10, 1908.

Peyrey, François. Les élèves de Wilbur Wright. In his *Les oiseaux artificiels*, Paris: H. Dunod et E. Pinat, 1909, pp. 212–227, illus.

Schmidt, Georg. *Die Flug-Maschine der Gebrüder Wright.* [Westerland Sylt: Druck von Fr. Rossberg, 1909], 8 pp.

Wright Bros. Biplane. In Jane, Fred T., *All the World's Air-Ships*, London: Sampson Low, Marston & Co., Ltd., 1909, pp. 276–277, illus.

Besides specifications includes list of machines built, building, or on order.

1910

Loening, Grover C. Description of the Successful Types of Aeroplanes: 4. Wright. *Aeronautics*, New York, Jan. 1910, vol. 6, pp. 2, 5, illus.

Includes references.

Jaray, Paul. Die Flugmaschinen von Wright und Blériot. *Technische Blätter; Vierteljahrschrift des deutschen Polytechnisches Vereines in Böhmen*, heft 1, 1910, vol. 42, pp. 31–40, illus.

Wright Glider Launching Apparatus. *Flight*, Jan. 8, 1910, vol. 2, p. 22, illus.

Apparatus constructed by T. W. K. Clarke and Co. for Mr. Alec Ogilvie's glider at Camber.

Ogilvie, Alec. Wright Glider Launching Apparatus. *Flight*, Jan. 15, 1910, vol. 2, p. 47.

Statement on modifications made to original apparatus.

Who Was the First? *Aero*, London, Jan. 18, 1910, vol. 2, p. 51.

Cites *Century Magazine* article as source for data on Wrights' first flight.

Wright Biplane in Australia. *Aero*, London, Jan. 25, 1910, vol. 2, no. 36, p. 62.

Harrop, F. C. The Measurements of the Wright Machine. *Aero*, London, Feb. 8, 1910, vol. 2, p. 109.

Meitner, F. Neuerungen am Wright - Flieger. *Der Motorwagen*, Feb. 28, 1910, vol. 13, p. 126.

Das neue Wright - Flugzeug. *Flugsport*, Mar. 5, 1910, vol. 2, pp. 140–142, illus.

Announcement and description of new German - built Wright machine equipped with wheels.

The Wright–Biplane. *Flight*, Mar. 12, 1910, vol. 2, pp. 174–177, illus.

Short - Wright Comparisons. *Flight*, Mar. 26, 1910, vol. 2, p. 228.

Humphreys, Frederic E. The Wright Flyer and its Possible Uses in War. *Professional Memoirs*, Mar.–Apr. 1910, vol. 2, pp. 99–107, illus.

Reprinted in *Journal of the United States Artillery*, Mar.–Apr. 1911, vol. 33, pp. 144–147, illus.

Matvieev, A. Pervaia vozdukhoplavatel'nai͡a vystavka v Rigie. [The Wright Aeronautical Exhibition at Riga.] *Vi͡estnik vozdukhoplavanii͡a*, Apr. 1910, no. 6, pp. 59–60, illus.

Account of exhibition held in Riga at which a German-built Wright aeroplane was the central attraction.

Ochoa, V. L. Are the Wrights Pirates? *Aircraft*, Apr. 1910, vol. 1, pp. 55–57, illus.

Author cites early flying machines and inventions from which the Wrights may have received ideas for their successful aeroplane.

[The Wright Elevator.] *Flight*, May 14, 1910, vol. 2, p. 380, illus.

Ruhl, Arthur. Up in the Air with Orville. *Collier's*, July 2, 1910, vol. 45, no. 15, pp. 16–17, 19, illus.

Author's description of his flight with Orville Wright at Simms pasture, Dayton, in June.

Die Metamorphose des Wright–Flyers. *Fachzeitung für Flugtechnik*, July 17, 1910, vol. 4, pp. 16–19, illus.

Post, Augustus. How to Learn to Fly. The Different Machines and What They Cost. *World's Work*, Sept. 1910, vol. 20, pp. 13389–13402, illus.

Includes description of Wright machine.

Brewer, Griffith. With the Wrights in America. *Flight*, Sept. 3, 1910, vol. 2, pp. 706–708.

Account of Wright work shop, flight instruction at Simms Station, and author's ride with Orville.

The New Wright Biplane. *Scientific American*, Sept. 3, 1910, vol. 103, p. 180, illus.

Description of new model in which the double-surface horizontal front rudder is removed.

The Wright Brothers and Their Flying Machine up to Date. *Gleanings in Bee Culture*, Sept. 15, 1910, vol. 38, pp. 602–604.

Details of the New Wright. *Aero*, St. Louis, Oct. 8, 1910, vol. 1, no. 1, pp. 8–10, illus.

Announces adoption of a rear elevator.

Noel, E. Percy. First Pictures from a Wright Biplane. [Signed *E. P. N.*] *Aero*, St. Louis, Oct. 22, 1910, vol. 1, no. 3, pp. 11–12, illus.

Account of flight over Kinloch aviation field, St. Louis, October 16.

Gill, Howard W. Details of the Wright Roadster. *Aero*, St. Louis, Oct. 29, 1910, vol. 1, no. 4, p. 10.

Loening, Grover C. The Leading Aeroplanes: 4. The Wright Biplane. *Scientific American Supplement*, Oct. 29, 1910, vol. 70, p. 276, illus.

General details on the construction of Wright aeroplanes. Includes "References."

Wright Racer. *Aero*, St. Louis, Nov. 5, 1910, vol. 1, no. 5, p. 8.

The "Baby Wright" model designed for the Gordon-Bennett aviation cup competition.

Hall, Edward H. Aeronautical Exhibitions. In his *The Hudson-Fulton Celebration, 1909*, Albany, N.Y.: 1910, vol. 1, pp. 486–497, vol. 2, pp. 1241–1251, illus.

Has extensive account of the preparations for and a description of Wilbur Wright's flights which formed a part of the celebration. These comprised three flights, September 29, including one in which he circled the statue of Liberty, and the flight of October 4, from Governors Island up the Hudson to Grant's Tomb and return.

Kennedy, D. Ross. *The Aeroplane Portfolio*. London: Percival Marshall & Co., 1910, 14 pp.

Contains scale drawings and descriptions of nine contemporary aeroplanes including the Wright 1908 aeroplane.

Les principaux types d'aéroplanes. Appareils sans queue. L'Aéroplane Wright. In *Rapport Officiel sur la première exposition internationale de locomotion aérienne*, Paris: Librairie Aéronautique, 1910, pp. 33–35, illus.

Wright Bros. Biplane. In Jane, Fred T. *All the World's Airships, Aeroplanes and Dirigibles, 1910–11*, London: Sampson Low, Marston & Co., Ltd., 1910, pp. 379–380.

Includes full list of owners of Wright aeroplanes, corrected to October 3, 1910.

1911

McCutcheon, Phillip. Construction of a Wright Model. *Fly Magazine*, Jan. 1911, vol. 3, no. 3, pp. 10, 20.

Phipps, W. H. The New York Aero Show. *Aircraft*, Feb. 1911, vol. 1, pp. 436–437, illus.

Summary of the main features of the exhibits forming a part of the Automobile Show, December 31, 1910–January 7, 1911, including the Wright "Roadster" and Wright standard Model B.

The Baby Wright. *Aero*, London, Apr. 1911, vol. 5, p. 17, illus.

Illustration and few details on Wright machine exhibited by Alec Ogilvie at the Olympia Aero exhibition, London.

When the Wrights Flew the First Aeroplane. *The Air-Scout*, Apr. 1911, vol. 1, no. 6, p. 13.

Includes two photographs of the Wrights in flight, May 1908, at Kitty Hawk, N.C.

The Wright Company. *Aircraft*, Apr. 1911, vol. 2, p. 51.

Brief mention of Wright model B aeroplane exhibited at the Boston Aero Show, February 1911.

Orville Wright Flies at Dayton. *Aero*, St. Louis, Apr. 29, 1911, vol. 2, no. 4, p. 86.

Flights, April 18, at Simms Station.

Orville Wright Takes a Joy Ride. *Aero*, July 29, 1911, vol. 2, p. 371.
Report of flights on July 19 in aeroplane built for the United States Navy.

The Wright Biplane, Model "B". *Aeronautics*, New York, Sept. 1911, vol. 9, pp. 93–100, illus.
Published also, without chronological series of photographs, in *Scientific American Supplement*, Dec. 9, 1911, vol. 72, pp. 380–382.
Besides a detailed description of the model B there is also included a series of photographs showing the chronological development of the Wright aeroplane, 1900–1910.

The New Wright Glider. *Town & Country*, Oct. 28, 1911, vol. 66, p. 21, illus.
Brief mention of gliding experiments conducted by Orville Wright at Kitty Hawk, N.C., in October.

The Wright Rumours. *Aero*, London, Nov. 1911, vol. 5, p. 229.
Relates to the recent Wright glider experiments.

Beatty, George W. How to Make the Wright Rib. *Aero*, New York, Nov. 4, 1911, vol. 3, p. 95, illus.

Loening, Grover C. The Recent Gliding Experiments of the Wrights. *Scientific American*, Nov. 4, 1911, vol. 105, pp. 404–405, illus.
Statement on the significance of the flights with special mention of those on October 23 and October 24, when Orville soared for 9¾ minutes for a distance of a quarter mile at an estimated height of 200 feet to establish a record which endured for many years.

The Wright Gliding Experiments. *Aeroplane*, Nov. 9, 1911, vol. 1, p. 544, illus.

Harwood, Van Ness. Flying Without a Motor. *Collier's*, Nov. 11, 1911, vol. 48, no. 8, p. 20, illus.
Account of Orville Wright's glider experiments at Kitty Hawk in October.

Mallet, R. F. Les Essais des Wright et le vol à voile. *L'Aérophile*, Nov. 15, 1911, vol. 19, pp. 531–533, illus.

Der motorlose Zweidecker der Gebrüder Wright. *Flugsport*, Nov. 29, 1911, vol. 3, pp. 860–862.

The Secret Experiments of the Wright Brothers. *Popular Mechanics*, Dec. 1911, vol. 16, pp. 797–804, illus.
Details on the construction and the operation of the Wright 1911 glider.

Der neueste Apparat der Wrights. *Wiener Luftschiffer-Zeitung*, Dec. 1, 1911, vol. 10, pp. 437–438.
Some details on the recent Wright gliding experiments based on an interview with them as reported in the *Frankfurter Zeitung*.

De zweefproeven der Wright's. *Avia*, Dec. 1, 1911, vol. 1, p. 213.

Orville Wright's Flights in a Glider at Kitty Hawk. *Scientific American*, Dec. 2, 1911, vol. 119, p. 495.

Sandick, R. A. van. Vliegen zonder motor. *De Ingenieur*, Dec. 30, 1911, vol. 26, pp. 1099–1100.
Includes letter of Orville to J. A. Heringa, November 18, 1911, giving some details on recent gliding experiments at Kitty Hawk.

Gaston, Raymond de. L'Aéroplane Wright. In his *Les Aéroplanes de 1911*, Paris: Librairie Aéronautique, 1911, pp. [122–126], illus.

Kaempffert, Waldemar. Some Typical Biplanes: The Wright Biplane. In his *The New Art of Flying*, New York: Dodd, Mead and Company, 1911, pp. 209–214.

La Vaulx, Henri de. École américaine et école française. In his *Le triomphe de la navigation aérienne*, Paris: Librairie illustrée Jules Tallandier, 1911, pp. 307–330, illus.

Presents summary of Wright flights in France, 1908, and 1909, with discussion and comparison of the Wright aeroplane with subsequent French aeroplane types.

Loening, Grover C. Wright Biplanes. In his *Monoplanes and Biplanes, Their Design, Construction and Operation; the Application of Aero Dynamic Theory with a Complete Description and Comparison of the Notable Types.* New York: Munn & Company, Inc., 1911, pp. 230–245, illus.

Includes descriptions of Wright 1909, Model R, and 1911 Model B aeroplanes.

Veĭgelin, Konstantin E. Biplany amerikanskago tipa. [American [Wright] type biplanes.] In his *Zavoevanie vozdushnogo okeana*, S. Peterburg: Knigoizdatel'stvo P. P. Soĭkina [1911], pp. 82–87, illus.

Zahm, Albert F. [Wright Brothers]. In his *Aerial Navigation*, New York and London: D. Appleton and Company, 1911, pp. 245–251, 270–282, illus.

Discusses the Wrights' early flights, 1900–1905, and flights conducted in 1908–1909.

1912

De Havilland, Geoffrey. Aeroplane Undercarriages: Wright Biplane. *Aero*, London, Mar. 1912, vol. 6, p. 84.

Seshun, Karl. Motorlose Schwebeflieger. *Fachzeitung für Automobilismus und Flugtechnik*, Apr. 21, 1912, vol. 6, pp. 17–19, illus.

Mitchell, J. W. Army Tests Curtiss and Wright Planes. *Aero*, St. Louis, May 25, 1912, vol. 4, p. 195.

Report on the testing at College Park, Maryland, of a new weight-carrying Wright machine with a new 6-cylinder engine.

The Wright Model C. *Aeronautics*, New York, May–June 1912, vol. 10, pp. 152–156, illus.

Loukianoff, G. S. Tragflächen-Untersuchungen des Aerodynamischen Laboratoriums der Technischen Hochschule Moskau. *Zeitschrift für Flugtechnik und Motorluftschiffahrt*, June 29, 1912, vol. 3, pp. 153–159, illus.

Includes account of experiments carried out by Professor Nikolaĭ Zhukovskiĭ in 1910 in the Aerodynamical Laboratory of the Royal Technical High School, Moscow, on profiles used by the Wrights and other contemporary fliers.

Wright Doppeldecker Modell C, Militärtyp. *Flugsport*, July 3, 1912, vol. 4, pp. 534–536, illus.

Wright Bros. Biplanes. In Jane, Fred T., *All the World's Aircraft*, London: Sampson Low, Marston & Co., 1912, pp. 324–325.

Includes data and drawings of the Wright Model B.

1913

Busse, C. Das neue Militär-Wright-Flugzeug. *Motorwagen*, Mar. 10, 1913, vol. 16, pp. 164–166, illus.

Le Vino, Albert S. The Army and the Aeroplane. *Leslie's Illustrated Weekly Newspaper*, May 1, 1913, vol. 116, p. 467, illus.

Short account of negotiations leading to the purchase of the Wright aeroplane by the United States Army.

Squier, George. The Wright Brothers—A Bit of History. *Flight*, June 14, 1913, vol. 5, pp. 651–652.

Published also in *Aeronautical Journal*, July 1913, vol. 17, pp. 186–187.

Remarks made at the first Wilbur Wright Memorial Lecture, giving particulars on early War Department negotiations with the Wrights.

New Model "CH" Wright. *Aeronautics*, New York, July 1913, vol. 13, pp. 11–12, illus.

Report on testing of Wright seaplane by Orville Wright on Miami River at Dayton.

Loening, Grover C. The Wright Company's New Hydro-Aeroplane Model C–H. *Aircraft*, Sept. 1913, vol. 4, pp. 152–153, illus.

——— The Wright Hydro-Aeroplanes. *Flying*, Sept. 1913, vol. 2, no. 8, pp. 20–22, illus.

Mention of early Wright hydroplane experiments and details of new model "C–H" and discussion of future uses for this type of machine.

New Fast Wright Model. *Aeronautics*, New York, Sept. 1913, vol. 13, no. 3, p. 96.

Model E, first Wright machine with a single propeller.

The Model "C. H." Wright Waterplane. *Flight*, Sept. 6, 1913, vol. 5, pp. 978–979, illus.

New Wright Model E. *Aeronautics*, New York, Oct. 1913, vol. 13, no. 4, pp. 140–141, illus.

Ten Years' Marvels Since Wrights' First Air Flight. *New York Times Magazine Section*, Oct. 12, 1913, pp. 1–2, illus.

The Wright Aeroboat. *Aeronautics*, New York, Nov. 1913, vol. 13, no. 5, pp. 169–171, illus.

The Wright Model G, designed by Grover Loening under the direction of Orville Wright.

Expressions of Appreciation of Tenth Anniversary of First Aeroplane Flight. *Flying*, Dec. 1913, vol. 2, no. 11, pp. 8–9, Jan. 1914, no. 12, pp. 8–9, Feb.-Mar. 1914, vol. 3, pp. 8–9.

Collection of statements from prominent people and organizations solicited by the Aero Club of America.

Tenth Anniversary of Flight. *Aeronautics*, New York, Dec. 1913, vol. 13, 208–209, 220, illus.

Presents brief résumé of Wright flights. Also reports meeting of the Aeronautical Society, December 18, honoring Orville Wright at which a set of engrossed resolutions and a bronze figure by Auguste Moreau were presented to him. Includes remarks by Orville on the present status of his stabilizer.

Wright Aeroboat Shows Unusual Efficiency. *Aero and Hydro*, Dec. 13, 1913, vol. 7, pp. 132–133, illus.

First Successful Power Flight Commemorated. *Aero and Hydro*, Dec. 27, 1913, vol. 7, pp. 153–154.

Reporting First Flight of Wright

269-517—68——6

Bros. *Aero and Hydro*, Dec. 27, 1913, vol. 7, p. 155, illus.

Erroneously presents five photographs as having been taken at Kitty Hawk in 1904. These are photographs taken by James H. Hare and other correspondents in 1908.

The Wright Aeroboat. Model "G." Dayton, Ohio: The Wright Co. [1913]. 4p., illus.

Leaflet issued by the Wright Company advertising the Model G aeroplane.

Wright Bros. Biplanes. In Jane, Fred T., *All the World's Aircraft 1913*, London: Sampson Low, Marston & Co., 1913, pp. 218–219, illus.

Includes data on Models B, C, EX, and E, and drawings of Models B and C.

1914

Williams, Henry. The New Wright Flying Boat. *Aircraft*, Jan. 1914, vol. 4, pp. 243–245, illus.

Orville Wright has stated that only two machines of this Model "G" aeroboat were built.

The Model E Wright Biplane. *Flight*, Jan. 3, 1914, vol. 6, p. 18, illus.

The Model E, built for the U.S. Army, was the first Wright machine with a fuselage.

Das Wright Flugboot. *Flugsport*, Feb. 18, 1914, vol. 6, pp. 85–86, illus.

Loening, Grover C. The New Wright Aeroboat Type "G." *Aeronautics*, New York, June 15, 1914, vol. 14, pp. 170–171, illus.

Similar account published in *Aircraft*, July 1914, vol. 5, pp. 335–337.

A New Wright Aeroboat. A Marine Aeroplane of the Pontoon Type. *Scientific American Supplement*, July 25, 1914, vol. 78, p. 55, illus.

Based on Loening's description above.

Wright Bros. Biplanes. In Jane, Fred T., *All the World's Aircraft*, London: Sampson Low, Marston & Co., 1914, pp. 200–201, illus.

Includes data on Models C, CH, E, and G, and drawings of Models E and G. Identical data in 1916 edition, pages 241–242.

1915–1920

Wright Tractor, Type "L". *Aerial Age Weekly*, July 10, 1916, vol. 3, pp. 508–509, illus.

Details and three-view drawings of single-place light-scout military biplane. By the time this model was available for sale Orville Wright's connection with the Wright Company had ceased.

Wright Light Scout Tractor Biplane. *Aircraft*, Aug. 1916, vol. 7, pp. 9–10, illus.

Includes scale drawings.

The New Wright Tractor Biplane–Type L. *Flight*, Aug. 10, 1916, vol. 8, 664–666, illus.

The Wright Model L Light Scout. *Aeroplane*, Aug. 30, 1916, vol. 11, pp. 376, 378, illus.

The Beginnings of Human Flight. New York: The Wright Company [1916], 4 pp. illus.

Leaflet issued on the occasion of the exhibit of the 1903 Wright aeroplane at the Massachusetts Institute of Technology, Boston.

Fourteen Years of the Aeroplane. *Scientific American*, Feb. 24, 1917, vol. 116, p. 196.

Editorial comment on the occasion of the exhibit of the Wright 1903 aeroplane at the first Pan American Aeronautic Exposition, New York, 1917.

Woodhouse, Henry. The Wright Experiment. In his *Textbook of Naval Aeronautics*, New York: The Century Co., 1917, pp. 179–180, illus.

Account of Wright 1907 experiments with hydroplanes, quoting extensively from original report in the *Dayton Daily News*, March 21, 1907.

1921–1925

Ogilvie, Alec. Some Aspects of Aeronautical Research. *The Aeronautical Journal*, Oct. 1922, vol. 26, pp. 381–389.

Abridged in *Aeroplane*, June 21, 1922, vol. 22, pp. 443–446; *Flight*, June 22, 1922, vol. 14, p. 362.

Tenth annual Wilbur Wright Memorial Lecture, June 15, 1922. Includes reference to author's associations with Wilbur Wright at Le Mans, December 1908, and at Eastchurch in 1911, and an account of the early experimental work of the Wrights.

Loening, Grover C. The Significance of the Early Work of the Wright Brothers. *U.S. Air Services*, Dec. 1922, vol. 7, no. 11, pp. 16–17.

Stefansson, Vilhjalmur. Human Flight a Triumph of Reason. *U.S. Air Services*, Dec. 1922, vol. 7, no. 11, p. 18.

Impressions of the author's first flight and of his visit to Orville Wright's workshop.

Calderara, Mario. The Wright Brothers' Discovery. *U.S. Air Services*, Dec. 1923, vol. 8, no. 12, pp. 11–12.

Dollfus, Charles. Les vols du 17 décembre 1903 [Signed *Ch.D.*] *L'Aéronautique*, Dec. 1923, vol. 10, p. 531.

Hammer, William J. A Brief Consideration of the Work of the Wright Brothers. *U.S. Air Services*, Dec. 1923, vol. 8, no. 12, pp. 16–17, illus.

The Airplane's Twentieth Anniversary, by our McCook Field Correspondent. *Air Service News Letter*, Jan. 7, 1924, vol. 8, no. 1, pp. 1–4.

Account of ceremonies in Dayton, December 17, 1923. Includes text of speech, which was broadcast, written by Orville for the occasion.

The Airplane's Twentieth Anniversary. *Aeronautical Digest*, Feb. 1924, vol. 4, p. 97, illus.

Lahm, Frank S. Wilbur Wright's First Flights in France. *U.S. Air Services*, Aug. 1924, vol. 9, no. 8, pp. 29–31, illus.

Jones, Ernest L. The 15th Anniversary of our Air Service. *Aviation*, Aug. 4–11, 1924, vol. 17, pp. 830–831, 863–865, illus.

Story of the origins of United States military aviation with an account of the Wright negotiations with the Army which led to the signing of a contract and the subsequent delivery of a Wright aeroplane to it upon successful completion of specified tests on July 30, 1909.

The Anniversary of Flight. *National Aeronautic Association Review*, Dec. 1925, vol. 3, no. 12, pp. 187–188.

1926–1930

Rodgers, John. My Acquaintance with the Wrights. *Slipstream*, Jan. 1926, vol. 7, no. 1, p. 18.

Speech delivered at a dinner of the National Aeronautic Association on the 22nd anniversary of the 1903 Kitty Hawk flights.

Commemoration of First Airplane Flight. *Congressional Record*, Dec. 17, 1926, vol. 68, pp. 630–631.

Remarks by Hiram Bingham of Connecticut.

Horsfall, Jesse E. The First Flight. *The Annals of the American Academy of Political and Social Science*, May 1927 vol. 131, pp. 14–19.

Résumé of the Wright 1903 experiments and their successful December 17, 1903, flights.

First Flight of Heavier-than-Air Machine. *Aviation Stories and Mechanics*, Aug. 1927, vol. 1, no. 2, pp. 38–39, illus.

Claudy, Carl H. The Army's First Airplane, *Aero Digest*, Dec. 1927, vol. 11, pp. 636–640, illus.

Reminiscences by one-time reporter for the *New York Herald*, who witnessed and reported Orville Wright's 1908 and 1909 Fort Myer flights and who obtained the first interview with Orville after the September 17, 1908, accident.

West, Rupert E. When the Wrights Gave Wings to the World. *U.S. Air Services*, Dec. 1927, vol. 12, no. 12, pp. 19–23, illus.

Based on facts supplied by Capt. W. J. Tate.

Foreign Expressions Concerning Wright Brothers' Plane. *Slipstream*, Apr. 1928, vol. 9, no. 4, pp. 16–17, 19, illus.

Marsh, Lockwood. The First Flight of All. The Original Wright Biplane is now on View at the Science Museum, South Kensington. *Airways*, Apr. 1928, vol. 4, pp. 291–293, illus.

Author's description of the Wright aeroplane as seen in the Science Museum.

What Science Owes to the Wright Brothers; a Complete Résumé of the Early Wright Experiments. *Slipstream*, Apr. 1928, vol. 9, no. 4, pp. 9–15, 18, illus.

The First Flight—Twenty-Five Years Ago. Remarkable Progress in Aviation in Intervening Quarter Century. *Aeronautic Review*, Aug. 1928, vol. 6, pp. 116–119, illus.

Orlovius, Heinz. Die Erfüllung der Ikarus-Sehnsucht. (Zum 25. Gedanktage des ersten Motorfluges der Brüder Wright.) *Aëronautica*, Dec. 1928, vol. 2, pp. 242–244, illus.

Tate, William J. With the Wrights at Kitty Hawk—Anniversary of First Flight 25 Years Ago. *Aeronautic Review*, Dec. 1928, vol. 6, no. 12, pp. 188–192.

The Wright Brothers. *Popular Aviation*, Dec. 1928, vol. 3, no. 6, pp. 11–16, 116–117, illus.

Popular account of the Wright experiments and flights through the year 1909.

The Wrights' First Flights. *Aero Digest*, Dec. 1928, vol. 13, pp. 1104–1109, 1290–1294, illus.

Summary of early Wright flights and experiments, 1900–1908.

Neville, Leslie E. The Original Wright Biplane. *Aviation*, Dec. 1, 1928, vol. 25, pp. 1724–1726, illus.

Slosson, Edwin E. How Man Learned to Fly. *Science News Letter*, Dec. 8, 1928, vol. 14, pp. 349–351.

Résumé of early Wright experiments and flights.

G[rey], C. G. On Twenty-Five Years of Flying. *Aeroplane*, Dec. 19, 1928, vol. 35, pp. 965–968, illus.

Twenty-Five Years of Flying. *Flight*, Dec. 20, 1928, vol. 20, pp. 1061–1062.

Editorial comment on twenty-fifth anniversary of 1903 Wright flights.

Wilbur Wright Anniversary Banquet. *Flight*, Dec. 20, 1928, vol. 20, p. 1064–1067.

Account of banquet held by the Royal Aeronautical Society in the Science Museum, London, December 17, 1928, celebrating the 1903 Wright flights. Quotes extensively from address delivered by Griffith Brewer reviewing the early Wright experiments.

U.S. Congress. House. *Joint Resolution to Appoint a Congressional Committee to Attend the Exercise Celebrating the Twenty-Fifth Anniversary of the First Airplane Flight Made by Wilbur and Orville on December 17, 1903, at Kill Devel Hills, Kitty Hawk, North Carolina.* [Washington: United States Government Printing Office, 1928] 2 pp. (70th Congress, 2d Session. H. J. Res. 332).

Introduced by Mr. Lindsay Warren of North Carolina; referred to the Committee on Rules.

U.S. Congress. House. Congressional Committee to Attend 25th Anniversary of 1st Airplane Flight, Kitty Hawk, N.C. *Report to Accompany H. J. Res. 342* [to appoint Congressional Committee to attend exercises celebrating 25th anniversary of 1st airplane flight made by Wilbur and Orville Wright on Dec. 17, 1903, at Kill Devil Hills, Kitty Hawk, N. C.]: submitted by Mr. Snell. December 8, 1928. Washington. Government Printing Office, 1928, 1 p. (70th Congress, 2d session. House. Report 1931.)

Joint Resolution to Appoint a Congressional Committee to Attend the Exercises Celebrating the Twenty-Fifth Anniversary of the First Airplane Flight Made by Wilbur and Orville Wright on December 17, 1903, at Kill Devil Hills, Kitty Hawk, North Carolina. *United States Statutes at Large*, 1927–29, vol. 45, pt. 1, p. 1020.

Public Resolution 71, approved December 11, 1928.

Veĭgelin, Konstantin E. Taĭna Raĭtov. [Wright secret] In his *Zanimatel'ni͡a avi͡atsi͡a*, Leningrad: "Vremia," 1928, pp. 109–114, illus.

I brevetti de fratelli Wright. *Aeronautica*, Jan. 1929, vol. 3, pp. 10–14, illus.

Includes Wrights' March 12, 1906, statement to the Aero Club of America, a résumé of their 1908 flights, and digest of their early patents.

Kitty Hawk 25 Years After the Event. Secretary of War and Other Officials Honor the Wright Brothers. *U. S. Air Services*, Jan. 1929, vol. 14, no. 1, pp. 28–31.

Report of group pilgrimage from Washington to Kitty Hawk and of ceremonies there at laying of the cornerstone of the national memorial to the Wright brothers, December 17, 1928.

Wright Anniversary Dinner. December 17th, 1928. *Journal of the*

Royal Aeronautical Society, Jan. 1929, vol. 33, pp. 83–90.

Abridged *Aeroplane*, Dec. 19, 1928, vol. 35, pp. 968, 970.

Account of the dinner held at the Science Museum, London, with inclusion of messages received on the occasion of the dinner and the address in appreciation of the Wright brothers delivered by Griffith Brewer who was closely associated with them for many years.

A Lighthouse Keeper's Connection with Pioneers in Aviation. *Lighthouse Service Bulletin*, Jan. 2, 1929, vol. 3, pp. 272–273.

Keeper W. J. Tate's relations with Wrights.

Aviation's Twenty-Five Birthday Candles. *Literary Digest*, Jan. 5, 1929, vol. 100, no. 1, pp. 47, 50, 52–56, illus.

Bacon, David. The Airplane Observes Its Silver Anniversary. *Air Travel News*, Feb. 1929, vol. 3, no. 2, pp 3–5, illus.

Ohio. General Assembly. *Joint Resolution Providing for a Testimonial to Orville Wright and Wilbur Wright, Deceased, Inventors of the Airplane on the 26th Anniversary of the First Human Flight in a Heavier-Than-Air Machine*. Columbus: 1929, 2 pp. (Senate Resolution No. 23).

Resolution adopted, April 1, 1929.

Foulois, Benjamin D. Cross Country. *Collier's*, Jan. 11, 1930, vol. 85, no. 2, pp. 28–33.

Account of first cross-country flight by the author and Orville Wright in 1909.

McMahon, John R. An Extra Spectator at the First Flight. *Aero Digest*, July 1930, vol. 17, no. 1, pp. 73, 202, 204, illus.

Author sets forth claim of Robert L. Westcott, member of the Kitty Hawk life saving crew, who testified in the Montgomery patent suit against the United States that he witnessed the December 17, 1903 flights from the life saving station through a spyglass.

1931–1935

Wright Brothers. [Signed N.] *Air*, Jan. 1931, vol. 4, pp. 10–12 illus.

Written on the occasion of a visit to the Science Museum, London, and quotes from a section on the Wrights in its *Handbook of the Collections Illustrating Aeronautics*.

Newton, Byron R. One of the Greatest Achievements in the Story of the Human Race. *U. S. Air Services*, Dec. 1931, vol. 16, no. 12, pp. 19–24, illus.

Reminiscences by a one-time aeronautic editor of the *New York Herald* with frequent reference to the Wright brothers. Reproduces Wilbur Wright's letter of January 20, 1910, to the author and Frank S. Lahm's letter of July 5, 1908, to him from France written on the eve of Wilbur's flights there.

——— They Said it was Neither Fact nor Fiction and Promptly Turned it Down. *U.S. Air Services*, July 1932, vol. 17, no. 7, pp. 20–24, port.

Author's story of the Wright flights at Kitty Hawk, May 1908, rejected at the time by magazines and other publications. Reprints letter of Orville to the author, June 7, 1908, regarding flights.

Montgomery, Frank A., Jr. Kitty Hawk. *Sportsman Pilot*, Dec. 1932, vol. 8, no. 6, pp. 22–25, 38, 47, illus.

Résumé of Kitty Hawk experiments.

Moore, Alvin E. The Dawn of Flight. *U.S. Air Services*, Dec. 1932, vol. 17, no. 12, pp. 35–39.

Popular account of the early Wright flying experiments which culminated in their successful December 17, 1903, flights.

McCormick, Anne O'Hare. The Epic Etched in Kitty Hawk Sands. *New York Times Magazine*, Dec. 1, 1932, pp. 4–5, 18, illus.

Allder, Walter. Pioneer Airmen: Part 1. The Wright Brothers. *Canadian Aviation*, Jan. 1933, vol. 6, no. 1, pp. 22–23.

Veit, Sidney B. France and the Wright Brothers. *Legion d'Honneur*, Apr. 1933, vol. 1, no. 4, pp. 207–215, illus.

Claudy, Carl H. Wright Flies! *The Quill*, Oct. 1933, vol. 21, no. 9, pp. 5, 12–13.

Lahm, Frank P. Training the Airplane Pilot. *Journal of the Royal Aeronautical Society*, Oct. 1933, vol. 37, pp. 916–941 and discussion pp. 941–942.

Author includes reference to early associations with Wrights and tells of Wright 1909 instruction methods.

Morelli, Ercole. A chi spetta il primato della costruzione degli aeroplani. *Le Vie dell' aria*, Nov. 12, 1933, vol. 5, p. 3, col. 1–2.

Celebrating the 30th Anniversary of Flight. *National Aeronautic Magazine*, Dec. 1933, vol. 11, no. 12, p. 12.

Celebration Commemorating the Thirtieth Anniversary of the Flight of the Wright Brothers at Kitty Hawk. *Journal of the Franklin Institute*, Feb. 1934, vol. 217, pp. 237, 256.

Account of exercises held at the Franklin Institute, December 17, 1933.

Lancken-Wakenitz, baron von der. Flying with Wright. *Living Age*, Sept. 1934, vol. 347, pp. 63–65.

Translation from *Berliner Tageblatt*.

Author, then German chargé d'affaires in Paris, describes flight with Wilbur Wright, October 24, 1908, and claims that he was the first German to fly in a heavier-than-air machine.

Coffyn, Frank. I Got Up Early, as Told to W. B. Courtney. *Collier's*, Dec. 15, 1934, vol. 94, pp. 25, 55–57, illus.

Reminiscences of the Wrights by a member of the Wright Exhibition Team.

1936–1940

The 32nd Anniversary is Celebrated. *U.S. Air Services*, Jan. 1936, vol. 21, no. 1, p. 10.

Dos Passos, John. Campers at Kitty Hawk. *New Republic*, July 8, 1936, vol. 87, pp. 262–264.

Reprinted in Dos Passos' *The Big Money*, New York: Harcourt, Brace and Co., 1936, pp. 278–285; translation, *L'Ala d'Italia*, Feb. 15, 1939, vol. 17, no. 4, pp. 49–52; also in Fadiman, Clifton, *Reading I've Liked*, New York: Simon and Schuster, 1941, pp. 154–160; Van Doren, Carl, and Carmer, Carl, *American Scriptures*, New York: Boni & Gaer; 1946, pp. 91–98; Brown, Leonard S., and others, eds., *Literature for Our Time*, New York: Henry Holt, 1947, pp. 99–102; Jensen, Paul, ed., *The Fireside Book of Flying, Stories*, New York: Simon and Schuster, 1951, pp. 33–39; and in Roberts, Joseph B. and Briand, Paul L., *The Sound of Wings*, New York: Henry Holt, 1957, pp. 56–61.

Memorial to the Wright Brothers. 29th Paris Prize in Architecture, Final Competition. Judgment of June 1, 1936. *The Bulletin of the Beaux Arts Institute of Design*, Sept. 1936, vol. 12, pp. 6–8, illus.

Illustrations and critiques of first three prize-winning designs.

Greene, Laurence. Flying Machine Soars Three Miles (Norfolk *Virginian-Pilot*). In his *America Goes to Press*, Indianapolis, New York: The Bobbs-Merrill Company, 1936, pp. 319–322.

Reprints account of the December 17, 1903, flights as originally published in the Norfolk *Virginian-Pilot*, Dec. 18, 1903.

Industry's Message to Orville Wright. *U.S. Air Services*, Jan. 1937, vol. 22, no. 1, p. 16.

Text of telegram sent to Orville Wright, December 17, 1936, by the Aeronautical Chamber of Commerce of America.

December 17, Anniversary of Famous Flight of Wright Brothers, Again Observed as National Aviation Day. *Air Commerce Bulletin*, Jan. 15, 1937, vol. 8, pp. 159–160.

Whitehouse, Arch. Happy Landings. The "Wright Biplane" Never Flew. *Flying Aces*, Feb 1937, vol. 25, no. 3, pp. 33–35, 93, illus.

Moszkowski, Walter. Figures et souvenirs de l'aviation. Les véritables débuts des frères Wright. *L'Aéro*, Mar. 26, 1937, no. 1504, p. 2, Apr. 2, no. 1505, p. 2, Apr. 9, no. 1506, p. 2, Apr. 16, no. 1507, p. 2, Apr. 23, no. 1508, p. 2.

Sullivan, Harry. Half a Lifetime Encompasses Entire History of the Modern Airplane Since the First Flight. *Congressional Record*, Dec. 17, 1937, vol. 82, pp. 1721–1722.

Reprinted from *Washington Post*, Dec. 12, 1937, and introduced into the record by Congressman Reynolds of North Carolina.

Durand, William F. The Wright Brothers. *Journal of the Institute of the Aeronautical Sciences*, Jan. 1938, vol. 5, pp. 111–112.

Brief address delivered at the Honors Night Meeting of the Institute of the Aeronautical Sciences commemorating the thirty-fourth anniversary of the first flights of the Wright brothers. Orville Wright attended as an Honorary Fellow.

The First Army Air Crash. *Look*, Feb. 1, 1938, vol. 2, no. 3, pp. 56–57, illus.

Seven photographs of accident at Fort Myer, September 17, 1908, in which Orville Wright was injured and Lieut. Thomas E. Selfridge killed.

Lahm, Frank P. The Wright Brothers as I Knew Them. *U.S.A. Recruiting News*, May 1938, pp. 4–7, illus.

Published also in *Journal of the Aeronautical Sciences*, Feb. 1939, vol. 6, pp. 165–167; *Air Corps News Letter*, Mar. 15, 1939, vol. 22, no. 6, pp. 1–4; *Sperryscope*, Apr. 1939, vol. 8 no. 10, pp. 1–5; translation *El Ejercito constitucional*,

Havana, June–July 1939, vol. 42, pp. 58–59; *Southern Flight*, July 1939, vol. 11, no. 7, pp. 5–7; *Quartermaster Review*, July–Aug. 1939, vol. 19, pp. 14–17, 73–74, with title, "Pioneers of the Air"; *American Foreign Service Journal*, Apr. 1940, vol. 17, pp. 194–195, 214–218, illus.

Bauer, Charles J. Ed Sines, Pal of the Wrights. *Popular Aviation*, June 1938, vol. 22, no. 6, pp. 40–78, illus.

Reminiscences of the Wrights by an early partner in their printing establishment.

Mayer, Robert. Kitty Hawk Cachet. *Stamps*, June 4, 1938, vol. 23, pp. 33–34, illus.

Description of cachet used on mail dispatched from Kitty Hawk, May 18, on the occasion of National Air Mail Week, May 15–21, 1938.

Iacobescu, Gh. Orville și Wilbur Wright. *România aeríană*, July–Aug. 1938, vol. 12, no. 7–8, pp. 20–24, illus.

Lewis, George W. The Contributions of the Wright Brothers to Aeronautical Science and Engineering. In The Edison Institute, *Dedication of the Wright Brothers Home and Shop in Greenfield Village*. Dearborn, 1938, pp. 26–35.

Published also in *U.S. Air Services*, May 1938, vol. 23, no. 5, pp. 13–15.

Address delivered at dedication exercises, April 16, 1938.

Purchase Date of First Army Airplane. *Air Corps News Letter*, Jan. 15, 1939, vol. 22, no. 2, p. 15.

The First Airplane Bought by Any Government. *U.S. Air Services*, Aug. 1939, vol. 24, no. 8, p. 7.

Editorial comment on thirtieth anniversary of sale of Wright aeroplane to U.S. Army, August 2, 1909.

Story of Aviation in Capitol's Rotunda. *U.S. Air Services*, Aug. 1939, vol. 24, no. 8, p. 9.

Reports favorable action on H.J. Res. 123, introduced by Thomas A. Jenkins of Ohio, to complete the unfinished frieze in the rotunda of the Capitol with a history of aviation including the invention of the aeroplane by the Wright Brothers.

Thirty Years Ago—and It Seems Like Only Yesterday. Orville Wright Flew Lieutenant Foulois from Ft. Myer to Alexandria, Va. *U.S. Air Services*, Aug. 1939, vol. 24, no. 8, pp. 11–14, illus.

Account of ceremonies planned for anniversary of contract signed, August 2, 1909, with Wright brothers, providing for purchase of an aeroplane by the U.S. Army.

Chronology of Army Wright. *Chirp*, Aug. 6, 1939, no. 25, p. 4.

Ingells, Douglas J. They Gave the World Wings. *Model Airplane News*, Oct. 1939, vol. 21, no. 4, pp. 6–7, 40–46, illus.

Popular summary of early Wright experiments and flights written on occasion of the thirtieth anniversary of the purchase by the U.S. Army of a Wright aeroplane. Quotes from Orville Wright's interview with reporters prior to thirty-fifth anniversary celebration of the 1903 Kitty Hawk flights.

Kelly, Fred C. How the Wright Brothers Began. *Harper's Magazine*, Oct. 1939, vol. 179, pp. 473–484.

Popular account of the Wright brothers' boyhood and youth, their operation of a print-shop and later a bicycle repair shop, their gliding experiments, and finally their successful powered flights in 1903.

Montgomery, Frank A., Jr. Kitty Hawk—Where Man First Flew. *Air Trails*, Dec. 1939, vol. 13, no. 3, pp. 25, 46–47, illus.

Thirty-Six Years After. *U.S. Air Services*, Jan. 1940, vol. 25, no. 1, p. 7.

Brewer, Griffith. A Visit to America in Wartime. *Flight*, May 30, 1940, vol. 37, pp. 494d–495, illus.

Author's account of visit to the home of Orville Wright.

Kelly, Fred C. They Wouldn't Believe the Wrights Had Flown. *Harper's Magazine*, Aug. 1940, vol. 181, pp. 286–300.

Abridged in *Reader's Digest*, Feb. 1941, vol. 38, pp. 39–43.

An analysis of the public attitude and reaction to the Wright flights, 1904–1908. Includes reference to reports of flights by Robert Coquelle of *L'Auto*, A. I. Root, editor of *Gleanings in Bee Culture*, Henry M. Weaver, and mentions other witnesses including Dan Kumler of the *Dayton Daily News*, Luther Beard of the Dayton *Journal*, D. Bruce Salley, and Byron R. Newton of the *New York Herald*.

Griscom, Lloyd C. *Diplomatically Speaking*. Boston: Little, Brown, and Company, 1940. 476 pp.

Includes brief account of flight with Wilbur Wright at Rome, pages 318–319. Griscom was then United States ambassador to Italy.

1941–1945

Cleaves, Freeman. What Happened at Kitty Hawk. *Air Youth Horizons*, Dec. 1941, vol. 2, no. 10, pp. 3–4, 20–21, illus.

Thirty-Eight Years Ago at Kitty Hawk. *U.S. Air Services*, Jan. 1942, vol. 27, no. 1, p. 20.

Reprint of editorial from the *New York Times* on the 38th anniversary of the first flight.

An Englishman's Tribute to the Wright Brothers. *U.S. Air Services*, Jan. 1943, vol. 28, no. 1, p. 46.

Quotation from Lord Brabazon's speech before the Royal Aeronautical Society, London.

Stout, Rex. It Was Something That Happened at Kitty Hawk. *U.S. Air Services*, Jan. 1943, vol. 28, no. 1, p. 19.

Remarks made December 6, 1942, over CBS radio station.

39th Anniversary World's First Flight. *U.S. Air Services*, Jan. 1943, vol. 28, no. 1, p. 19.

Report on visit of Orville Wright to Washington, December 16–17, 1942.

Jablonsky, Bruno. The First Aeroplane. *Aeroplane*, Jan. 1, 1943, vol. 64, p. 28.

Letter by a pupil of Orville Wright in 1909, written in reply to C. G. Grey's article of same title in *Aeroplane*, December 4, 1942, which tended to belittle the original Wright aeroplane.

Jeanjean, Marcel. L'Affaire Wright. *L'Aérophile*, Apr.–June, 1943, vol. 51, pp. 74–75, 89–90, 113–114, illus.

A part of his series entitled "Histoire illustrée de l'aviation." Summary of aviation during the period, 1905–1907, and the intensive controversy which raged in France regarding the Wright brothers and their claims for the achievement of heavier-than-air flights.

Kelly, Fred C. The Mysterious Visitor. *Technology Review*, June 1943, vol. 45, pp. 408, 410.

Author's letter to the editor contending that visitor to Huffman Prairie in September 1905 was Charles M. Manly.

Johnston, S. Paul. Still Mysterious. *Technology Review*, June 1943, vol. 45, pp. 410, 458.

Letter to the editor refuting Mr. Kelly's claim that the visitor to Huffman Prairie in September 1905 was Charles M. Manly.

Jeanjean, Marcel. La "Campagne de France" de Wilbur Wright. *L'Aérophile*, July–Aug. 1943, vol. 51, pp. 134–135, 154–155, illus.

Continuation of author's previous account giving brief description of Wright aeroplane and engine and summary of Wilbur Wright's 1908 flights in France.

Gardner, Lester D. The Wright Flyer. *Technology Review*, Nov. 1943, vol. 46, p. 12.

Letter to the editor setting forth details on exhibition of the 1903 Wright aeroplane at the Massachusetts Institute of Technology in 1916.

U.S. Congress. House. *Joint Resolution Commemorating the Fortieth Anniversary of the First Airplane Flight by Wilbur and Orville Wright.* [Washington: United States Government Printing Office, 1943], 2 pp. (78th Congress, 1st Session. H.J. Res. 175).

Introduced by Mr. Harry P. Jeffrey of Ohio, Oct. 20, 1943; referred to the Committee on the Library; passed House, Nov. 24; referred to Senate Committee on Commerce, Nov. 26; passed Senate with amendment, Dec. 3.

Broughton, J. Melville. The Fortieth Anniversary of the Flight of a Heavier-Than-Air Machine. *Science*, Nov. 5, 1943, vol. 98, pp. 400–401.

Published also in *Pegasus*, Dec. 1943, vol. 2, no. 6, p. 12 and abridged *U.S. Air Services*, Dec. 1943, vol. 28, no. 12, p. 30.

Text of proclamation of the governor of North Carolina, issued October 6, 1943, designating December 17, 1943, as "Kitty Hawk Day."

U.S. Congress. House. *Commemorating 40th Anniversary of 1st Airplane Flight by Wilbur and Orville Wright. Report to accompany H.J. Res. 175. Submitted by Mr. O'Toole. Nov. 16, 1943.* Washington: United States Government Printing Office, 1943, 1 p. (78th Congress, 1st Session. House. Report 869.)

Arnold, Henry H. They Gave Us a New World. *U.S. Air Services*, Dec. 1943, vol. 28, no. 12, p. 21.

Tribute to the Wright brothers.

Bonnalie, Allan F. The Wrights Solved All Fundamental Problems of Flight. *U.S. Air Services*, Dec. 1943, vol. 28, no. 12, pp. 25–26, illus.

Author draws comparisons between modern aeroplanes and the Wright 1903 aeroplane.

Forty Years of Heavier-than-Air. *National Aeronautics*, Dec. 1943, vol. 21, no. 12, p. 14.

Announcement of plans being made for the fortieth anniversary of the Wright 1903 flights.

Foulois, Benjamin D. Two Vital Problems of the Wright Brothers. *U.S. Air Services*, Dec. 1943, vol. 12, no. 12, p. 22.

Genesis. *Trade Winds*, Dec. 1943, vol. 7, pp. 7–8, 14, illus.

Part of fortieth anniversary of 1903 flight issue.

Kelly, Fred C. The Revolution at Kitty Hawk. What the Achievement of the Airplane Owed to the Past and Presages for the Future. *Technology Review*, Dec. 1943, vol. 46, pp. 83–84, 96, illus.

Brief survey of the accomplishments of some of the Wright predecessors whom the author asserts contributed inspiration but little technical help and knowledge to the brothers.

Lewis, George W. Contributions of Wilbur and Orville Wright to Aeronautical Sciences. *U.S. Air Services*, Dec. 1943, vol. 28, no. 12, pp. 19–20.

Tribute to the Wrights on the fortieth anniversary of their first power flights, December 17, 1903.

Martin, Glenn L. Let Us Pause to Honor Orville and Wilbur Wright. *U.S. Air Services*, Dec. 1943, vol. 28, no. 12, p. 23.

Published also in *Martin Star*, Dec. 1943, vol. 2, p. 17, with a photograph of Orville Wright and Glenn Martin at an early aircraft show.

Merner, Mary. Kill Devil Hills. *Airlanes*, Dec. 1943, vol. 8, no. 12, pp. 2–3, illus.

Milling, T. De Witt. Orville and Wilbur—the Immortal Brothers. *U.S. Air Services*, Dec. 1943, vol. 28, no. 12, p. 21.

Reminiscences by one of Orville Wright's pupils in 1911.

North Carolina Honors the Fathers of Flight. *Pegasus*, Dec. 1943, vol. 2, no. 6, pp. 13–14, illus.

Reed, Thomas R. Wrights Were the Discoverers of Secret of Flight. *U.S. Air Services*, Dec. 1943, vol. 28, no. 12, p. 24, illus.

Wright Brothers. First of the Skymasters. *Aviation and Yachting*, Dec. 1943, vol. 11, no. 7, pp. 19, 33, 48, illus.

U.S. Congress. Senate. *Commemorating 40th Anniversary of 1st Airplane Flight by Wilbur and Orville Wright. Report to Accompany H.J. Res. 175. Submitted by Mr. Bailey, Dec. 3, 1943.* Washington: United States Government Printing Office, 1943, 1 p. (78th Congress, 1st Session. Senate. Report 568).

Owen Russell. The Dream That Found Wings. *New York Times Magazine*, Dec. 12, 1943, pp. 8, 45, illus.

Wright fortieth anniversary article.

Joint Resolution Commemorating the Fortieth Anniversary of the First Airplane Flight by Wilbur and Orville Wright. *United States Statutes at Large*, 1943, vol. 57, pt. 1, p. 605.

Approved December 17, 1943.

Speech of Hon. Lindsay Warren. Extension of Remarks of Hon. Herbert C. Bonner. *Congressional Record*, Dec. 18, 1943, vol. 89, appendix p. A5577.

Speech delivered December 17, 1943, at celebration honoring Orville Wright, Washington, D.C.

Fortieth Anniversary. *Model Airplane News*, Jan. 1944, vol. 30, no. 1, pp. 10–11, 45–46, illus.

The Fortieth Anniversary. The World Honors the Wright Brothers. *National Aeronautics*, Jan. 1944, vol. 22, no. 1, pp. 12–13, 54, illus.

The Orville Wright Dinner. *U.S. Air Services*, Jan. 1944, vol. 29, no. 1, p. 10.

Brief report on fortieth anniversary dinner given by the Aero Club of Washington, December 17, 1943, and attended by Orville Wright.

Wright Bros. Flier. *Model Airplane News*, Jan. 1944, vol. 30, p. 10.

Scale plans drawn by W. A. Wylam.

P[arish], W[ayne] W. The Wright Dinner — Moral Lesson. *American Aviation*, Jan. 1, 1944, vol. 7, no. 15, pp. 23–24, illus.

Wright Brothers Honored on Flight Anniversary. *Aero Digest*, Jan. 1, 1944, vol. 44, pp. 191, 201.

Blake, Bob. 41 Years of Flight. *Aviation and Yachting*, Dec. 1944, vol. 12, no. 7, pp. 32–33, 35–36, illus.

Anniversary account of Wright 1903 flights.

Carnegie, Dale. They Made History in Twelve Seconds [Wright Brothers]. In his *Dale Carnegie's Biographical Roundup; Highlights in the Lives of Forty Famous People*, New York: Greenberg, 1944, pp. 228–233.

Included also in British edition (Kingswood, Surrey: The World's Work, Ltd., 1946), pp. 190–195.

Orville Wright Attends 41st Anniversary Celebration. *U.S. Air Services*, Jan. 1945, vol. 30, no. 1, pp. 18–19.

Report on Orville Wright's attendance at meeting of the National Aeronautic Association and the Institute of the Aeronautical Sciences, Washington, D.C., December 17, 1944. On this occasion, as a previous recipient of the Robert Collier Trophy, he was presented with a certificate of award for the year 1913.

Builders of America; Picture Biography. *Scholastic*, Apr. 30, 1945, vol. 46, p. 11, illus.

Account of Wright brothers.

Kelly, Fred C. For the Wright Record. *Technology Review*, June 1945, vol. 47, pp. 484–485, illus.

An account of the arrangements made by the Wrights for recording data on their December 17, 1903 flights. The recording devices used were a revolution counter, anemometer, and stop watch. Based on information furnished by Orville Wright in a letter to the author, January 17, 1945.

Wylam, William. Wright Brothers Original Flier. In his *Scale Models by Wylam. Book II.* New York: Air Age, Inc., 1945, frontispiece.

1946–1950

Hettick, John. Twelve Seconds for the Wrights. *Aero Digest*, Apr. 1946, vol. 52, no. 4, pp. 29, 156, illus.

Story of the early Wright experiments published in the author's series of articles entitled, "Gallery of Aviation's Frontiersmen—No. 4".

Sidram, Louis. When the Aeroplane First Saluted Liberty. *Esquire*, May 1946, vol. 25, no. 5, pp. 48–50, illus.

Wilbur Wright's flight of September 29, 1909, from Governors Island around the Statue of Liberty and return; accompanied by a colored lithograph of this event by Harper Goff.

Wylam Masterplans: Wright Model A, Wright Model B. *Model Airplane News*, Mar. 1947, vol. 36, pp. 34–35.

Kelly, Fred C. First Night Flight. *Technology Review*, July 1947, vol. 49, p. 521.
Account of Orville Wright's flight, September 1909 at Dormstedt (i.e. Bornstedt) military parade ground near Potsdam.

Mattioli, Guido. L'Aero Club di Roma onora Wilbur Wright, ed i pionieri dell'aria di tutto il mondo. *L'Aviazione*, Oct. 26, 1947, vol. 30, p. 1, illus.

The Army-Wright Contract. *Chirp*, Mar. 1948, no. 37, p. 4.
Brief summary of events leading to the signing of a contract between the U.S. Army and the Wrights, February 10, 1908.

Deux lettres des frères Wright. *Forces aériennes françaises*, Mar. 1948, pp. 880–883.
Letters of December 29, 1903, and November 4, 1905, from Wright brothers to Captain Ferber.

Kitty Hawk in 1908. *Chirp*, Mar. 1948, no. 37, p. 5.
Summary of Wright flights, May 1908.

Orville Flies Army Plane. *Chirp*, Mar. 1948, no. 37, p. 6.
Chronology of Orville Wright's Fort Myer flights, September 1908.

The Wayward Press with Due Apology to *The New Yorker*. *U.S. Air Services*, Mar. 1948, vol. 33, no. 3, pp. 7–9.
Concerning articles about Wright brothers following the death of Orville Wright on January 30, 1948.

The Wright Brothers. *Journal of the Royal Aeronautical Society*, Mar. 1948, vol. 52, pp. 141–150.
Statement on the work of the Wrights written on the occasion of Orville's death. Includes impressions of the Wrights written by Griffith Brewer, Sir Francis McClean, Lord Brabazon of Tara, Sir Roy Fedden, and Dr. H. Roxbee Cox and his brief bibliography.

Wright Brothers Records. *Chirp*, Mar. 1948, no. 37, p. 6.
Tabulation of record performances, December 14, 1903–September 18, 1909.

McSurely, Alexander. New Historical Booklet Disregards Wright's Aviation Contribution [signed A. McS.]. *Aviation News*, Mar. 11, 1946, vol. 5, pp. 10–11.
Review of Albert F. Zahm's *Early Powerplane Fathers* with Orville Wright's comments as set forth in a letter to McSurely, February 5, 1946.

The Wright Negotiations. *Chirp*, Aug. 1948, no. 38, pp. 1, 7–8.
Chronological summary of negotiations for the sale of their aeroplane to the United States Government, 1905–1908.

Courtney, W. B. Twelve Seconds that Shrank the Earth. *Collier's*, Dec. 25, 1948, vol. 122, p. 94, illus.

Aviation's Shrine. *Newsweek*, Dec. 27, 1948, vol. 32, p. 43.

Davy, Maurice J. B. [Wright Brothers]. In his *Interpretive History of Flight; a Survey of the History and Development of Aeronautics With Particular Reference to Contemporary Influences and Conditions*. London: H. M. Stationery Off., 1948, pp. 103–109, 113–117, 122–123, illus.
Included also in 1937 edition (London: H. M. Stationery Off., 1937), pp. 121–127, 131–136, 142–143, 147.
Deals primarily with the development of the Wright aeroplane through 1905.

The First Controlled Human Flight—the Wright Brothers. In U.S. National Air Museum, *National Aircraft Collection*, Washington: Smithsonian Institution, 1949, pp. 14–19, illus.

Engel, Leonard. Between Wind and Water; in Forty-Five Years as a Telegrapher on the Only Line Serving the Carolina Banks, near Cape Hatteras, Alpheus Drinkwater Has Seen More Shipwrecks than any other Man Alive. *True Magazine*, Jan. 1949, vol. 24, no. 140, pp. 54–55, 57.

Includes account of sending of telegram, December 17, 1903, from Wrights to Dayton.

Kelly, Fred C. Traits of the Wright Brothers. *Technology Review*, June 1949, vol. 51, pp. 504–507.

Representative anecdotes about the Wrights, emphasizing their modesty, thoroughness, and practical common sense.

L'Aviazione italiano onora i fratelli Wright. *L'Aviazione*, July 15, 1949, vol. 31, p. 1, illus.

Pedace, Giovanni. Gli albori dell'aviazione militare italiano 1909. *L'Aviazione*, July 15, 1949, vol. 31, pp. 1–2.

First Wright Glider. *Chirp*, Nov. 1, 1949, no. 48, pp. 10–12.

Al Williams in Charge of Celebration at Kitty Hawk. *U.S. Air Services*, Dec. 1949, vol. 34, no. 12, p. 17.

Lindbergh, Charles A. A Lesson from the Wright Brothers. *Aviation Week*, Dec. 26, 1949, vol. 51, no. 26, p. 42.

Address delivered, December 17, 1948, at Washington, D.C. on the occasion of the 46th anniversary of the 1903 flight.

Il primo volo di W. Wright. *L' Aviazione*, Jan. 30, 1950, vol. 32, p. 1.

Reproduces Ambassador James Clement Dunn's letter of December 21, to Guido Mattioli acknowledging tribute to the Wrights in Mattioli's letter of December 17, to Dunn.

Arnold, Henry H. Dayton and the Wright Brothers 1911; Learning to Fly. *National Air Review*, Apr. 1950, vol. [1], pp. 26–32.

Originally published in his *Global Mission*, New York; Harper & Brothers, 1949, pp. 16–29.

Kitty Hawk. *Chirp*, Apr. 1, 1950, no. 43, pp. 3–4.

Account of Frank Lahm's participation in the forty-sixth anniversary celebration of the Wrights' first flights.

Langewiesche, Wolfgang. What the Wrights Really Invented. *Harper's Magazine*, June 1950, vol. 200, pp. 102–105.

Published also in *U.S. Air Services*, Aug. 1950, vol. 35, no. 8, pp. 13, 16–17, illus.

Author stresses their achievement of control of flight, particularly the control of bank by the use of wing-warping in conjunction with a controllable vertical tail-rudder.

Beck, Charles P. It Happened at Kitty Hawk; First Plane Flight at Kitty Hawk. *Instructor*, Dec. 1950, vol. 60, p. 23, illus.

1951–1955

[Findley, Earl N.] If a Lie is Repeated Often Enough Someone Will Believe It. *U.S. Air Services*, Sept. 1951, vol. 36, no. 9, pp. 5–6.

Editorial taking exception to statements by C. G. Grey that

Ader was the first to achieve powered flight in an article entitled, "The First Half-Century of Aviation," *Interavia*, June 1951, vol. 6, p. 319.

Brown, Aycock. The Kill Devil Story. *Air Force*, Dec. 1951, vol. 34, no. 12, pp. 11–12.
Statement on aims and purpose of the Kill Devil Hill Memorial Association and its plans to become a national organization with name Kill Devil Hill Memorial Society.

Lahm, Frank P. Memoirs of Fort Myer. *Aeronautica*, Jan./Mar. 1952, vol. 4, no. 1, pp. 1, 9–10, illus.
Description of Wright first military aeroplane.

Golden Anniversary of Flight to be Observed Fittingly. *National Aeronautics*, Dec. 1952, vol. 31, p. 2.
Announces plans for the nationwide, yearlong observance of the fiftieth anniversary of powered flight.

Wright Memorial Observance. *Aviation Week*, Dec. 29, 1952, vol. 57, p. 15.
Summary of events held in Kitty Hawk, N.C., Dayton, Ohio, and Washington, D.C. on December 17, 1952, in celebration of forty-ninth anniversary of the Wright brothers' first successful flights.

Ludovico, Domenico. I Realizzatori dell'Aeroplano: Wright. In his *L'Aeroplano; Soluzione ed Evoluzione del Problema del Volo*. 3. ed. Rome: Associazione Culturale Aeronautica, 1952, pp. 25–32, illus.

Rolfe, Douglas. Wrights' Biplane. *Air Progress; History of Aviation*, 1952, pp. 62–63.

Allen, Carl B. The Concept of Flight That Worked. *Bee-Hive*, Jan. 1953, vol. 28, no. 1, pp. 3–6, illus.
Account of early Wright brothers' experiments and research which led to their successful powered flights of December 17, 1903.

Ceremonies Held at Kitty Hawk. *National Aeronautics*, Jan. 1953, vol. 32, p. 5.
Account of Wright brothers' anniversary celebration, December 17, 1952.

Haven, Gil. The Wrights at the Stick. *Bee-Hive*, Jan. 1953, vol. 28, no. 1, pp. 12–15, illus.
Account of the development of controls and piloting techniques of Wrights.

Johnson, Jesse S. Kitty Hawk Ceremonies Inaugurate 50th Year Wright Flight Anniversary. *Airpost Journal*, Jan. 1953, vol. 24, pp. 108, 126.

Ushering in the Golden Anniversary of Flight. *U.S. Air Services*, Jan. 1953: vol. 38, no. 1, pp. 1–2.

Fravel, Ira F. The Wright Brothers, B. F. (Before Flying). *U.S. Air Services*, Feb. 1953, vol. 38, no. 2, p. 16.

Whitener, Ralph V. Fly-By at Kitty Hawk. *Air Force*, Feb. 1953, vol. 36, no. 2, pp. 54–56, illus.
Account of Wright brothers 49th anniversary ceremonies at Kitty Hawk, December 17, 1952.

U.S. Congress. House. *Joint Resolution To Provide for Proper Participation by the United States Government in a National Celebration of the Fiftieth Anniversary Year of Controlled Powered Flight Occurring During the Year from Dec. 17, 1952, to Dec. 17, 1953*. Washington: United States Government Printing Office, 1953,

3 pp. (83rd Congress, 1st Session. H.J. Res. 193)

Introduced Feb. 18, 1953 by Mr. Hinshaw of California; referred to the Committee on the Judiciary.

Allen, C. B. Earl N. Findley, Chronicler of the Era of Powered Flight. *Pegasus*, Apr. 1953, vol. 20, no. 4, pp. 6–12, illus.

Includes extensive reference to Findley's associations and friendship with the Wrights.

Harper, Harry. I Watched Wilbur Fly. *Air Trails*, May 1953, vol. 40, no. 2, pp. 24–25, illus.

Author's recollections of Wilbur Wright at Le Mans, France, in the summer of 1908.

Fiftieth Anniversary of Powered Flight. Extension of Remarks of Hon. Peter F. Mack, Jr. *Congressional Record*, May 28, 1953, vol. 99, appendix pp. A3206–A3207.

Description of commemorative stamp marking the 50th anniversary of the Wright brothers' flight provided for in a bill introduced by Congressman Mack.

The Birth of Flight. *Air University Quarterly Review*, Summer 1953, vol. 6, p. 2, illus.

Photograph of the Wrights' first powered flight on December 17, 1903, made from the original glass-plate negative in the collections of the Library of Congress.

Chester, Ralph. Astonished Reporters and Skeptical Editors. *The State*, July 18, 1953, vol. 21, pp. 6–7.

Davis, Chester. North Carolina's Twelve Great Seconds. *The State*, July 18, 1953, vol. 21, pp. 3–5, 50.

Bonney, Walter T. Prelude to Kitty Hawk. Part V. *Pegasus*, Sept. 1953, vol. 21, pp. 6–11, illus.

The last in a series of five articles deals with the Wright brothers and their successful flights on December 17, 1903.

Lipp, Frederick J. "Let her go, Wilbur!"—The Wright Brothers of Ohio Led the Way to the Skies. *Inside Ohio Magazine*, Sept. 1953, vol. 2, pp. 70–72.

The Wrights' Airplane in Europe. *Bee-Hive*, Fall 1953, vol. 28, pp. 28–29, illus.

Brief report on Wrights' European flights, 1908–1909.

Wright Golden Anniversary to Last 4 Days this Year. *Air Force Times*, Sept. 26, 1953, vol. 14, p. 8.

Big Four Day Observance at Kitty Hawk. *National Aeronautics and Flight Plan*, Nov. 1953, vol. 32, p. 7.

Announces plans for Wright brothers celebration, December 14–17, 1953.

Barnaby, Ralph S. Gliding Experiments That Made the 50th Anniversary of Powered Flight Possible. *Soaring*, Nov./Dec. 1953, vol. 17, pp. 2–3, 10, 14, 26.

Summarizes available data on the Wright gliders and Wright gliding experiments, 1900–1902, and 1911.

Broomfield, G. A. The Wright Brothers in Europe. *Esso Air World*, Nov./Dec. 1953, vol. 6, pp. 68–71, illus.

An account of the Wrights' flights in and visits to England, France, Germany, and Italy, 1908–1911.

Lodi, Angelo. Agli inizi di una era nuova. *Rivista Aeronautica*, Nov./Dec. 1953, vol. 29, pp. 801–807, illus.

Anniversary article dealing with the Wright brothers and their flights, 1900–1909, ending with their flights at Centocelle, Italy, in April 1909.

269-517—68——7

Dollfus, Charles. First Powered Flights; New Historical Facts Justify International Recognition of the Wright Brothers. *Flight Magazine*, Dec. 1953, vol. 40, pp. 38–39, 44, 49–54, illus.

Analyses claims of Clément Ader, Alberto Santos-Dumont, and the Wright brothers to being the first to fly.

Fifty Years of Flight; 31 Historic Photographs. *National Geographic*, Dec. 1953, vol. 104, pp. 740–756.

The first six photographs are of flights by Wilbur and Orville Wright, 1903–1908.

Harper, Harry. I Watched Wilbur Fly. *Royal Air Force Flying Review*, Dec. 1953, vol. 9, pp. 19–20, 43.

Author's recollection of his observation of a flight by Wilbur at Le Mans, France, in 1908.

Kelly, Fred C. Web of Circumstance. *Air Force*, Dec. 1953, vol. 36, p. 40.

The author's observations on Wilbur Wright's statement in a letter to Octave Chanute, October 28, 1906, that the successful 1903 flights were due "to peculiar combinations of circumstances which might never occur again."

——— The Wright Brothers' Worst Brush-Off. *Air Force*, Dec. 1953, vol. 36, pp. 38–40, 42, illus.

An account of the Wright brothers' negotiations, 1905–1908, with the U.S. War Department for the purchase of their aeroplane.

Muller, Jane S. Kitty Hawk Jubilee. *Compressed Air Magazine*, Dec. 1953, vol. 58, pp. 337–339, illus.

A popular fiftieth anniversary article which confuses the dates of death of Wilbur and Orville, page 338, in the sentence, "Orville died in 1912, but Wilbur lived through two wars in which aviation was a major factor."

Orville et Wilbur Wright effectuaient, il y a cinquante ans, leurs premiers vols. *Aero France*, Dec. 1953, pp. 179–180.

Anniversary article based on original reports published in *L'Aérophile*, January 1904 and December 1905.

Rutledge, William. Birth of Flight. *Royal Air Force Flying Review*, Dec. 1953, vol. 9, pp. 17–18.

A fiftieth anniversary article dealing with the Wrights' December 17, 1903, flights at Kitty Hawk, N.C.

Unos segundos para la historia [signed J. H.]. *Revista Nacional de Aeronautica*, Dec. 1953, vol. 13, pp. 26–29, illus.

Warring, Ron. 50 Years Ago–. *Model Aircraft*, Dec. 1953, vol. 12, pp. 552–554, illus.

Instructions for making a scale model of the Wright 1903 aeroplane.

Wright Papers Appear to Top '50th' Events. *Air Force Times*, December 1953, vol. 14, p. 17.

Havemann, Ernest. The Day That Man First Flew. Wrights' Papers Recall Great Event 50 Years Ago. *Life*, Dec. 7, 1953, vol. 35, pp. 162–176, illus.

Summary of letters from the *Papers of Wilbur and Orville Wright* dealing with their early flights, especially the flights of December 17, 1903.

De Wright "Flyer" van 1903. *Avia-Vliegwereld*, Dec. 10, 1953, vol. 2, pp. 652–653, illus.
Detailed drawing.

Development of the Wright Flyer. *Engineering*, Dec. 11, 1953, vol. 176, pp. 737–739, illus.
An account of the early Wright aeroplane, gliders, and flights, culminating in their successful powered flights on December 17, 1903.

50 Jahre Motorflug; Ein Rückblick zur 50-Jahr-Feier des 1. Motorfluges der Gebrüder Wright am 17. Dez. 1903. *Technica: illustrierte technische Rundschau*, No. 26, 1953, vol. 2, pp. 1–3.

Burgunder, Hans. Das Wunder von Kitty Hawk. *Technische Rundschau*, Dec. 18, 1953, vol. 45, pp. 1–2, illus.

Meacock, F. T. Twelve Significant Seconds. *Aeroplane*, Dec. 18, 1953, vol. 85, pp. 817–819, illus.
Brief account of early work of the Wright brothers which culminated in their successful flight of twelve seconds' duration on December 17, 1903.

Slater, A. E. Gliding Notes. *Aeroplane*, Dec. 18, 1953, vol. 85, p. 852, illus.
Review of early Wright gliding flights and gliders, 1900–1902.

British Celebration of the Wright Jubilee. *Engineering*, Dec. 25, 1953, vol. 176, p. 823.
Brief report on British exhibitions, lectures, and celebrations arranged to commemorate the fiftieth anniversary of the Wrights' first powered flights, December 17, 1903.

Wright Brothers Jubilee Exhibition at the Science Museum. *Illustrated London News*, Dec. 26, 1953, vol. 223, p. 1061.

Brown, Aycock. *The Birth of Aviation, Kitty Hawk, N.C.* Winston-Salem, N.C.: The Collins Company, 1953, [64] pp., illus.
Deals especially with the glider and aeroplane experiments and flights conducted at Kitty Hawk and Kill Devil Hills by Wilbur and Orville Wright in 1900, 1901, 1902, 1903, 1908, and 1911.

Meynell, Laurence. "Guess I'll Take You Up." In his *Rolls: Man of Speed; a Life of Charles Stewart Rolls and Some Account of the Early Days of Motoring and Flying*. London: The Bodley Head, 1953, pp. 125–138.
An account of Rolls' flight with Wilbur at Le Mans, France, October 8, 1908. Rolls, piloting a French-built Wright aeroplane, was killed in a crash at the Bournemouth Air Meet, in England, July 12, 1910, the first English pilot to die in an aircraft accident.

A New Dimension for Travel—the Wrights. In *Fifty Years of Aviation; Background Information on Aviation's First Fifty Years*. Washington: National Committee to Observe the 50th Anniversary of Powered Flight [1953] pp. 5–9.

Thomas, H. A. The Wright Biplane. *Air Trails Model Annual*, 1953, pp. 30–31, 80.
Scale plans for building the original Wright 1903 aeroplane.

Throm, Edward L., and Crenshaw, James S. *Popular Mechanics Aviation Album*. Chicago: Popular Mechanics Company, 1953, 192 pp., illus.
Popular pictorial history including three chapters on the Wrights, "A Short Run and A

Jump," "12 Seconds Over Kitty Hawk," and "Yankee Ingenuity Wins Again," pp. 37–56.

There were Celebrations Galore. *U.S. Air Services*, Jan. 1954, vol. 39, p. 18.

A list of the Wright brothers' fiftieth anniversary celebrations.

Flight's Biggest Birthday Party. *Air Force*, Feb. 1954, vol. 37, pp. 18–19, 42, illus.

Summary of the special events and ceremonies held at Kitty Hawk, N.C., December 17, 1953, commemorating the fiftieth anniversary of the Wright brothers' first successful flights.

Turns Liberty's Head. Wright's Epoch Making Flight Accomplished. Bronze Goddess Receives Queerest Visitor in Her History. *U.S. Air Services*, Nov. 1954, vol. 39, pp. 16–17.

An account of Wilbur Wright's flight from Governors Island to the Statue of Liberty and return on September 29, 1909, as reported in the *New York Tribune* on September 30, 1909.

Powell, William S. First Flight. *American Heritage*, Winter 1954 issue, vol. 5, pp. 40–43, 57, illus.

A fiftieth anniversary article on the Wright brothers and their first flights at Kitty Hawk, N.C., December 17, 1903, by the news editor of *American Heritage.*

Golden Anniversary Observance of Man's First Successful Powered Flight. Proceedings at the Exercises Held at Wright Brothers National Memorial, December 14–17, 1953, in Commemoration of the Fiftieth Anniversary of the First Flight of an Airplane Made by Wilbur and Orville Wright. Washington: U.S. Govt. Print. Off., 1954, 27p. (83d Cong., 2d Sess. House. Document no. 480).

Includes the texts of the addresses presented, list of dignitaries in attendance, list of sponsors of the celebration, list of sponsors of the reconstruction of the Wright brothers' buildings at Kill Devil Hill, and the programmed events of the four special days which were "Pioneer & Private Flyers Day," "Industry Day," "Defense Day," and "Anniversary Day."

Wright Day Celebrations Mark Flight Anniversary. *Air Force Times*, Dec. 24, 1955, vol. 16, p. 4.

1956–1966

Drinkwater, Alpheus W. I Knew Those Wright Brothers Were Crazy. *Reader's Digest*, Nov. 1956, vol. 69, pp. 188–189, 192, 194.

Account of the Wrights' 1903 and 1908 flights at Kitty Hawk by the Weather Bureau telegraph operator at Manteo, N.C.

McKnew, Thomas W. Fledgling Wings of the Air Force. *National Geographic*, Aug. 1957, vol. 112, pp. 266–271, illus.

An eyewitness account of the Wrights' 1908 and 1909 Fort Myer flights by the Vice-President and Secretary, National Geographic Society.

North Carolina, Ohio, D.C. Mark 54th Anniversary of Wright Flight. *Air Force Times*, Dec. 28, 1957, vol. 18, p. 13.

Bruccoli, Matthew J. Flight to Eternity. *Flying*, Jan. 1958, vol. 62, pp. 43, 76, 78.

An account of Orville Wright's first trial flight at Kitty Hawk, N.C., on December 17, 1903.

AFA Takes Part at Kitty Hawk. *Air Force*, Feb. 1958, vol. 41, p. 37.

Account of the fifty-fourth anniversary tribute to the Wright brothers participated in by the Air Force Association, Kill Devil Hills Memorial Society, National Park Service, and the U.S. Air Force.

Delgove, Henri. A Fiftieth Anniversary. *Aeroplane*, Aug. 8, 1958, vol. 95, p. 190, illus.

Anniversary account of Wilbur's stay at Les Hunaudières, France, in 1908 and his flight of August 8, 1908, with photograph of stone memorial marking the site of the flight.

Fifty Years Ago The Journal Covered the First Military Aviation Tests. *Army, Navy, Air Force Journal*, Aug. 30, 1958, vol. 95, pp. 1,23, illus.

Excerpts dealing with Orville Wright's Fort Myer flights in 1908, originally published in the *Army Navy Journal*, Aug. 22, Sept. 5, 12, 19, 26, 1908.

Ingells, Douglas J. The Fort Myer Incident. *Saturday Evening Post*, Sept. 13, 1958, vol. 231, pp. 48–49, 82–83, 86.

Deals with Orville's September 1908 flights for the U.S. Signals Corps and the fatal crash of September 17 in which he was injured and his passenger, Lieut. Thomas E. Selfridge, killed.

First United States Military Aircraft Accident, 17 September 1908, Mr. Orville Wright and Lt. Thomas E. Selfridge. Norton Air Force Base, Calif.: Deputy the Inspector General, USAF [1958?]. 10p. and appendices.

Copy of the official accident report prepared in 1908.

Kennedy, George. The Rambler R ports on Early Flights. *Congressional Record*, July 30, 1959, vol. 105, p. 14734.

Originally published in the *Washington Star*, July 30, 1959, and introduced into the record by Sen. A. S. Mike Monroney on the occasion of the fiftieth anniversary of Orville Wright's successful aeroplane demonstration at Fort Myer, July 30, 1909.

Gibbs-Smith, Charles H. How Wilbur Wright Taught Europe to Fly. *American Heritage*, Feb. 1960, vol. 11, pp. 60–63, 107.

Emphasizes the role of Wilbur's 1908 flights near Le Mans, France, in stimulating flying in Europe. Illustrated by unique photographs from an album dedicated by Wilbur to Elizabeth Bollée, daughter of Léon Bollée, French automobile manufacturer and friend of Wilbur.

Aviation Log Wright Hydroaeroplane Navy No. B–1 (AH–4). 15 July 1911 to 5 June 1913. [Washington: Bureau of Naval Weapons, Navy Dept., 1960]. Looseleaf.

Prepared for internal Navy distribution from original copy in the Capt. W. Irving Chambers Papers in the Navy Historical Foundation records deposited in the Library of Congress.

Aviation Log Wright Hydroaeroplane Navy No. B–2 (AH–5). 27 October 1912. [Washington: Bureau of Naval Weapons, Navy Dept., 1960]. Looseleaf.

Prepared for internal Navy distribution from original copy in the Capt. W. Irving Chambers Papers in the Navy Historical Foundation records deposited in the Library of Congress.

Brown Aycock. Birthplace of Aviation; Aviation History Began at North Carolina's Outer Banks. *National Aeronautics*, Dec. 1961, vol. 40, pp. 4–7, illus.

Moore, Alvin E. Dawn of Flight. In Sunderman, James F., ed., *Early Air Pioneers, 1862–1935*, New York: Franklin Watts, 1961, pp. 22–36. (The Watts Aerospace Library).

Garber, Paul E. Historian Seeks Data on Wright Planes. Wright Aircraft Listed. *Chirp*, Oct. 1962, No. 69, pp. 12–13.

Lists 31 aircraft associated with the Wright brothers, 1899–1920. Scale models of most are in the National Air and Space Museum.

Air Leaders Boost 60th Anniversary. *National Aeronautics*, Oct./Dec. 1963, vol. 42, p. 9.

Lists scheduled events for the sixtieth observance of Wright brothers' Kitty Hawk flights.

Soule, Gardner. How the Wright Brothers Learned to Fly. With Quotations from the Papers of Wilbur and Orville Wright. *Popular Science*, Dec. 1963, vol. 183, pp. 51–57.

Stewart, Oliver. Did the Wright Brothers Fly First? *Spectator*, Dec. 20, 1963, vol. 213, p. 816.

Discusses the claims of the Wrights and Clément Ader of being the first to fly. The author concludes that both flew and that "Ader's aircraft probably lacked controllability; the Wrights' aircraft probably lacked power for weight."

Kitty Hawk—Mission Accomplished. *National Aeronautics*, Mar. 1964, vol. 43, p. 8.

Résumé of 1963 Wright anniversary events including the dedication of the First Flight Airport at Kill Devil Hill, N. C.

Gibbs-Smith, Charles H. *The World's First Aeroplane Flights (1903–1908) and Earlier Attempts to Fly*. London: Her Majesty's Stationery Office, 1965, 32 pp., illus.

Section entitled "The First Successful Flights" discusses and illustrates early Wright flights, pp. 10–12, 20. Chronological "Table of Powered Take-offs and Flights (1903–1908)" lists 16 Wright flights made 1903, 1904, 1905, and 1908. Section entitled "Aviation Date List (1799 to 1908)," pp. 30–32, lists 15 events associated with Wright brothers.

—— *A Directory of and Nomenclature of the First Aeroplanes, 1809–1909*. London: Her Majesty's Stationery Office, 1966, 120 pp.

Wright aeroplanes and engines are discussed and listed, pp. 79–85, 98. Section entitled "Surviving Aircraft," pp. 101–102, lists four Wright aircraft; section entitled "Surviving Engines," pp. 102–103, lists six Wright engines; and section entitled "The First Aerodromes," pp. 107–110, discusses "Huffman Prairie" and "Kitty Hawk, and the Kill Devil Hills."

Powerplant

Motor

Wright Brothers' 28- to 30-Horsepower Aeroplane Motor. *Scientific American*, Dec. 15, 1906, vol. 95, pp. 448–449, illus.

Brief note on exhibition of Wright four-cylinder engine at

the Second Annual Exhibition of the Aero Club of America, December 1906.

Nicolleau, Auguste. L'Aeronautique en Amérique. *L'Aérophile*, Jan. 1907, vol. 15, pp. 13–15, illus.
Includes report on "Le nouveau moteur des frères Wright," page 15, which is based on the account in the *Scientific American*, December 15, 1906.

Moteurs à cylindres verticaux et parallèles. 1er moteur Wright. *Le Génie civil*, June 19, 1909, vol. 55, p. 152, illus.
The Wright engine built by Bariquand et Marre in France.

Dierfeld, [Benno]. Der Wright-Motor der Neuen Automobil-Gesellschaft in Oberschöneweide bei Berlin. *Zeitschrift Verein der Deutscher Ingenieure*, May 28, 1910, vol. 54, pp. 886–888, illus.
Details of the Wright engine manufactured in Germany by the Neue Automobil-Gesellschaft at Oberschöneweide.

Dyke, Andrew L. Features of the Standard Wright Motor. *Aero*, New York, Nov. 5, 1910, vol. 1, no. 5, p. 15, illus.
Four-cylinder engine used in the "Baby Wright," 1910.

Aero Engines: Wright. In *All the World's Airships . . . 1910–11*, London: Sampson Low, Marston & Co., Ltd., 1910, p. 434.
Scant details in 1910–1914 editions.

André, Henri. Moteur Wright (Salon 1909). In his *Moteurs d'aviation et de dirigeables*, Paris: L. Geisler, 1910, pp. 151–152, illus.
The four-cylinder Wright engine built by Bariquand et Marre and exhibited 1909 in Paris.

Brewer, Robert W. A. Wright Engine. In his *The Art of Aviation*, London: Crosby, Lockwood and Son, 1910, pp. 66–68.
The Bariquand et Marre engine.

Lumet, Georges. Le Moteur Wright. In his *Les Moteurs d'aviation*, Paris: H. Dunod et E. Pinat, 1910, pp. 60–61.
Short description of the four-cylinder Wright engine manufactured by Bariquand et Marre.

Vorreiter, Ansbert. Motor der Gebrüder Wright. In his *Motoren für Luftschiffe und Flugapparate*, Berlin: Richard Carl Schmidt & Co., 1910, pp. 110–112, illus.
Brief description of improved four-cylinder Wright engine being built in Germany by the Neue Automobil—Gesellschaft for the Flugmaschine Wright-Gesellschaft.

Wright Aeroplane Motor Type "6–60." Dayton, Ohio: The Wright Co., [1913], 4 pp., illus.
Leaflet issued by the Wright Company advertising this motor.

Phipps, Walter H. Leading Aeronautical Motors of the World: Wright. *Aircraft*, June 1913, vol. 4, pp. 88, 90.
Brief specifications of the four- and six-cylinder engines.

The New Wright Six-Cylinder Motor. *Aeronautics*, New York, Oct. 1913, vol. 13, p. 141, illus.
Account of use in Wright type hydroplane piloted by Harry A. Atwood.

Loening, Grover C. The New Wright Six-Cylinder Motor. *Aircraft*, Nov. 1913, vol. 4, p. 210, illus.

The 6-Cylinder 60-Horsepower Wright Motor. *Aeronautics*, New

York, Nov. 1913, vol. 13, pp. 177–179, illus.
Detailed account of "6–60" engine.

Wrights Produce Economical Six. *Aero and Hydro*, Nov. 15, 1913, vol. 7, p. 87, illus.
The "6–60" engine.

The New Wright Flexible Drive. *Scientific American*, June 13, 1914, vol. 190, p. 484.
Auxiliary shaft as adopted in the new aeroboat model.

Angle, Glenn D. Wright [Engines]. In his *Airplane Engine Encyclopedia*, Dayton, Ohio: Otterbein Press, 1921, pp. 521–523, illus.
Brief description of Wright 4, 6, and 8 cylinder and 6–60 engines.

Lawrance, Charles L. The Development of the Airplane Engine in the United States. In International Civil Aeronautics Conference, Washington, D.C., December 12–14, 1928, *Papers Submitted by the Delegates for Consideration by the Conference*, Washington: United States Government Printing Office, 1928, pp. 409–421.
In his discussion of the "Early Period" author has brief description of early Wright engines, pages 412–414.

McSurely, Alexander. The Horsepower at Kitty Hawk. *Bee-Hive*, Jan. 1963, vol. 28, no. 1, pp. 7–11, illus.
Account of the development of the first Wright aeroplane engine.

Propeller

Brown, Harold S. A Defense of the Wright System of Propellers. *Scientific American*, Dec. 26, 1908, vol. 99, p. 471.
Letter to the editor, December 1908, commenting on Wrights' use of twin propellers and stating belief that propeller was not the immediate cause of the Fort Myer accident.

Margoulis, Wladimir. Wright & Voisin. Le Rendement des hélices Wright (réponse à M. Lefort). *L'Aérophile*, Mar. 1909, vol. 17, p. 101.
Brief comment on previous article in *L'Aérophile*, February 1, 1909, pages 51–54 entitled, "L'Aéroplane Wright et les aéroplanes français."

Eberhardt, Carl. Die Wright'sche Luftschraube und der Fahrwiderstand der Wright'schen Flugmaschine. *Der Motorwagen*, Aug. 20. 1909, vol. 12, pp. 630–632, illus.
Published also in his *Theorie und Berechnung der Luftschrauben*, Berlin: Verlag von M. Krayn, 1910, pp. 94–98, illus.
Details and calculations on the Wright propeller by a German engineer attached to the Royal Prussian Aerial Battalion in Berlin.

Wrights' Propeller Efficiency. *Aeronautics*, New York, Nov. 1909, vol. 5, pp. 174–175, illus.
Based on calculations of Captain Eberhardt above.

Aston, W. G. A Consideration of Some Existing Propellers. *Aero*, London, May 3, 1910, vol. 2, pp. 348–349, illus.
Includes the Wright brothers' propeller.

Dallwitz-Wegner, Richard von. Die Wright-Schraube. In his *Der Treibschrauben - Konstrukteur*, Rostock, i. M.: C. J. E. Volckmann, 1911, pp. 139–140, illus.

James, Sydney V. Aerial Screw Practice. *Aero and Hydro*, Dec. 7, 1912, vol. 5, pp. 180–182, illus.

Includes description of the Wright propeller with discussion of blade outline, pitch, cross section, line of center of pressure, and construction.

McSurely, Alexander. The Wrights and the Propeller. *Bee Hive*, Spring 1953, vol. 28, no. 2, pp. 20–24, illus.

Account of the early Wright propeller experiments and the Wright brothers' later operating experiences with their propellers.

Automatic Stabilizer

Wrights Patent Automatic Stability. *Flight*, July 10, 1909, vol. 1, pp. 406–407, illus.

Abstract in *Rivista Tecnica di Aeronautica*, July, 1909, vol. 6, pp. 232–233; *Aeronautics* [New York], Sept. 1909, vol. 5, pp. 90–91.

Based on specifications of the Wrights' British patent No. 2913, filed February 6, 1909, and granted September 9, 1909. The automatic stabilizing device, used in actual flights by the Wrights as early as 1908, was first described in their American patent No. 1,075,533, filed February 10, 1908.

Orlovskiĭ, Petr. Novyĭ avtomaticheskiĭ stabilizator sistemy br. Raĭt [Wright brothers' new automatic stabilizer]. *Viestnik vozdukhoplavaniia*, Dec. 1909, no. 2, pp. 21–22, illus.

Automatic Stabilizing System of the Wright Brothers. *Scientific American Supplement*, Jan. 14, 1911, vol. 71, pp. 20–21, illus.

Based on British and French patent specifications.

Aubigny, Eugène d'. Le Nouveau planeur Wright. *L'Aéro*, Oct. 29, 1911, vol. 5, no. 272, p. 1, illus., Oct. 30, no. 273, p. 1.

Includes comments by Ernest Archdeacon, Marcel Armengaud, and René Quinton.

Der Wright-Stabilisator. *Flugsport*, Feb. 28, 1912, vol. 4, pp. 171–172, illus.

Report on use in 1911 glider flights at Kitty Hawk, N.C.

Wright Automatic Stability System. *Aeronautics* [New York], Oct. 1913, vol. 13, pp. 138–139, 142, illus.

Abridgment of Wright patent No. 1,075,533, filed February 10, 1908, and granted October 14, 1913.

Loening, Grover C. The Wright Automatic Stabilizer. *Flying*, Jan. 1914, vol. 2, no. 12, p. 29.

Brief general statement of operating principles, with an account of test by Orville.

Dienstbach, Carl. The Wright Automatic Stabilizer for Aeroplanes. *Scientific American*, Jan. 3, 1914, vol. 110, pp. 17, 36–37, illus.

Discussion of Wright patent (1913) with statement of modifications.

Stabilizer Qualifies Wright for Trophy. *Aero and Hydro*, Jan. 10, 1914, vol. 7, p. 179.

Excerpts from the official report to the Aero Club of America by the committee which witnessed 17 flights by Orville at Dayton, December 31, 1913.

Le Stabilisateur automatique Wright. *L'Aérophile*, Jan. 15, 1914, vol. 22, p. 37.

Brief note based on American announcement of award of Collier Trophy to Orville.

The Wright Automatic Stabilizer. *Aeronautics* [New York], Jan. 15, 1914, vol. 14, pp. 3–4.
Supplements note in October issue with explanation of modifications made after filing of patent application.

The Collier Trophy of the Aero Club of America for 1913 Awarded to Mr. Orville Wright for the Development and Demonstration of the Wright Stabilizer. *Flying*, Feb. 1914, vol. 3, no. 1, illus., pp. 6–7.
Another account of demonstrations by Orville Wright at Simms Station, Dayton, December 31, 1913, before committee of the Club.

James, Paul. Le Stabilisateur automatique Wright. *L'Aérophile*, Feb. 1, 1914, vol. 22, p. 59, illus.
Based on descriptions in recent issues of American trade journals.

Le Stabilisateur automatique Wright. *Le Génie civil*, Feb. 14, 1914, vol. 64, p. 318, illus.
Based on description in *Scientific American*, January 3, 1914.

Orville Wright's Fool-Proof Plane. *Literary Digest*, Feb. 21, 1914, vol. 48, p. 374.

Der automatische Wright-Stabilisator für Flugzeuge. *Deutsche Luftfahrer Zeitschrift*, Mar. 4, 1914, vol. 18, p. 110, illus.
Brief note based on patent specifications.

Sée, Alexandre. Considérations sur le stabilisateur automatique Wright. *L'Aérophile*, Mar. 15, 1914, vol. 25, pp. 134–135.

Das Versprechen von Wright. *Wiener Luftschiffer-Zeitung*, Mar. 15, 1914, vol. 13, pp. 27–29.
Summary of recent press reports on automatic stabilizer.

Bejeuhr, Paul. Der automatische Wright-Stabilisator. *Die Umschau*, Aug. 22, 1914, vol. 18, pp. 684–685, illus.

Orville Wright's New Stabilizer Almost Perfected. *Aviation and Aeronautical Engineering*, Dec. 15, 1915, vol. 1, p. 331.
Published also in *Aerial Age Weekly*, Dec. 18, 1916, vol. 4, p. 359.
Report on series of tests conducted by Orville in November with a new stabilizer based on gravity principle.

Orville Wright inventa un estabilizador para aeroplanos. *Tohtli*, Feb. 1917, vol. 2, pp. 51–52.
Based on description published in *El Pueblo*, January 8, 1917.

Control Devices

Die Steuerung des Wrightschen Fliegers. *Flugsport*, Feb. 5, 1909, vol. 1, pp. 100–103, illus.
Outline of the steering mechanism of the Wright aeroplane.

The Wright Control. *Aero*, New York, Nov. 5, 1910, vol. 1, no. 5, p. 7.
Brief note and explanatory statement by Wilbur Wright on the interconnection of the wing warping lever and the rudder.

Mitchell, John W. Wrights' Improved Anemometer. *Aeronautics*, New York, Jan. 1911, vol. 8, no. 1, p. 15.
The Wrights' first crude side-

slip "indicator," here incorrectly called an anemometer, is described as a soaked and grimy piece of rag supposedly regarded by the Wrights as superior to a pendulum or other similar device.

The New Wright Control. *Aeronautical Journal*, Jan. 1911, vol. 15, pp. 28–29, illus.
Drawings and detailed description of the new control furnished by an American correspondent.

Illustrating the Control System of Wright Planes. *Aero*, St. Louis, Mar. 25, 1911, vol. 1, p. 228, illus.
Diagram only.

Loening, Grover C. Controlling Apparatus. 8. Wright. In his *Monoplanes and Biplanes; Their Design, Construction and Operation* . . . New York: Munn & Company, Inc., 1911, pp. 287–290.

The Wright Company. *Incidence Indicator.* [Dayton, Ohio, 1913.] 1 p., illus.
Advertising leaflet with illustration and brief description of operating principles of the indicator. The indicator described was a simple wind vane controlling a pointer moving over a dial which was controlled by a special mechanical contrivance which eliminated gravity influence.

Wright Incidence Indicator. *Aeronautics*, New York, Aug. 1913, vol. 13, pp. 56, 58. illus.
Announces availability of the new incidence indicator and gives brief description.

Wright Incidence Indicator Brought Out. *Aero and Hydro*, Aug. 9, 1913, vol. 6, p. 380, illus.
Published also in *Aircraft*, Sept. 1913, vol. 4, p. 159.

A Wright Incidence Indicator. *Flight*, Oct. 15, 1913, vol. 5, p. 1178, illus.
Brief descriptive note.

Wrights Adopt New Type Control. *Aero and Hydro*, Feb. 21, 1914, vol. 7, pp. 263–264, illus.
Description of new automobile-type steering wheel in combination with a rotatable rudder handle which replaces older lever system.

Loening, Grover C. The New Wright Control. *Flying*, Mar. 1914, vol. 3, no. 2, p. 60, illus.

The New Wright Control. *Flight*, Mar. 7, 1914, vol. 6, p. 240, illus.

Wright Wheel Control. *Aeronautics*, New York, Mar. 15, 1914, vol. 14, no. 5, p. 69.
Brief descriptive note.

Wright Improves Elevator Control. *Aero and Hydro*, Apr. 25, 1914, vol. 8, p. 40.
Report on flight of Orville Wright with a new type elevator control on April 17.

Jones, Ernest L. New Model Wright Incidence Indicator. *Aeronautics*, London, Feb. 16. 1916, vol. 10, p. 116, illus.
Apparently identical with 1913 model.

The Wright Control System. In Gibbs-Smith, Charles H., *The Invention of the Aeroplane (1799–1909)*, New York: Taplinger Publishing Co., Inc., 1966, pp. 308–312, illus.
Included in discussion of control systems in use in 1909 in Wright, Voisin, Blériot, Antoinette, Henry Farman, and Curtiss aircraft.

Patents and Patent Suits

Patents

United States

Orville Wright and Wilbur Wright, of Dayton, Ohio. Flying-Machine. No. 821,393. Specification of Letters Patent. Application Filed March 23, 1903. Patented May 22, 1906. Washington: United States Patent Office, 1906, 10 pp., illus.

Abridged in *The Official Gazette of the United States Patent Office*, May 22, 1906, vol. 122, pp. 1257–1258, and reprinted in *Vehicles of the Air*, by Victor Lougheed, Chicago: The Reilly and Britton Co., 1909, pp. 451–457.

The basic Wright patent, incorporating the constructions and combinations of the Wright 1902 glider.

Orville Wright and Wilbur Wright, of Dayton, Ohio, Assignors to the Wright Company, a Corporation of New York. Flying-Machine. 1,075,533. Specification of Letters Patent. Application Filed February 10, 1908. Patented Oct. 14, 1913. Washington: United States Patent Office, 1913, 14 pp., illus.

Abridged in *The Official Gazette of the United States Patent Office*, Oct. 14, 1913, vol. 195, p. 353.

Device for maintaining automatic stability.

Orville Wright and Wilbur Wright, of Dayton, Ohio. Mechanism for Flexing the Rudder of a Flying Machine or the Like. No. 908,929. Specification of Letters Patent. Application Filed July 15, 1908. Patented Jan. 5, 1909. Washington: United States Patent Office, 1909, 5 pp., illus.

Abridged in *The Official Gazette of the United States Patent Office*, Jan. 5, 1909, vol. 138, p. 164.

Orville Wright and Wilbur Wright, of Dayton, Ohio, Assignors to the Wright Company, a Corporation of New York. Flying-Machine. 987,662. Specification of Letters Patent. Application Filed February 17, 1908. Patented Mar. 21, 1911. Washington: United States Patent Office, 1911, 5 pp., illus.

Abridged in *The Official Gazette of the United States Patent Office*, Mar. 2, 1911, vol. 164, p. 711.

Orville Wright and Wilbur Wright, of Dayton, Ohio, Assignors to the Wright Company, a Corporation of New York. Flying-Machine. No. 1,122,348. Specification of Letters Patent. Application Filed February 17, 1908. Patented Dec. 29, 1914. Washington: United States Patent Office, 1914, 10 pp., illus.

Abridged in *The Official Gazette of the United States Patent Office*, Dec. 29, 1914, vol. 209, p. 1357.

Orville Wright and James M. H. Jacobs, of Dayton, Ohio, Assignors to Dayton-Wright Company, of Dayton, Ohio, a Corporation of Delaware. Airplane. 1,504,663. Application Filed May 31, 1921. Patented Aug. 12, 1924. Washington: United States Patent Office, 1924, 8 pp., illus.

Abridged in *The Official Gazette of the United States Patent Office*, Aug. 12, 1924, vol. 325, p. 374.

Invention designed to increase the lift of an airfoil through the use of a split flap.

Orville Wright of Oakwood, Ohio, Assignor to the Miami Wood Specialty Company, of Dayton, Ohio, a Corporation of Ohio. Toy. 1,523,989. Application Filed November 10, 1923. Patented Jan. 20, 1925. Washington: United States Patent Office, 1925, 4 pp., illus.

Abridged in *The Official Gazette of the United States Patent Office*, Jan. 20, 1925, vol. 330, pp. 662–663.

The toy consists of a device by which an object, such as a doll, is thrown through the air and caused to be engaged and to be supported by a swinging bar.

Austria

Wilbur Wright und Orville Wright in Dayton (Ohio, V. St. A.) Österreichische Patentschrift Nr, 23174. Flugmaschine. Angemeldet am 23 März 1904. Beginn der Patentdauer: 15. September 1905. Ausgegeben am 26. Februar 1906. Wien: Kais. Königl. Patentamt, 1906, 8 pp., illus.

Wilbur Wright und Orville Wright in Dayton (Ohio, V. St. A.) Österreichische Patentschrift Nr. 36566. Drachenflieger. Angemeldet am 24. Februar 1908. Beginn der Patentdauer: Oktober 15. 1908. Ausgegeben am 10. März 1909. Wien: Kais. Königl. Patentamt, 1909, 4 pp., illus.

Belgium

Wright (O.) et Wright (W.) 176292. Imp. Perfectionnements aux machines aéronautiques. 23 mars 1904 (brevet américain du 23 mars 1903). *Recueil des brevets d'invention*, 1904, vol. 52, p. 509.

Wright (W.) et Wright (O.) 211970. Imp. Perfectionnements aux machines aéronautiques. 13 novembre 1908 (brevet français du 18 novembre 1907, sous le bénéfice de la convention internationale du 20 mars 1883). *Recueil des brevets d'invention*, 1908, vol. 56, pp. 1919–1920.

Wright (W.) et Wright (O.) 211971. Imp. Perfectionnements aux machines aéronautiques. 13 novembre 1908 (brevet français du 18 novembre 1907, sous le bénéfice de la convention internationale du 20 mars 1883). *Recueil des brevets d'invention*, 1908, vol. 56, p. 1920.

Wright (W.) et Wright (O.) 213823. Inv. Perfectionnements aux machines volantes, invention pour laquelle le breveté déclare avoir déposé aux États–Unis d'Amérique, le 10 février 1908, sous le bénéfice de la convention internationale du 20 mars 1883, une première demande de brevet non encore accordée à la date du 4 février 1909. *Recueil des brevets d'invention*, 1909, vol. 57, p. 224.

Wright (W.) et Wright (O.) 217586. Inv. Perfectionnements au mécanisme servant à présenter un gouvernail de machine aéronautique sous une forme concave, faisant l'objet d'une première demande de brevet déposée aux États–Unis d'Amérique, le 15 juillet 1908, sous le bénéfice de la convention internationale du 20 mars 1883 et non encore accordée à la date du 8 juillet 1909. *Recueil des brevets d'invention*, 1909, vol. 57, p. 1230.

France

MM. Orville Wright et Wilbur Wright résidant aux États–Unis d'Amérique. Brevet d'invention N° 342.188. Perfectionnements aux machines aéronautiques. Demandé le 22 mars 1904. Délivré le 1er juillet 1904. Publié le 1er septembre 1904. [Paris] Office National de la Propriété Industrielle, 1904, 4 pp., illus.

MM. Wilbur Wright et Orville Wright résidant aux États–Unis d'Amérique. Brevet d'invention N° 384.124. Perfectionnements aux machines aéronautiques. Demandé le 18 novembre 1907. Délivré le 27 janvier 1908. Publié le 30 mars 1908. [Paris] Office National de la Propriété Industrielle, 1908, 6 pp., illus.

MM. Wilbur Wright et Orville Wright résidant aux États–Unis d'Amérique. Brevet d'invention N° 384.125. Perfectionnements aux machines aéronautiques. Demandé le 18 novembre 1907. Délivré le 27 janvier 1908. Publié le 30 mars 1908. [Paris] Office National de la Propriété Industrielle, 1908, 4 pp., illus.

MM. Wilbur Wright et Orville Wright résidant aux États-Unis d'Amérique. Brevet d'invention N° 401,905. Perfectionnements aux machines volantes. Demandé le 8 février 1909. Délivré le 14 août 1909. Publié le 21 septembre 1909. [Paris] Office National de la Propriété Industrielle, 1909, 8 pp., illus.

MM. Wilbur Wright et Orville Wright résidant aux États–Unis d'Amérique. Brevet d'invention N° 404,866. Perfectionnements au mécanisme servant à présenter un gouvernail de machine aéronautique sous une forme concave. Demandé le 8 juillet 1909. Délivré le 30 octobre 1909. Publié le 14 decembre 1909. [Paris] Office National de la Propriété Industrielle, 1909, 3 pp. illus.

Germany

Orville Wright und Wilbur Wright in Dayton, (V. St. A.) Patentschrift. Nr. 173378. Klasse 77h. Gruppe 7. Mit wagerechtem Kopfruder und senkrechtem Schwanzruder versehener Gleitflieger. Patentiert im Deutschen Reiche vom 24. März 1904 ab. Ausgegeben den 16. Juli 1906. Berlin: Kaiserliches Patentamt, 1906, 4 pp. illus.

Orville Wright und Wilbur Wright in Dayton, V. St. A. Patentschrift. Nr. 240181. Klasse 77h. Gruppe 5. Vorrichtung zur Erhaltung eines bestimmten Einfallwinkels der Luftströmung zur Tragfläche vom Flugsmachinen. Patentiert im Deutschen Reiche vom 7. Februar 1909 ab. Ausgegeben den 28. Oktober 1911. Berlin: Kaiserliches Patentamt, 1911, 7 pp., illus.

Orville Wright und Wilbur Wright in Dayton, V. St. A. Patentschrift Nr. 240702. Klasse 77h. Gruppe 5. Steuer für Flugmaschinen bei welchem Vorderkante und Hinterkante gegen den Wind in verschiedenem Winkel einstellbar sind. Patentiert im Deutschen Reiche vom 15. Juli 1909 ab. Ausgegeben den 15. November 1911. Berlin: Kaiserliches Patentamt, 1911, 3 pp., illus.

Orville Wright in Dayton, V. St. A. Patentschrift Nr. 259339. Klasse 77h. Gruppe 5. Flugzeug mit verwendbaren durch senkrechte Stützen gelenkig verbundenen Tragflächenrahmen. Patentiert im Deutschen Reiche vom 13. November 1908 ab. Ausgegeben den 3. Mai 1913. Berlin: Kaiserliches Patentamt, 1913, 3 pp., illus.

Orville Wright in Dayton, V. St. A. Patentschrift Nr. 258732.

Klasse 77h. Gruppe 5. Steuerung für Flugzeuge mit verwindbaren Tragflächen. Patentiert im Deutschen Reiche vom 23. November ab. Ausgegeben den 17. Mai 1913. Berlin: Kaiserliches Patentamt, 1913, 3 pp., illus.

Orville Wright in Dayton, V. St. A. Patentschrift Nr. 259811. Klasse 77h. Flugzeug mit beiderseits von der Maschinenmitte bezüglich ihres Neigungswinkels gegen den Wind verschieden einstellbaren Tragflächen. Patentiert im Deutschen Reiche vom 13. November 1908 ab. Ausgegeben den 14. Mai 1913. Berlin: Kaiserliches Patentamt, 1913, 3 pp., illus.

Orville Wright in Dayton, V. St. A. Patentschrift Nr. 260050. Klasse 77. Gruppe 5. Flugzeug mit verwindbaren Tragflächen. Zusatz zum Patent 173378. Patentiert im Deutschen Reiche vom 13. November 1908 ab. Längsten Dauer: 23. März 1919. Ausgegeben den 17. Mai 1913. Berlin: Kaiserliches Patentamt, 1913, 3 pp., illus.

Great Britain

[Orville Wright and Wilbur Wright] Improvements in Aeronautical Machines. Complete specification. No. 6732. Date claimed for Patent under Patent Act, 1901, being date of first foreign application (in United States), 23rd Mar., 1903. Date of application (in the United Kingdom), 19th Mar., 1904. Accepted, 12th May, 1904. London: His Majesty's Stationery Office, 1904, 5 pp., illus.

[Wilbur Wright and Orville Wright] Improvements in or Connected with Flying Machines. Complete specification. No. 24,076. Date claimed for patent under Patents and Designs Act, 1907, being date of first foreign application (in France), 18th Nov., 1907. Date of application (in the United Kingdom), 10th Nov., 1908. Accepted 1st Apr., 1909. London: His Majesty's Stationery Office, 1909, 8 pp., illus.

[Wilbur Wright and Orville Wright] Improvements in or Connected with Flying Machines. Complete specification. No. 24,077. Date claimed for patent under Patents and Designs Act, 1907, being date of first foreign application (in France), 18th Nov., 1907. Date of application (in the United Kingdom), 10th Nov., 1908. Accepted, 18th Feb., 1909. London: His Majesty's Stationery Office, 1909, 5 pp., illus.

[Orville Wright and Wilbur Wright] Improvements in or Connected with Flying Machines. Complete specification. No. 2913. Date claimed for Patent under Patents and Designs Act, 1907, being date of first foreign application (in the United States), 10th Feb., 1908. Date of application (in the United Kingdom), 6th Feb., 1909. Accepted, 9th Sept., 1909. London: His Majesty's Stationery Office, 1909, 13 pp., illus.

[Orville Wright and Wilbur Wright] Improvements in Mechanism for Actuating the Rudders or Controlling Planes of Aeronautical Machines. Complete specification. No. 16,068. Date claimed for patent under Patents and Designs Act, 1907, being date of first foreign application (in the United States), 15th July, 1908. Date of application (in the United Kingdom), 9th July, 1909. London: His Majesty's Stationery Office, 1909, 4 pp.

Hungary

Wright Wilbur és Wright Orville gyárosok Daytonban. Szabadalmi leirás 44407 szám. Röpülōgép. A bejelentés napja 1908 február hó 22-ike. Megjelent 1909. évi február hó 24-én. Budapest: Magy. Kir. Szabadalmi Hivatal, 1909, 5 pp., illus.

Wright Wilbur és Wright Orville gyárosok Daytonban. Szabadalmi leirás 44408 szám. Röpülōgép. A bejelentés napja 1908 február hó 22-ike. Megjelent 1909. évi február hó 24-én. Budapest: Magy. Kir. Szabadalmi Hivatal, 1909, 8 pp., illus.

Wright Wilbur és Wright Orville gyárosok Daytonban. Szabadalmi leirás 47943 szám. Röpülōgép. A bejelentés napja 1909 február hó 9–ike. Megjelent 1910. évi február hó 12–én. Budapest: Magy. Kir. Szabadalmi Hivatal, 1910, 15 pp., illus.

Italy

Wright Orville e Wright Wilbur a Dayton, Ohio (S. U. d'America). 227/184.81601. "Perfezionamenti nelle macchine aeronautiche," richiesto il 16 marzo 1906, prolungamento per anni 6 della privativa 189/181 de un anno dal 31 marzo 1904, già prolungato per un anno con l'attestato 204/38. *Bollettino della proprietà intellettuale*, June 30, 1906, vol. 5, p. 635.

Wright Wilbur e Wright Orville, a Dayton, Ohio (S. U. d'America). Perfectionnements aux machines aéronautiques. (Rivendicazione di priorità dal 18 novembre 1907). Registro generale 99047. 14.11.-1908. *Bollettino della proprietà intellettuale*, Dec. 15–31, 1909, vol. 8, p. 1277.

Wright Wilbur e Wright Orville, a Dayton, Ohio (S. U. d'America). Perfectionnements aux machines aéronautiques. (Rivendicazione di priorità dal 18 novembre 1907). Registro generale 99048. 14.11.-1908. *Bollettino della proprietà intellettuale*, Dec. 15–31, 1909, vol. 8, p. 1277.

Wright Wilbur e Wright Orville, a Dayton, Ohio (S. U. d'America). Perfectionnements aux machines volantes. (Rivendicazione di priorità dal 10 febbraio 1908). Registro generale 100791. 8.2. 1909. *Bollettino della proprietà intellettuale*, Jan. 31, 1910, vol. 9, p. 91.

Wright Wilbur e Wright Orville, a Dayton, Ohio (S. U. d'America). Perfectionnements au mécanisme servant à présenter un gouvernail de machine aéronautique sous une forme concave (Rivendicazione di priorità dal 15 luglio 1908). Registro generale 103685. 8.7.1909. *Bollettino della proprietà intellettuale*, Mar. 31, 1910, vol. 9, p. 368.

Wright Orville e Wright Wilbur, a Dayton, Ohio (S. U. d'America). Perfezionamenti nelle macchine aeronautiche. Registro generale 124336. 29.3.1912. *Bollettino della proprietà intellettuale*, Oct. 31, 1912, vol. 11, p. 1069.

Russia

[Orville Wright and Wilbur Wright] Opisanie ostova dvoĭnogo aeroplana. [Description of the framework of a biplane.] K privilegii inostrant͡sev O. Raĭta (O. Wright) i U. Raĭta (W. Wright), v.g. Deĭtone, v severoamerikanskom shtate, Ogaĭo, zai͡avlennoĭ 13 marta 1904 goda (okhr, svid. Mo. 23488, Gruppa V. No. 15010, 31 i͡anvari͡a, 1909 g. *Svod privilegii vydannykh v Rossii*, 1909, vyp. 1, pp. 59–61.

Mres. Wilbur Wright et Orville Wright. 44.332. Patente de invención por veinte años por "perfeccionamientos en máquinas para la aerostación." Presentada la solicitud en el Registro de este Ministerio en 11 de noviembre de 1908. Recibido el expediente en 12 de idem. Concedida la patente en 27 de idem. *Boletín oficial de la propriedad industrial*, Dec. 16, 1908, vol. 23, p. 1750.

Mres. Wilbur Wright et Orville Wright. 44.333. Patente de invención por veinte años por "Perfeccionamientos en máquinas para la aerostación." Presentada la solicitud en el Registro de este Ministerio en 11 de noviembre de 1908. Recibido el expediente en 12 de idem. Concedida la patente en 27 de idem. *Boletín oficial de la propriedad industrial*, Dec. 16, 1908, vol. 23, p. 1750.

Mres. Orville Wright et Wilbur Wright. 44.860. Patente de invención por veinte años por "Perfeccionamientos en máquinas voladoras." Presentada la solicitud en el Registro de este Ministerio en 6 de febrero de 1909. Recibido el expediente en 8 de idem. Concedida in patente en 20 de idem. *Boletín oficial de la propriedad industrial*, Mar. 16, 1909, vol. 24, p. 269.

Mres. Wilbur Wright et Orville Wright. 45.940. Patente de invención por veinte años por "Un mecanismo perfeccionado qué sirve para dar una flexión ó forma arqueada al timón de una máquina voladora ú otra por el estilo." Presentada la solicitud en el Registro de este Ministerio en 13 de julio de 1909. Recibido el expediente en 14 de idem. Concedida la patente en 7 de agosto de idem. *Boletín oficial de la propriedad industrial*, Sept. 1, 1909, vol. 24, p. 905.

Court Records

The Wright Company vs. The Herring-Curtiss Company and Glenn H. Curtiss

Brief for Complainant and Abstract of Evidence on Motion for Preliminary Injunction. United States Circuit Court, Western District of New York. Springfield, O.: The Young & Bennett Co. [1909], 163 pp.

Submitted December 1909 in appeal by the Wright Company, filed August 18, 1909, to enjoin the Herring-Curtiss Company and Glenn H. Curtiss from manufacturing, selling, or using for exhibition purposes the Curtiss aeroplane.

Opinion by John R. Hazel, District Judge. Circuit Court of the United States, Western District of New York. New York: C.G. Burgoyne [1910], 7 pp.

Published also in *Federal Reporter*, May–June 1910, vol. 177, pp. 257–261.

Opinion of January 4, 1910 granting a preliminary injunction to the Wright Company. Published together with Judge Hand's decision of February 17 in the Wright Company *vs.* Louis Paulhan suit affirming this decision.

Transcript of Record, Appeal from the Circuit Court of the United States for the Western District of New York. United States Circuit Court of Appeals for the Second Circuit. [New York: 1910], 476 pp. illus.

Includes affidavits of Wilbur Wright given at Dayton, Ohio, September 18, 1909, pages 13–40, December 11, 1909, pages 252–253, at New York, March 12, 1910 pages 431–434, at Buffalo, March 19, 1910, pages 462–471; of Orville Wright at Dayton,

269-517—68——8

Ohio, December 11, 1909, pages 251–252; and of Wilbur and Orville Wright at New York, November 27, 1909, pages 203–250, at Dayton, Ohio, December 11, 1909, pages 261–271, and March 7, 1910, pages 421–431.

Also includes corroborating Wright testimony, defendant's affidavits as well as photographs, exhibits, and numerous other documents introduced into the record.

Brief for Defendants-Appellants, United States Circuit Court of Appeals for the Second Circuit. New York: C. G. Burgoyne [1910], 53 pp.

Mr. Bull's Brief for Defendants-Appellants. United States Circuit Court of Appeals for the Second Circuit. New York: C. G. Burgoyne [1910], 17 pp.

Brief for Complainant-Appellee, and Abstract of Evidence, on Appeal from an Order Granting a Preliminary Injunction. United States Circuit Court of Appeals, for the Second Circuit. Springfield, Ohio: The Young & Bennett Co. [1910], 189 pp.

Submitted May 1910.

Brief [of Mr. Wetmore] for Complainant-Appellee. United States Circuit Court of Appeals for the Second Circuit. [New York: 1910], 7 pp.

[Opinion of Lacombe, Coxe, and Noyes, Circuit Judges, June 14, 1910], In *Federal Reporter*, Sept.–Oct., 1910, vol. 180, pp. 110–111.

Reverses earlier order for a preliminary injunction.

Defendant's Record. United States District Court, for the Western District of New York. New York: Appeal Printing Company [1912], 2 vols. [1142 pp.]

Includes deposition of Wilbur Wright, New York, September 13–14, 16, 1911, vol. 1, pages 78–125, and other pertinent Wright articles, correspondence, and documents including the "file wrapper and contents" of the original Wright patent issued May 22, 1906.

Complainant's Record. United States District Court, Western District of New York. [Dayton, Ohio: 1912], 820 pp.

Includes extensive "First Rebuttal Deposition of Wilbur Wright," Dayton, Ohio, February 15–23, 1912, pages 473–614 (abstracted in *Aeroplane*, June 21–28, 1916, vol. 10, pp. 990, 992, 1034 and in *Aeronautical Journal*, July–Sept. 1916, vol. 20, pp. 115–124) and a "Second Rebuttal Deposition," February 26–March 2, 1912, pages 615–690 and also, in part, the testimony of Wilbur Wright as originally given in the Charles H. Lamson *vs.* The Wright Company suit, March 30, and April 3, 1912, pages 780–808.

Also includes extensive testimony by William J. Hammer and James W. See and by other witnesses with introduction of Wright correspondence, records, and documents into the record.

Complainant's Record-Appendix. Exhibits Reproduced. United States District Court, Western District of New York. [Dayton, Ohio: 1912], 151 pp. illus.

Includes reproduction of original Wright patent, photographs of the Curtiss, Willard, and Wright aeroplanes, text of Wright-Burgess and Wright Aeronautic Company licenses, St. Louis aviation 1910 and 1911 meet licenses, and extensive reference to Albert F. Zahm's patent application no. 550,606, filed March 21, 1910, and to that of Glenn H. Curtiss, no. 586,425, filed June 23, 1910.

Brief and Digest of the Evidence for Complainant on Final Hearing. United States District Court, Western District of New York. Springfield, Ohio: The Young & Bennett Co. [1912], 221 pp.
Submitted October 1912.

Closing Arguments of Frederick P. Fish and Edmund Wetmore. United States District Court, Western District of New York. Boston: L. H. Lane [1912], 55 pp.
Arguments for the complainant before Judge Hazel, November 19, 1912.

Argument of J. Edgar Bull, Esq., for Defendants. United States District Court, Western District of New York. New York: The C. G. Burgoyne Printing Business [1912], 44 pp.

[Opinion of John R. Hazel, District Judge, February 21, 1913.] In *Federal Reporter*, June-July 1913, vol. 204, pp. 597–614.

[*Transcript of Record on Appeal from the Decree of Court, April 8th, 1913*.] United States Circuit Court of Appeals. [New York: 1913], 3 vols. (2184 pp.)
Compilation and reprinting of pertinent records in the action including *Complainant's Record* and *Defendants' Record* above.

Brief for Complainant-Appellee. United States Circuit Court of Appeals for the Second District. Springfield, Ohio: The Young & Bennett Co. [1913], 147 pp., and appendix, IX pp.

Brief for Appellants. United States Circuit Court of Appeals, for the Second District. New York: Appeal Printing Company [1913], 205 pp.

Supplemental Brief on the Question of Infringement. United States Circuit Court of Appeals for the Second Circuit. New York: C. G. Burgoyne [1913], 26 pp.

Complainant's Reply Brief on Question of Infringement. United States Circuit Court of Appeals for the Second Circuit. Boston: L. H. Lane [1913], 24 pp.

[Opinion of Lacombe, Coxe, and Ward, Circuit Judges, January 13, 1914.] In *Federal Reporter*, Apr.-May 1914, vol. 211, pp. 654–655.
Affirms earlier interlocutory decree upholding the validity of the Wright patent.

The Wright Company vs. The Curtiss Aeroplane Co.

Bill of Complaint. In the United States District Court, for the Western District of New York. [Dayton, Ohio: November 16, 1914], 11 pp. [Typescript.]
Filed with supporting affidavits of A. F. Barnes and Orville Wright in a preliminary injunction motion November 17, 1914, against the Curtiss Aeroplane Company. Because of the sale of the Wright Company, October 15, 1915, subsequent delays, and the aircraft manufacturers' cross-licensing agreement of July 1917, this case was not brought to trial.

Affidavit of Orville Wright. [Dayton, Ohio: November 16, 1914], 5 pp., illus [Typescript.]
States that, despite earlier court decrees and judgments in favor of the Wright Company, the Curtiss Aeroplane Company is continuing to manufacture, use, and sell flying machines which infringe the Wright patent and gives a detailed report

on the infringing features of the Curtiss aeroplane.

Affidavit of Alpheus F. Barnes. [New York: November 16, 1914], 8 pp. [Typescript.]

Affidavit of Edward C. Huffaker. [Hammondsport, N.Y.: December 28, 1914], 7 pp. [Typescript.]

Affidavit of Grahame H. Powell. [Washington: December 28, 1914], 4 pp., illus. [Typescript.]

Affidavit of Robert L. Reed. [Hammondsport, N.Y.: December 28, 1914], 23 pp. [Typescript.]

Affidavit of Thomas W. Smillie. [Washington, D.C.: December 28, 1914], 2 pp., illus. [Typescript.]

Affidavit of Charles Gurtler. [Rochester, N.Y.: January 5, 1915], 5 pp. illus. [Typescript.]

Affidavit of Edson Gallaudet. [New York: January 8, 1915], 11 pp., illus. [Typescript.]

Affidavit of Charles M. Manley. [New York: January 9, 1915], 42 pp., illus. [Typescript.]

Manly Second Affidavit. [New York: January 9, 1915], 4 pp. [Typescript.]

Affidavit of Harry Benner. [Hammondsport, N.Y.: January 11, 1915], 3 pp. [Typescript.]

Affidavit of Glenn H. Curtiss. [Buffalo, N.Y.: January 11, 1915], 20 pp. [Typescript.]

Affidavit of Henry C. Genung. [Buffalo, N.Y.: January 11, 1915], 2 pp. [Typescript.]

Affidavit of G. Ray Hall. [Buffalo, N.Y.: January 11, 1915], 9 pp. [Typescript.]

Affidavit of John A. D. McCurdy. [Buffalo, N.Y.: January 11, 1915], 13 pp. [Typescript.]

Affidavit of Henry T. Wehman. [Hammondsport, N.Y.: January 11, 1915], 4 pp. [Typescript.]

Affidavit of Dr. Albert F. Zahm. [Hammondsport, N.Y.: January 11, 1915], 13 pp. and 11 photos. [Typescript.]

Affidavit of William Elwood Doherty. [Hammondsport, N.Y.: January 12, 1915], 3 pp. [Typescript.]

Additional Affidavit of John A. D. McCurdy. [Buffalo, N.Y.: January 12, 1915], 3 pp. [Typescript.]

Charles M. Manley's 2nd Additional Affidavit. [New York: January 13, 1915], 5 pp. [Typescript.]

Affidavit of Charles A. Stiles. [New York: March 18, 1915], 3 pp. [Typescript.]

Affidavit of Roy Knabenshue. [Dayton, Ohio: March 25, 1915], 2 pp. [Typescript.]

Affidavit of Harry C. Watts. [Los Angeles: March 27, 1915], 1 p. [Typescript.]

Affidavit of Walter R. Brookins. [Dayton, Ohio: April 16, 1915], 5 pp. [Typescript.]

Affidavit of Orville Wright. [Dayton, Ohio: April 24, 1915], 48 pp., illus. [Typescript.]

A reply to a number of the affidavits filed above with a discussion also of prior art and extensive testimony on the "Langley Machine" and "Tests at Hammondsport," pages 31–48.

Affidavit of Walter R. Brookins. [Newcastle, Pa.: April 30, 1915], 7 pp. [Typescript.]

Affidavit of Orville Wright. [Dayton, Ohio: May 10, 1915], 3 pp. [Typescript.]

States that he has reason to believe but has been unable to prove that knocked-down Curtiss aeroplanes were being shipped to England and assembled there with the incorporation of a double acting aileron control.

E. E. Winkley vs.
Orville & Wilbur Wright

Brief for Wright & Wright. In the United States Patent Office. Consolidated Interference No. 32,042 Flying Machines. Springfield, Ohio: The Young & Bennett Printers [1912], 10 pp.

Submitted, May 1912, in an interference which was declared on August 12, 1910, by the Commissioner of Patents in an action by Erastus E. Winkley, an inventor, who developed an automatic control for sewing machines and conceived the idea that this control could be applied to the regulation of flying machine wings and claimed its disclosure at an earlier date than that of the Wrights.

A decision by the examiner of interference, August 7, 1912, awarding priority of invention to the Wrights. This was appealed but the original decision was affirmed by the examiner in chief, May 26, 1913.

Flying Machines, Testimony in Behalf of Wright & Wright. United States Patent Office Interference No. 32,042. [Interferences Nos. 32,042, 32,302, 32,304, 32,305 and 32,306 Consolidated.] Dayton, Ohio: [1912], 37 pp., illus.

Includes depositions taken at Dayton, Ohio, January 9–10, 1912, of Orville Wright, pages 7–19, and of Wilbur Wright, pages 19–25, with testimony on the conception of their patent no. 415,105, filed February 10, 1908, and introducing into the record several drawings used for their patent application and correspondence with Katharine Wright and H. A. Toulmin regarding it.

The Wright Company vs.
Louis Paulhan

Brief for Complainant on Motion for Injunction. In the United States Circuit Court, Southern District of New York. [Springfield, Ohio: 1910], 46 pp.

Submitted in appeal by the Wright Company for an injunction to restrain Louis Paulhan, French aviator, from using several flying machines, claimed to infringe the Wright patents, which were imported into the United States for exhibition purposes.

Exhibit Book [New York: 1910], 113 pp., illus.

Compilation of complainant's and defendant's exhibits, comprising patents, drawings, blueprints, and photographs relating to points at issue.

Opinion of Judge Hand Granting Preliminary Injunction in Favor of the Wright Company, Complainants, against Louis Paulhan, Defendant. Circuit Court of the United States, Southern District of New York. [New York: 1910], 15 pp.

Published also in *Federal Reporter*, May–June 1910, vol. 177, pp. 261–271 and, together with Judge Hazel's opinion of January 4, 1910, in the Wright Company *vs.* Herring-Curtiss Company suit, New York: C. C. Burgoyne, 1910, 16 pp.

Decision rendered February 17, 1910, affirming earlier decision of Judge Hazel, January 4, 1910.

Brief for Defendant-Appellant. United States Circuit Court of Appeals for the Second Circuit. [New York: The Evening Post Job Printing Office, 1910], 54 pp.

Appeal from Judge Hand's order of February 24 granting preliminary injunction to the Wrights restraining Paulhan "from importing, exhibiting and using . . . Farman and Blériot machines," alleged to infringe the original Wright patent.

Brief for Complainant-Appellee, and Abstract of Evidence, on Appeal from an Order Granting a Preliminary Injunction. United States Circuit Court of Appeals, for the Second Circuit. [Springfield, Ohio: 1910], 69 pp.

Submitted May 1910. Quotes from testimony of Wilbur Wright, pages 3, 21–22, 26–29, 32–34, 40–41, and that of Orville Wright, pages 36–37.

Transcript of Record. Appeal to the Circuit Court of the United States for the Southern District of New York [New York: 1910], 427 pp.

Includes affidavits of Wilbur Wright, January 6, 1910, pages 21–24, January 22, pages 25–27, February 5, pages 256–292, March 15, pages 360–370, March 16, pages 391–395, and March 23, pages 396–398, and that of Orville Wright, January 5, pages 17–20.

[Opinion of Lacombe, Ward, and Hayes, Circuit Court Judges, June 14, 1910.] In *Federal Reporter*, Sept.-Oct. 1910, vol. 180. p. 112.

Reverses earlier order for a preliminary injunction.

Charles H. Lamson vs. The Wright Company

Defendant's Record. In Equity, No. 6611. The United States District Court, Southern District of Ohio, Western Division. Springfield, Ohio: The Young & Bennett Co., Printers [1913], 153 pp.

Records, 1910–1912, in a suit filed by Charles H. Lamson against the Wright Company for alleged infringement of his kite patent no. 666,427, issued January 22, 1901. Includes deposition of Wilbur Wright, taken at Dayton, Ohio, March 30–April 2, 3, 4, 1912, pages 13–76, and deposition of Orville Wright, April 5, pages 77–90, telling of their early experiments, particularly their kite experiments in 1899.

The Wright Company vs. Claude Grahame-White

Bill of Complaint. In Equity on Letters Patent no. 821,393. In the United States Circuit Court, Southern District of New York. [New York: 1910], 10 pp. [Typescript.]

Filed November 29, 1910, in suit for $29,000 for infringement and accounting by reason of defendant's use of Farman and Blériot machines in the United States. These machines were alleged to infringe the Wright patent. A judgment of $1,700 for the complainant was decreed January 24, 1912.

Answer. In Equity on Letters Patent no. 821,393. In the United States Circuit Court, Southern District of New York. [New York: 1911], 11 pp. [Typescript.]

Filed February 6, 1911.

Testimony on Behalf of Complainant. In Equity on Letters Patent no. 821, 393. In the United States

Circuit Court, Southern District of New York. [New York: 1911], 69 pp. (Typescript.)

Includes testimony of William J. Hammer, consulting engineer, and of James W. See, mechanical engineer, taken February 13 and 15 at the office of H. A. Toulmin, Dayton, Ohio.

Brief for Complainant on Final Hearing. In the United States Circuit Court, Southern District of New York. [New York: 1911], 32 pp.

Submitted November 1911. The court ordered that printing of records in this action be dispensed with October 19, 1911.

Complaint. In the United States Circuit Court, Southern District of New York. [New York: 1911], 6 pp. [Typescript.]

Filed December 11, 1911.

Answer. United States District Court, Southern District of New York. [New York: 1912], 10 pp. [Typescript.]

Filed January 25, 1912.

Answer to Amended Complaint. United States District Court, Southern District of New York. [New York: 1912], 10 pp. [Typescript.]

Filed January 25, 1912.

The Wright Company vs. Aero Corporation Limited

Wright Co. *vs.* Aero Corporation, Limited. *New York Supplement,* April 10–May 22, 1911, vol. 128, pp. 726–727.

Decision denying motion for an injunction in suit brought December 6, 1910, by the Wright Company to recover $15,000 from the Aero Corporation, Ltd., which managed the Belmont Park Meet in September–October, 1910. It was dismissed by Justice Cohalan of the New York Supreme Court, January 19, 1912, on grounds that the Wrights had insufficient cause for action.

Case on Appeal. Supreme Court, Appellate Division—First Department. [New York]: Press of Fremont Payne, [1912], 163 pp.

The record and case were filed in the Appellate Division, New York State Supreme Court, March 25, 1912. Includes direct and cross examination of Wilbur Wright, January 15, 1912, pages 30–36, 102–103, and 111–118 as well as plaintiff's exhibits consisting of the agreements entered into and correspondence relating thereto.

Appellant's Points. Supreme Court. Appellate Division—First Department. [New York]: Press of Fremont Payne, [1912], 36 pp.

Appellant's Points in Reply. Supreme Court, Appellate Division—First Department. [New York]: Press of Fremont Payne [1912], 10 pp.

The motion was denied and this judgment later was affirmed with costs.

Regina Cleary Montgomery et al. vs. The United States

Evidence for Defendant. Court of Claims of the United States, No. 33,852. [Washington: Government Printing Office, 1923], pp. 607–858.

Suit for infringement filed against the Government of the United States by the heirs of John J. Montgomery, original owner of patent no. 831,173, granted September 18, 1906. The decision was against the heirs and the petition ordered dismissed, May 28, 1928.

Includes depositions of Orville Wright, taken at Dayton, Ohio, January 13, 1920, pages 651–691, 857, and on February 2, 1921, pages 694–714. Corroborating depositions by Spratt, Fansher, Meyer, Taylor, Westcott, and Dough, covering the prior development work of the Wright brothers, were also submitted and included.

Exhibit Book. Defendant's Wright Exhibits. [Exhibits Nos. 1–40.] Court of Claims, no. 33,852. [Washington: 1920–21, 140 pp.], illus.

Includes photographs of the Wright kite 1899, the 1901 and 1902 gliders, and the 1903 and 1904 aeroplanes, facsimiles of Octave Chanute and G. A. Spratt and Spratt-Wright correspondence, 1899–1907, and other data relating to their early experiments.

In the Court of Claims of the United States. No. 33852. *Defendant's Brief.* Washington: Government Printing Office, 1926, pp. xvi, 1067–1621.

Includes "work of Wright brothers in accomplishing flight," pages 1170–1193, "Wrights' use of curved wings," pages 1284–1324, "two-rudder control used by Wrights in 1902," pages 1463–1469, and "plaintiffs' argument in the Wright patent," pages 1538–1546.

Regina Cleary Montgomery et al. vs. Wright-Martin Aircraft Corporation

[Deposition and Cross Examination of Orville Wright on Behalf of Defendant. Dayton, Ohio: January 13, 1920, 78 pp.] [Typescript.]

Deposition submitted in suit filed contemporaneously with that above in the Court of Claims. Depositions were taken jointly in the two cases and these are identical with those cited in the preceding case. On plaintiffs' motion of June 6, 1921, the suit was dismissed by Judge Learned Hand, June 25, 1921.

[Deposition and Cross Examination of Orville Wright in Behalf of Defendant. Dayton, Ohio: February 2, 1921, 34 pp.] [Typescript.]

Identical testimony to that presented in the case of Regina Cleary Montgomery et al. *vs.* The United States above.

[Deposition and Cross Examination of Charles Edward Taylor. Dayton, Ohio: February 2, 1921, 11 pp.] [Typescript.]

Testimony about Taylor's activities as Wright mechanic, 1901–1905.

Wright Aeronautical Corporation vs. Handley Page, Limited, Aircraft Disposal Company, Limited, and William H. Workman.

Brief for Plaintiff on Motion for Preliminary Injunction. In Equity No. 19–16. On Wright Patent No. 821,393. United States District Court, Southern District of New York. New York: The Evening Post Job Printing Office [1920], 40 pp.

Submitted December 3, 1920, in suit for infringement of the original Wright patent no. 821,393. Has extensive references to the Wright Company and quotes from affidavit of Orville Wright, pages 7–8, 12–14, on its organization and on the British Wright Company.

George Francis Myers vs. The United States

George Francis Myers vs. *The United States.* In the Court of

Claims of the United States No. C–700 (Decided December 5, 1938). [Washington: United States Government Printing Office, 1938], 35 pp., illus.

Decision against the plaintiff in a suit brought June 2, 1923, against the United States Government by George Francis Myers alleging infringement of his patent no. 1,226,985 for a flying machine, granted May 22, 1917. This was granted on his application of September 20, 1905, which the plaintiff asserted was a continuation in part of his earlier application of January 29, 1897.

[*Deposition of Orville Wright for Defendant.* Dayton, Ohio: October 28, 1925], 52 pp. [Typescript.]

Deposition of Orville Wright. [Dayton, Ohio: February 28, 1927], 23 pp. [Typescript.]

Deposition of Orville Wright. [Dayton, Ohio: October 14, 1935], 13 pp. [Typescript.]

His Majesty, the King, Plaintiff, vs. Myers Canadian Aircraft Co., Ltd., et al., and George Francis Myers, Defendants

His Majesty, the King, Plaintiff, and Myers Canadian Aircraft Company, Ltd., et al, Defendants. *Canada Law Reports (Exchequer Court)*, 1931, pp. 146–158.

Judgment May 18, 1931, for plaintiff in action instituted October 1930, to annul Myers' patents nos. 146,917 and 187,882. Quotes from testimony of Orville Wright on Myers' United States patent no. 1,226,985, pages 157–158.

[*Deposition and Cross Examination of Orville Wright.* Dayton, Ohio: October 9–10, 1930, 51 pp.] [Typescript.]

Extensive testimony on the early Wright experiments and early Wright aeroplanes.

Published References to Patents and Patent Suits

Cléry, A. Derniers perfectionnements connus des machines volantes Wright. *L'Aérophile*, Jan. 1906, vol. 14, pp. 23–26, illus.

Based largely on specifications of Wright French patent no. 342,188, published September 1, 1904.

The American Flying-Machine Patented in England. *Illustrated London News*, Jan. 25, 1908, vol. 132, pp. 136–137.

Includes drawing by W. B. Robinson from documents in the British Patent Office.

Lucas-Girardville, [P.-N.] Les Brevets des frères Wright. *Revue d'artillerie*, Mar. 1908, vol. 71, pp. 400–403, illus.

Discussion and comparison of the French 1904 Wright patent and the two new French Wright patents, nos. 384124 and 384125.

Les plus récents brevets des Wright. *L'Aérophile*, May 1, 1908, vol. 16, pp. 161–168, illus.

Reprinting of French patents no. 384,124 and no. 384,125; published March 30, 1908.

Dominik, Hans. Die Patent der Gebrüder Wright. *Der Motorwagen*, May 31, 1908, June 10, 1908, vol. 11, pp. 397–398, 424–427.

I brevetti Wright. *Bollettino della Società Aeronautica Italiana*, July 1908, vol. 5, pp. 252–253.

Italian translation of Captain Ferber's letter to Georges Besançon originally published in *L'Aérophile*, July 1, 1908.

Ferber, Louis F. Que valent des brevets Wright? *L'Aérophile*, July 1, 1908, vol. 16, pp. 252–253.
Letter of June 22, 1908, addressed to the director, Georges Besançon, commenting on recent French patents.

Les brevets des frères Wright. *L'Aéro-Mécanique*, Oct. 10, 1908, vol. 1, no. 3, pp. 1–2, Nov. 10, no. 4, pp. 2–3, illus.
Résumé of Wright Belgian patents.

British Patent Specifications. 24077. *Flight*, Mar. 20, 1909, vol. 1, p. 168.
Abstract of British Wright patent granted March 4, 1909.

Wright Brothers' New British Patent. *Aeronautics*, New York, Apr. 1909, vol. 4, pp. 141–142, illus.
Based on specifications of British patent no. 24076 applied for November 10, 1908 and granted March 4, 1909.

Il nuovo brevetto dei fratelli Wright. *Bollettino della Società Aeronautica Italiana*, no. 5, 1909, vol. 6, pp. 182–183, illus.

Wrights' British Patents. *Flight*, May 1, 1909, vol. 1, pp. 249–250, illus.
Abstract of Wright British patent no. 24076.

Ein neues Wright-Patent. *Flugsport*, May 21, 1909, vol. 1, pp. 299–300, illus.
Brief note on Wright British patent.

A New Wright Patent. *Aero*, London, May 25, 1909, vol. 1, p. 16.
Abridgement of Wright British patent no. 24,076.

The Validity of the Wright Patents. Mr. S. F. Cody's Claim as Prior User Considered. *Aero*, London, June 15, 1909, vol. 1, p. 61.
Cody claimed that a machine employing automatic stability was commenced by him in October 1907, a month before the Wright patents were filed.

Latest Wright Patent. *Aeronautics*, New York, July 1909, vol. 5, pp. 7–8, 39–40, illus.
Abstract of British Wright patent no. 24076.

Wrights Patent Automatic Stability. *Flight*, July 10, 1909, vol. 1, pp. 406–407, illus.
Abstract of British Wright patent no. 2913.

A Patent Fight in America. *Flight*, Aug. 28, 1909, vol. 1, p. 523.
Announcement of the filing of a bill of complaint by the Wrights against Glenn H. Curtiss.

The Wright Aeroplane Infringement Suit. *Scientific American*, Aug. 28, 1909, vol. 115, p. 138.
Editorial commenting on infringement claims of the Wrights in their suit against the Aeronautic Society of New York.

Orville Wright und Wilbur Wright (V.S.A.). Mit wagerechtem Kopfruder und senkrechtem Schwanzruder versehener Gleitflieger. Patentiert im deutschen Reiche von 24 März 1904 ab. *Flugsport*, Sept. 5, 1909, vol. 1, pp. 662–665, illus.
Wright German patent no. 173378.

Über die Gültigheit der Wright-Patente. *Flugsport*, Sept. 5, 1909, vol. 1, p. 661, illus.

Includes claim by the Schröter-Motorenfabrik that it has employed wing warping in its machines for period of 13 years.

Hill, Thomas A. Status of the Wrights' Suit. *Aeronautics*, New York, Oct. 1909, vol. 5, pp. 122–123, 164.

Traces actions of the Wrights and Government patent examiners which led to the granting of Wright patent no. 821,393, dated May 22, 1906, and gives Wright claims as set forth in their suit against Aeronautic Society.

Wright Brothers Bring Suit. *Aeronautics*, New York, Oct. 1909, vol. 5, p. 135.

Announcement of filing of suits against the Aeronautic Society, Herring-Curtiss Co., and Glenn H. Curtiss.

The Wrights' Legal Action. *American Aeronaut*, Oct. 1909, vol. 1, pp. 110–112.

Reprints photographs and accounts of Herring's machine from *American Engineer and Railroad Journal*, January 1895, which editor contended contained all principles claimed by the Wrights except wing warping.

Taris, Étienne. La question des brevets Wright. *La Revue aérienne*, Oct. 25, 1909, vol. 2, pp. 621–624.

The Wright-Curtiss Suit. *Aeronautics*, New York, Nov. 1909, vol. 5, pp. 169–172, illus.

Abstract of Wright patent specifications.

Armengaud, Jules. A Propos des brevets Wright. *L'Aérophile*, Nov. 15, 1909, vol. 17, p. 515.

Sénemaud, Ch. Les Brevets Wright sont-ils valables? *L'Aviation illustrée*, Nov. 15, 1909, vol. 1, no. 35, pp. 5–6, illus.

Originally published in *L' Automobile.*

Apitz, J. Über die Bedeutung der deutschen Wright-Patente. *Flugsport*, Nov. 19, 1909, vol. 1, pp. 689–692.

Lecture delivered before the Verein Deutscher Flugtechniker giving detailed chronological account of the Wright patent actions, 1904–1905.

Der Prozess um die Wright-Patente. *Flugsport*, Nov. 19, 1909, vol. 1, pp. 688–689.

Note on Wright suits brought against the Aeronautic Society and against Glenn H. Curtiss.

The Wright Patents. *Aero*, London, Dec. 1909, vol. 1, p. 544.

Quotes from New York correspondent of the *Daily Telegram* on the Curtiss case.

Die Würdigung der Wright-Patente durch die Flugtechnische Gesellschaft. *Die Luftflotte*, Dec. 1909, vol. 1, pp. 7–8.

Based on lecture by John Rozendaal, November 25, before the Automobil- und Flugtechnische Gesellschaft, Berlin.

Über die Gültigheit des Wright-Patentes. *Flugsport*, Dec. 3, 1909, vol. 1, pp. 716–719.

Summary of Rozendaal lecture.

Noalhat, Henri. Stabilité Automatique des aéroplanes. Analyse du brevet Wright. *L'Aéronaute*, Dec. 11, 1909, vol. 42, pp. 133–137, illus.

Die Würdigung der Wright-patente durch die Flugtechnische

Gesellschaft. *Illustrierte Aeronautische Mitteilungen*, Dec. 15, 1909, vol. 15, pp. 1125–1129.

Discussion of Wright patent no. 173, 378.

Rozendaal, John. Das deutsche Reichspatent der Gebrüder Wright. *Der Motorwagen*, Dec. 31, 1909, vol. 12, pp. 918–925, illus.

Discussion, pp. 932, 934.

Address before the Automobil- und Flugtechnische Gesellschaft, Berlin, November 25, 1909. Includes comments on the Wright patent by Blériot, Farman brothers, Kress, Nimführ, and Wels.

The 1904 Wright Patent. *Flight*, Jan. 22, 1910, vol. 2, p. 55, illus.

From *Automotor Journal.*

Résumé of British Wright patent no. 6732.

Court Gives Wrights Injunction. *Aeronautics*, Feb. 1910, vol. 6, no. 2, pp. 63–68, illus.

Injunction granted January 3, restraining Herring-Curtiss Company and Glenn H. Curtiss from manufacturing, selling, or using for exhibition purposes the Curtiss aeroplanes. Includes extracts from briefs.

The Wright Injunction. *Scientific American Supplement*, Feb. 19–26, 1910, vol. 69, pp. 122–123, 135.

Extracts from the court's opinion and briefs.

Apitz, J. Bewertung des deutschen Wright-Patentes. *Zeitschrift für Flugtechnik*, Feb. 26, May 10, June 11, 1910, vol. 1, pp. 39–41, 109–111, 135–136.

Expansion of a lecture delivered before the Verein Deutscher Flugtechniker in Berlin.

Wright-Paulhan Suit. *Aeronautics*, New York, Mar. 1910, vol. 5, pp. 94–95.

Summarizes points at issue and quotes from affidavits in case which was decided February 17, in favor of the Wrights, by decision of Judge Hand.

Wright Brothers and Their Patents. *Flight*, Mar. 5, 1910, vol. 2, p. 164.

Wright *vs.* Paulhan. Extracts from Affidavits and Judge Hand's Decision in the Case of the Farman and Blériot Aeroplanes. *Scientific American Supplement*, Mar. 19–26, 1910, vol. 69, pp. 182–183, 198.

From Judge Hand's decision rendered February 17 in the United States Circuit Court, Southern District of New York.

Campbell-Wood, George F. The Wright-Paulhan Conflict. *Aircraft*, Apr. 1910, vol. 1, pp. 50–55, illus.

Summary of points at issue.

Ludlow, Israel. Criticism of the Court's Decision of February 17th in the Wright-Paulhan Suit. *Aircraft*, Apr. 1910, vol. 1, p. 75.

Counsel for Paulhan cites ten errors which he believes justify an appeal from the decision.

Paulhan, Louis. The Wrights' Contentions Groundless. *Aircraft*, Apr. 1910, vol. 1, p. 75.

Brief statement on the operating principles of the Blériot and Farman aeroplanes used by the author.

Toulmin, Harry A. Attacks on the Wright Brothers Wholly Unjustified. *Aircraft*, Apr. 1910, vol 1, pp. 93–94.

Statement by counsel of the Wrights.

Wright-Paulhan Opinion. *Aeronautics*, New York, Apr. 1910, vol. 6, pp. 144–146.

Excerpts from the opinion of Judge Hand handed down February 17.

The Great Wright Lawsuits in America. *Flight*, Apr. 16, 1910, vol. 2, pp. 284–285, illus.

Statement on principal points at issue.

A.C.A. Recognizes Wright Patent. *Aeronautics*, May 1910, vol. 6, p. 173.

Report on conference between Wilbur Wright and Andrew Freedman, representing the Wright Company, and an Aero Club of America committee at which an agreement was reached that the Aero Club recognize the Wright patent.

A Letter from Clément Ader. *Aircraft*, May 1910, vol. 1, pp. 100–101.

Letter of Ader, March 21, 1910, to Israel Ludlow denying statements made by Wilbur Wright in the Wright-Paulhan lawsuit about the Ader machine and its purported flights in 1897.

Ludlow, Israel. The Wright Company is a Menace to the Development of Aviation. *Aircraft*, May 1910, vol. 1, pp. 94–95.

Author contends that the newly incorporated Wright Company constitutes a possible monopoly.

Les brevets Wright et les épreuves d'aviation en Amérique. *L'Aérophile*, May 1, 1910, vol. 18, p. 210.

Gibson, Hugo C. The Wright and Selden Patents—a Comparison. *Aircraft*, June 1910, vol. 1, p. 144.

Advocates a low license fee for all aircraft infringing the Wright patent.

Hanna, John G. The Wright Company is an Incentive to the Development of Aviation. *Aircraft*, June 1910, vol. 1, pp. 151–152.

Author contends that the Wright patent is valid and that the patentees are entitled to all its benefits.

Letters from Sir Hiram Maxim, Blériot, and Esnault - Pelterie. *Aircraft*, June 1910, vol. 1, p. 138.

Response to editor's request for their views on Wright patents.

Bird-Men versus Bird-Men. *Law Notes*, July 1910, vol. 14, pp. 62–63.

Editorial.

Lamson *vs.* Wright Suit. *Aeronautics*, New York, July 1910, vol. 7, pp. 21–22.

Abstract: *Flight*, July 9, 1910, vol. 2, p. 527.

Announces the filing by Charles H. Lamson of an appeal for an injunction against the Wright Company and Wilbur and Orville Wright for alleged infringement of his kite patent No. 666,427, issued January 22, 1901.

Rummler, William R. The Wright Suits; Some Conclusions to be Drawn. *Aircraft*, July 1910, vol. 1, pp. 188–189.

Wright Injunction Vacated. *Aeronautics*, New York, July 1910, vol. 7, p. 21.

Reports that the injunction granted by Judge Hazel has been set aside by the United States Circuit Court of Appeals, June 14, 1910.

Wright Patents Litigation. *Flight*, July 9, 1910, vol. 2, p. 527.

Statement on current status of patent litigation.

Wright Suits. *Aeronautics*, New York, Aug. 1910, vol. 7, p. 60.

Report of denial of the United States Circuit Court of Appeals, June 30, of a Wright Company motion asking that the Curtiss Company put up a bond to protect the Wright Company against loss in the event of their winning the patent suit.

A Simple Explanation of the Principles Involved in the Wright Patent Suit. *Scientific American*, Aug. 13, 1910, vol. 117, pp. 128–129, illus.

The Patent Bugaboo. *Aero*, St. Louis, Nov. 19, 1910, vol. 1, no. 7, p. 12.

Wright Suits. *Aeronautics*, New York, Apr. 1911, vol. 8, p. 120.

The Present Status of the Wright Patents. *Aero*, New York, Apr. 15, 1911, vol. 2, no. 2, p. 45.

Imbrecq, J. Le Procès des brevets Wright, les jugements. *L'Aérophile*, May 15, 1911, vol. 19, pp. 227–228.

Decision rendered April 29, 1911, by the French Third Civil Tribunal. Although technically the judgment was rendered in favor of the Compagnie Générale de Navigation Aérienne, French concessionaire of the Wright patents, the final decision was withheld pending presentation of evidence by MM. Léauté, Renard, and Deprez purporting to prove that the Wrights were not the first to use the principles covered by their patents. The action against Santos-Dumont was dismissed on the ground that he constructed aeroplanes for his own use and did not infringe the patent law.

Translation by Buel H. Green with title "The Wright Patent Suit Decisions," *Aviation*, June 1911, vol. 1, no. 6, pp. 28–32.

The Wright Infringement Suit in France. *Scientific American*, June 17, 1911, vol. 118, p. 601.

Digest of French court decision of April 29 above.

French Court Favors Wrights. *Aeronautics*, New York, July 1911, vol. 9, pp. 12–13.

Summary of French court decision of April 29.

Wright Company to Start Wholesale Suits. *Aeronautics*, New York, Aug. 1911, p. 57.

Includes statement of Frank H. Russell, manager of the Wright Company.

Wholesale Litigation by the Wright Company in America. *Aeronautics*, London, Sept. 1911, vol. 4, p. 176.

Wrights Sue Grahame-White. *Aero*, St. Louis, Dec. 23, 1911, vol. 3, p. 234.

Suits served by Wrights to restrain Grahame-White from flying in the United States and to compel him to render an account of his profits.

Brevet d'invention. *Revue juridique internationale de la locomotion aérienne*, 1911, vol. 2, pp. 260–264, illus.

Text of Wright French patent no. 342,188.

Lorisson, Jacques. Le brevet Wright. *La Revue de l'aviation et des sports*, Jan. 1912, vol. 7, pp. 2–3.

Based on statements of André Henry-Coüannier.

Wright Company Loses a Suit. *Aero*, St. Louis, Feb. 3, 1912, vol. 3, p. 361.

Dismissal by Justice Cohalan of New York Supreme Court, of suit brought by the Wright Company to recover $15,000 from the Aero Corporation, Ltd., which managed the Belmont Park Meet in September 1910.

Wright Suit in Germany. *Aeronautics*, New York, Mar. 1912, vol. 10, p. 100.

Published also in *Aero*, London, Mar. 23, 1912, vol. 3, p. 499; *Scientific American*, Mar. 30, 1912, vol. 106, p. 287; *Fly Magazine*, Apr. 1912, vol. 4, no. 6, p. 10; *Flight*, Apr. 6, 1912, vol. 4, p. 305.

Wilbur Wright's letter of March 19 to the editor on the recent decision of the German Patent Office, February 22, nullifying the main claim of the German Wright patent, because of disclosures of the Wright system of control made before the filing of the Wright patent application in Germany. The disclosures cited were those contained in a report of a speech of Octave Chanute published in *L'Aéronaute*, May 1903, and by Wilbur Wright in his 1901 address before the Western Society of Engineers, a synopsis of which appeared in *Automotor*, February–March 1902.

Wrights Refuse to Make Concessions. *Aero*, St. Louis, Mar. 30, 1912, vol. 3, p. 514.

Note on refusal to permit participants in Gordon-Bennett Cup Race to engage in money-making exhibition flying.

Myers, Denys P. The Patent Situation. *Aircraft*, Apr. 1912, vol. 3, pp. 40, 48.

Analyzes Wright patent decisions to date and cites need for clear definition of privileges deriving from original Wright patent.

Quirk, James R. Those Wright Patents. *Popular Mechanics*, Apr. 1912, vol. 17, pp. 494–495.

Ludlow, Israel. The Wright Patent Situation. *Aero Club of America Bulletin*, July 1912, vol. 1, no. 6, p. 14.

Author states his belief that court decision will be a fair and just one.

Hayward, Charles B. Wright Patents in American and Foreign Courts. In his *Practical Aeronautics*, Chicago: American School of Correspondence, 1912, pp. 505–524.

Extensive summary of patent developments and status as of January 1912.

Jackman, William J., and Russell, Thomas J. Amateurs May Use Wright Patents. In their *Flying Machines; Construction and Operation*, Chicago: Charles C. Thompson Co., 1912, pp. 205–212.

Quotes from Judge Hand's 1910 injunction statement and the Wrights' statement on the use of their control system.

Les Brevets Wright en Allemagne. Instance en nullité du brevet allemand O. et W. Wright no. 173,378 intentée devant le Patentamt Impérial de Berlin par un consortium de constructeurs français. Jugement rendu le 22 février 1912 par la Section des Annulations. *Revue juridique internationale de la locomotion aérienne*, 1913, vol. 4, pp. 97–104.

Translation of German patent decision rendered February 22, 1912.

Bruneval. Les brevets Wright. *La Revue de l'aviation, de l'automobile et des sports*, Mar. 1913, vol. 8, p. 6.

Burridge, Lee S. Some Light on the Patent Situation. *Aeronautics*,

New York, Mar. 1913, vol. 12, pp. 91–92.

Court of Public Opinion. *Aeronautics*, New York, Mar. 1913, vol. 12, pp. 90–91.

Includes chronological history of the Wright suits and comments on the court decision of February 27, by Captain Thomas S. Baldwin, Thomas W. Benoist, Alan R. Hawley, and the Curtiss Aeroplane Company.

Merrill, Albert Adams. Wright versus Curtiss. *Aeronautics*, New York, Mar. 1913, vol. 12, pp. 93, 106.

Author attempts to differentiate Wright and Curtiss control systems.

Wright-Curtiss Litigation. *Aeronautics*, New York, Mar. 1913, vol. 12, pp. 85–89.

Quotes from opinion of court handed down February 27, 1913.

Wright vor dem Reichsgerichte in Berlin. *Fachzeitung für Automobilismus und Flugtechnik*, Mar. 2, 1913, vol. 7, p. 20.

German decision of February 26, 1913.

Another Decision Rendered in Wright Suit. *Aero and Hydro*, Mar. 8, 1913, vol. 5, pp. 417–418.

Judge John R. Hazel's decision of February 27, granting decree sought by Wrights.

German Court Favors Wright Patents. *Aero and Hydro*, Mar. 8, 1913, vol. 5, p. 419.

Quotes from telegram sent from Leipzig by Orville Wright.

The Wright Patent Litigation Abroad. *Flight*, Mar. 15, 1913, vol. 5, p. 300.

Quotes from statement by Orville Wright, March 7, to a representative of the Paris edition of the *New York Herald* and from an interview with Griffith Brewer.

The Decision in the Wright Aeroplane Patent Case. *Scientific American*, Mar. 22, 1913, vol. 108, p. 273.

Judge Hazel's decision on February 27 in the District Court of the United States for the Western District of New York upholding the Wright patents.

Curtiss, Greely S. On the Wright Patent Decision. *Aeronautics*, New York, Apr. 1913, vol. 12, p. 133.

American and foreign reaction to recent decisions.

Myers, Denys P. The Wright-Curtiss Decision. *Aircraft*, Apr. 1913, vol. 4, pp. 34–35.

The Wright Patents. *Aeronautics*, London, Apr. 1913, vol. 6, p. 155.

Brief résumé of court proceedings in France, Germany, and the United States.

The Wrights' Patent. *Flying*, Apr. 1913, vol. 2, no. 3, pp. 19–20.

The Wright Patent Suit Decided. *Flying*, Apr. 1913, vol. 2, no. 3, pp. 28–32.

Text of opinion rendered February 27 by Judge Hazel.

Wrights Victorious in Courts at Home and Abroad; Judge Hazel Sustains Infringement Suit Against Curtiss. *Fly Magazine*, Apr. 1913, vol. 5, no. 6, pp. 16–18, 22.

Les Brevets Wright et l'industrie française. *La Conquête de l'air*, Apr. 15, 1913, vol. 10, p. 134.

Decisions on the Wright Aeroplane Patents. *Popular Mechanics*, July 1913, vol. 20, pp. 64–65.
Brief statement by Orville Wright commenting on decisions on Wright patents in Germany, France, and the United States.

Wright Automatic Stability System. *Aeronautics*, New York, Oct. 1913, vol. 13, pp. 138–139, 142, illus.
Wright patent no. 1,075,533, filed February 10, 1908, and granted October 14, 1913.

Les Brevets Wright. *L'Aérophile*, Dec. 1, 1913, vol. 21, pp. 537–538.
Brief summary of patent decisions to date.

The Legal Triumph of the Wrights. *Scientific American*, Jan. 24, 1914, vol. 90, p. 76.
Editorial comment on the court decision of January 13 in favor of the Wrights in their infringement suit.

Wright-Curtiss Litigation Ended. *Aeronautics*, New York, Jan. 31, 1914, vol. 14, p. 21.
Opinion of Judges Lacombe, Coxe, and Ward handed down January 13.

The Wright-Curtiss Decision. *Aircraft*, Feb. 1914, vol. 4, pp. 262–263.
Decision of January 13.

The Wright Patents: American Courts' Decision. *Aeronautics*, London, Feb. 1914, vol. 7, pp. 48–49.

Wright Patent Situation. *Aeronautics*, New York, Feb. 28, 1914, vol. 14, p. 57.
Speculation on effects of court decision of January 13.

The Army and the Wright Patent. *Aeronautics*, New York, Mar. 15, 1914, vol. 14, p. 74.

The Wright Patents in America. *Flight*, Apr. 18, 1914, vol. 6, p. 403.
Editorial comment.

Curtiss, Glenn H. The Wright Patents. *Flight*, May 22, 1914, vol. 6, p. 558.
Letter to the editor.

——— The Wright Patents Decision. *Aeronautics*, London, June 1914, vol. 7, p. 186.

The Wright Patents and the Aeroplane Industry. *Aeroplane*, Oct. 14, 1914, vol. 7, p. 331.
Editorial comment on the acceptance by the British Wright Company of a settlement of £15,000 from British War Office in lieu of the original £25,000 asked for the use of the Wright patent.

Wright Company Starts New Infringement Suit. *Aeronautics*, Oct. 15, 1914, vol. 15, p. 100.
Suit filed November 15, 1914 against the Curtiss Aeroplane Company.

The Wright Patent and the British Government. *Flight*, Oct. 16, 1914, vol. 6, p. 1032.
Announces settlement price of £15,000 by British government for the use of Wright patents.

G[rey], C. G. On the Wright Patents and the Aircraft Industry. An Official Pronouncement. *Aeroplane*, Oct. 4, 1916, vol. 10, pp. 581–583.
Includes letter from Griffith Brewer setting forth official policy of the British Wright Company.

The Wright Patents. *Flight*, Oct. 12, 1916, vol. 8, p. 872.

269-517—68——9

Martin, James V. Clear Statement of the Bearing of the Martin Aerodynamic Stabilizer on the Wright Patent Infringement Controversy. *Flying*, Feb. 1917, vol. 6, p. 19.

Author claims that his principle of lateral stability is unlike that of the Wrights.

The Wright Patent in Congress. *Aerial Age Weekly*, Feb. 26, 1917, vol. 4, pp. 689–691.

Reprinted from *Congressional Record*, Feb. 6, 1917, vol. 54, pp. 2701–2703.

Discussion of Government purchasing of aircraft and possible purchase by the Government of the basic Wright patent.

Validity of Wright Patents Again Attacked. *Aircraft*, Nov. 1917, vol. 7, pp. 152–153.

Announcement of the filing of a suit September 24 by the heirs of John J. Montgomery against the Wright-Martin Aircraft Corporation.

Wright Patent Expires this Year. *Aerial Age*, Mar. 1923, vol. 16, pp. 139, 142.

States Wright patent will expire May 22, 1923.

Wright Patent Expiration and the Manufacturers Association. *Aerial Age*, Apr. 1923, vol. 16, p. 188.

Further discussion of implications of the expiration of the Wright patent.

Specifications of the Wright Patents, Filed March 23rd, 1903. *Aero Digest*, Dec. 1928, vol. 13, pp. 1111–1112, illus.

Watter, Michael. Modern Significance of the Wright Patent. *Aero Digest*, Dec. 1928, vol. 13, pp. 1110–1111, 1284.

Black, Archibald. The Patent Suits. In his *The Story of Flying*, New York: McGraw-Hill Book Company, Inc., 1940, pp. 92–98.

Published also in revised 1943 edition.

Brief résumé of the Wright patent suits.

Kelly, Fred C. Patent Suits. In his *The Wright Brothers*, New York: Harcourt, Brace and Company, 1943, pp. 287–299.

Summary of principal patent suits and points at issue.

Wright Companies and School

Wright a fini! *La Revue de l'aviation*, Oct. 1908, vol. 3, no. 23, 1 p. supplement following p. 6.

Reports that Wilbur Wright has completed tests of the Wright aeroplane and fulfilled conditions of the contract signed with Lazare Weiller for the formation of a French Wright company to be known as La Compagnie Générale de Navigation Aérienne.

Wright Aeroplanes in Germany. *Aeronautics*, London, June 1909, vol. 2, p. 67.

Announces formation of the Flugmaschine Wright G. m. b. H. which acquired the Wright German patents and the rights for manufacture of the Wright aeroplanes in Germany as well as sales rights for Sweden, Norway, Denmark, Luxemburg, and Turkey.

Flugmaschine Wright G. m. b. H. Berlin: [Vereinigte Verlagsanstalten G. Braunbeck & Gutenberg - Druckerei Aktiengesellschaft, 1909], 12 pp., illus.

Descriptive brochure issued by the Flugmaschine Wright G. m. b. H. giving details on the formation of the company and the Wright aeroplane and its performance.

Satzungen der Flugmaschine Wright Gesellschaft m. b. H. Berlin: Vereinigte Verlagsanstallten Gustav Braunbeck & Gutenberg-Druckerei Aktiengesellschaft [1909], 16 pp.
List of the board of directors, including Orville Wright, and statutes of the newly organized company.

Flugmaschine Wright-Gesellschaft. *Beteiligung an Schau-und Wettfliegen 1910.* Berlin: 1910, 12 pp., illus.
Gives details on the manufacture of the Wright machine and conditions for use of machines for exhibition purposes.

Flugmaschine Wright-Gesellschaft, m. b. H. *Wright-Flugzeug.* [Berlin: Hofdruckerei Gebr. Radetzki, 1910], 25 pp., illus.
Published also in English edition.
Illustrated brochure giving a brief account of the Wright 1908 and 1909 flights, records established, description of factory, details on the Wright aeroplane and motor, and conditions of sale.

Flugmaschine Wright-Gesellschaft, m. b. H. *Wright-Aeroplan.* [Berlin: Hofdruckerei Gebr. Radetzki, 1910], 25 pp., illus.
English translation of German edition above.

Wrights Form $1,000,000 Company. *Aeronautics*, New York, Jan. 1910, vol. 6, p. 11.
Statement of incorporation of the Wright Company, November 22, 1909, for the purpose of manufacturing and trading in flying machines.

Flying - Machine Manufacture. *Scientific American*, Jan. 1, 1910, vol. 116, p. 8.
Brief mention of formation of the Flugmaschine Wright, G. m. b. H. in Germany.

Leo. Wright Company. *Vozdukhoplavatel'*, Feb. 1910, vol. 5, pp. 179–181.

Wrights Form Exhibition Co. *Aeronautics*, New York, Apr. 1910, vol. 6, p. 127.
Brief note on formation of the "Aeroplane Exhibition Co.," exclusive licensee under the Wright brothers' patents, with Roy Knabenshue as manager.

The Wrights and the Gordon-Bennett Cup. *Flight*, Apr. 30, 1910, vol. 2, p. 329.
Reproduces Wright letter of April 8, 1910, agreeing not to take any legal action against aeroplanes which are imported into the United States solely for this competition.

Ludlow, Israel. The Wright Company is a Menace to the Development of Aviation. *Aircraft*, May 1910, vol. 1, pp. 94–95.
Counsel for the French aviator, Louis Paulhan, challenges right of Wrights to demand licensing of pilots for exhibition flights using machines infringing on their patent rights.

Ein Besuch in den Werkstatten der "Wright"-Flugmaschinen Gesellschaft. *Umschau*, May 31, 1910, vol. 14, pp. 413–415, illus.
Includes interior views of German Wright factory.

Aero Club of America Agreement Signed Between the Club and the Wright Company. *Aircraft*, June 1910, vol. 1, p. 153.

The Wright Brothers and the Aero Club of America. *Aeronautics*, London, June 1910, vol. 3, no. 6, pp. 78–79.
Reprints correspondence re-

lating to the agreement of April 8, between the Wright Company and the Aero Club of America, by which the latter agrees to sanction meets only through proper arrangements with the Wrights and includes text of agreement.

Wright School Closed. *Flight*, July 9, 1910, vol. 2, p. 531.
Announces that the Wright school in Montgomery, Ala., was closed in May.

Mitchell, John. Earnings of Aviators. *Saturday Evening Post*, Oct. 8, 1910, vol. 183, no. 15, pp. 14–15, 32, illus.
Includes discussion of Wrights as business men, page 14.

Aero Club of America. *Re Wright-Aero Club Agreement.* New York: Aero Club of America, 1910, 7 pp.
Agreement relates to foreign participation in a forthcoming contest for the Gordon-Bennett International Aviation Trophy scheduled to be held October 22, 1910.

The Wright Exhibition Co. *Aviation*, Jan. 1911, vol. 1, no. 1, p. 20.
Portraits of Walter Brookins, Roy Knabenshue, manager, Thomas Jackson, representative, and Phil Parmelee.

Harrison, George B. Progress of the Wright Brothers. *Aviation*, Apr. 1911, vol. 1, no. 4, pp. 12–15, illus.
Emphasizes the building up and organization of the Wright Company.

Pupils Learn at Dayton School. *Aero*, New York, Apr. 15, 1911, vol. 2, p. 40, illus.
Account of flight training at Wright Company flying field at Dayton under supervision of J. C. Turpin.

Steady Training Continues at Wright School. *Aero*, New York, Apr. 22, 1911, vol. 2, p. 59, illus.

The Wright Flyer. Dayton, Ohio: The Wright Co. [1911], 5 pp., illus.
Includes details and illustrations of the Model B, Model R, and the four-cylinder Wright motor.

Les Wright et la Coupe Gordon-Bennett d'aviation. *Schweizer Aero-Club Bulletin*, Feb. 1912, vol. 6, p. 42.
Reproduces letter from Wright Company, signed by Wilbur Wright, granting representatives of foreign countries right to participate in race for Gordon-Bennett Cup regardless of questions of patent infringement.

The First Flying Machine Factory in America. *Aviation News*, Mar. 23, 1912, vol. 1, no. 5, p. 15.
Reprinted from Toledo *Daily Blade*, June 4, 1910.
Account of visit to Wright factory in Dayton.

Wrights Win Damage Suit. *Aeronautics*, New York, July 1912, vol. 11, p. 37.
Decision against complainant, Morris Gorsuch, who brought suit for $25,000 damages because he suffered a broken arm when a Wright aeroplane crashed into the grandstand at Asbury Park, August 10, 1910.

Wright Company. *Wright Flyers.* [New York: Premier Press, 1912], 16 pp., illus.
Brochure with brief descriptive notes on the company, Models B, C, and D, the four and six-cylinder engines, the

Wright School of Aviation, and a list of forty-two graduates of the school.

The Wright Company School of Aviation. Dayton, Ohio: [The Wright Co., 1912], 3 pp., illus.
Advertising leaflet giving details on courses of instruction and rates.

Loening, Grover C. The Wright Aviation School at Simms Station. *Flying*, Apr. 1914, vol. 3, no. 3, pp. 76, 77, 94, illus.
Account of activities for the year 1913.

Wright Licenses Granted. *Aeronautics*, New York, May 30, 1914, vol. 14, p. 147.
Announces the granting of the first Wright license for exhibition flying to Lincoln Beachey on May 23.

Wright Buying up Company's Stock. *Aero and Hydro*, June 6, 1914, vol. 8, pp. 118, 124.
Statement of Orville's reasons for the purchase of outstanding stock.

Wright Licenses Users. *Aeronautics*, New York, June 15, 1914, vol. 14, no. 11, p. 172.
Announcement relative to the granting of licenses to users of machines.

Wright Continues Stock Purchases. *Aero and Hydro*, June 20, 1914, vol. 8, p. 143.
Confirmation on June 16 by Russell A. Alger of the sale by the board of directors of the Wright Company to Orville Wright three weeks ago.

Orville Wright Sells Aeroplane Rights to Syndicate. *Aerial Age Weekly*, Oct. 18, 1915, vol. 2, p. 105.
Brief note reporting sale.

Plans of New Wright Organization. *Aerial Age Weekly*, Oct. 25, 1915, vol. 2, pp. 130, 138.
States that Orville Wright will be retained as a director.

The Wright Company Sold to N.Y. Capitalists. *Flying*, Nov. 1915, vol. 4, p. 737.
Some details of the sale.

The Wright Organization. *Aircraft*, Feb. 1916, vol. 6, p. 539.
Details of the sale of the Wright Company with a statement by C. S. Jennison who arranged the purchase of the Wright Company stock.

The Wright Flying School. New York: Wright Flying Field, Inc., 1916. [16]p., illus.
Informational brochure issued for prospective students at the school located at Hempstead Plains Flying Field, New York.

Flint, Charles R. Early Reminiscences of the Wright Brothers. *Aviation*, Dec. 31, 1923, vol. 15, pp. 797–798.
Reprinted from his *Memories of an Active Life; Men and Ships, and Sealing Wax*, New York & London: G. P. Putnam's Sons, 1923, pp. 240–253.
Recollections by a partner of Flint & Co., the Wrights' business representative abroad.

History of the Wright Company. *U.S. Air Services*, Dec. 1928, vol. 13, no. 12, pp. 34–35.
Brief mention of the original Wright Company.

Ball, Fred S. The Genesis of Maxwell Field at Montgomery, Alabama. In *Maxwell Field, Army Air Corps*, Montgomery, Ala., 1929, pp. 7–13, illus.
Account of early Wright activities at their winter flying

269-517—68——10

school in 1910 at site of present Maxwell Air Force Base.

Coffyn, Frank T. Flying as it was—Early Days at the Wrights' School. *The Sportsman Pilot*, May 15, 1939, vol. 21, no. 5, pp. 14–15, 30–34, illus.

Author's reminiscences of his association with the Wright Flying School, 1910.

Kelly, Fred C. In Aviation Business. In his *The Wright Brothers*, New York: Harcourt, Brace and Company, 1943, pp. 268–286.

Summary of significant events in the history of the Wright Company, 1909–1915.

Brewer, Griffith. The British Wright Company. In his *Fifty Years of Flying*, London: Air League of the British Empire, 1946, pp. 104–107.

Author's account of his participation in formation of company in 1913.

Pin-Points in the Past. *Roundel*, May 1957, vol. 9, pp. 28–29, illus.

Slightly different version published also in *American Aviation Historical Society Journal*, Spring 1963 issue, vol. 8, pp. 40–41, with title "Canadians at the Wright School."

Deals with Canadians by birth or residence who were trained at Wright Brothers Field, Dayton, Ohio, 1913–1916, with list of the 41 whose names appear on a commemorative plaque at the Wilbur and Orville Wright Memorial in Dayton.

Wright-Smithsonian Institution Controversy

The Langley Medal. In *Annual Report of the Smithsonian Institution, 1910*, Washington: Government Printing Office, 1911, pp. 23–24.

Brief note on awarding of the Langley Medal to the Wrights. Orville Wright has stated (in "Why the 1903 Wright Airplane is Sent to a British Museum," *U.S. Air Services*, March 1928) that the Smithsonian Institution here misrepresented Wilbur's remarks on that occasion by attributing to him a statement used in a different connection at another time, viz, in his letter, November 8, 1906, to Octave Chanute, who quoted it in his Langley Memorial Address of December 3, 1906.

Original Langley Machine Flies. *Aeronautics*, New York, May 30, 1914, vol. 14, pp. 148–150, illus.

Describes original Langley machine shipped from the Smithsonian Institution to Hammondsport, New York, for testing to determine whether it was "capable of flight." Report states that it was reassembled, fitted with three pontoons, and flown with the original engine for a short distance, May 28.

Curtiss to Test Original Langley Plane. *Aero and Hydro*, May 30, 1914, vol. 8, pp. 105–106.

Note on preparations for test flights over Lake Keuka, Hammondsport, N.Y.

Proves Langley's First Practical Aeroplane. *Aero and Hydro*, June 6, 1914, vol. 8, pp. 117–118, illus.

Includes account of reported flight of May 28 with statement of Dr. Charles D. Walcott, Secretary of the Smithsonian Institution, to the press regarding it.

Zahm, Albert F. Testing the Langley Aerodrome, by Our Staff Correspondent at Hammondsport [Albert F. Zahm]. *Scientific American*, June 6, 1914, vol. 110, pp. 462–463.
Published also in Zahm, Albert F., *Aeronautical Papers, 1885–1945*, Notre Dame, Ind.: University of Notre Dame, 1950, vol. 1, pp. 345–346.
Brief note on preparations for launching of the machine on Lake Keuka with account of flight of May 28.

Testing the Langley "Aerodrome." *Flight*, June 12, 1914, vol. 6, pp. 630–631, illus.
Brief note on flight of May 28 to which is added an abbreviated history of Langley's studies and experiments supplied by Glenn H. Curtiss.

Dr. Langley, Discoverer of the Air. *Literary Digest*, June 13, 1914, vol. 48, p. 1451.

Langley's Aerodrome Flies Again. *Aero and Hydro*, June 13, 1914, vol. 8, p. 130.
Note on flights of June 2.

"Langley's Folly" Flies. *Outlook*, June 13, 1914, vol. 107, p. 326.
Editorial comment on announcement of successful flight of Langley machine.

Did Langley Fly? *Aeronautics*, June 15, 1914, vol. 14, p. 168, illus.
Note on Hammondsport trials.

Justice posthume à un grand précurseur; Curtiss vole avec l'appareil de Langley. *L'Aérophile*, June 15, 1914, vol. 22, pp. 279–280, illus.

Zahm, Albert F. The Langley Aeroplane Construction and Control Mechanism, by Our Staff Correspondent at Hammondsport [Albert F. Zahm]. *Scientific American*, June 20, 1914, vol. 110, pp. 499–500, illus.
Published also in Zahm, Albert F. *Aeronautical Papers, 1885–1945*, Notre Dame, Ind.: University of Notre Dame, 1950, vol. 1, pp. 347–352.
Progress report on Hammondsport trials.

Du Bois, H. M. The Langley Aerodrome Flown. *Flying*, July 1914, vol. 3, pp. 184–186, illus.

The Irony of "Langley's Folly." *World's Work*, July 1914, vol. 28, p. 254.
Editorial comment on flight of Langley machine May 28.

Mr. Brewer Criticizes Langley. *Scientific American*, July 4, 1914, vol. 111, p. 2.
Editorial based on letter of Griffith Brewer to the *New York Times*, June 21, protesting alterations made to the original Langley machine at Hammondsport.

Brewer, Griffith. The Langley Aerodrome Tests. *Flight*, July 17, 1914, vol. 6, pp. 765–766, illus.
Brewer's letter of June 21 to the *New York Times*.

Dienstbach, Carl. Did Prof. S. P. Langley Invent the First Practical Flying Machine? *Scientific American*, July 25, 1914, vol. 111, pp. 59, 65–66.
Discussion of aerodynamic characteristics of the Langley machine and its capability for flight.

The Wisdom of Langley's Folly. *Hearst's Magazine*, Aug. 1914, vol. 26, no. 2, p. 277.
Editorial comment on Langley machine.

Zahm, Albert F. Further Flights with Langley's Aeroplane, by Our Staff Correspondent at Hammondsport [Albert F. Zahm]. *Scientific American*, Oct. 10, 1914, vol. 111, p. 307, illus.

Published also in Zahm, Albert F., *Aeronautical Papers, 1885–1945*, Notre Dame, Ind.: University of Notre Dame, 1950, vol. 1, pp. 385–387.

Account of flights of Langley machine equipped with Curtiss 80-horsepower motor, September 17, 19, and October 1.

Langley's Aerodrome Flies Well in New Tests. *Aero and Hydro*, Oct. 17, 1914, vol. 9, pp. 25–26.

Huffaker, Edward C. Affidavit of Edward C. Huffaker. In *The Wright Company, against The Curtiss Aeroplane Company. United States District Court, Western District of New York.* [Hammondsport, N.Y.: December 28, 1914], 7 pp. [Typescript]

Testimony on experiments of Samuel Pierpont Langley by his assistant at the Smithsonian Institution, 1895–1899.

Reed, Robert L. Affidavit of Robert L. Reed. In *The Wright Company, against The Curtiss Aeroplane Company. United States District Court, Western District of New York.* [Hammondsport, N.Y.: December 28, 1914], 23 pp. [Typescript.]

Extensive testimony on the Langley flying machine by the foreman of flying machine work at the Smithsonian Institution.

Benner, Harry. Affidavit of Harry Benner. In *The Wright Company, against The Curtiss Aeroplane Company, United States District Court, Western District of New York.* [Hammondsport, N.Y.: January 11, 1915], 3 pp. [Typescript.]

Testimony of photographer giving details of photographs taken by him of the Langley flying machine on Lake Keuka, September 17 and 19, 1914.

Wehman, Henry T. Affidavit of Henry T. Wehman. In *The Wright Company, against The Curtiss Aeroplane Company. United States District Court, Western District Court of New York.* [Hammondsport, N.Y.: January 11, 1915], 4 pp. [Typescript.]

Testimony by the official Curtiss Aeroplane Company photographer giving details on photographs taken by him of the Langley flying machine on Lake Keuka, June 2, September 17 and 18, and October 1, 1914.

Zahm, Albert F. Affidavit of Dr. Albert F. Zahm. In *The Wright Company, against The Curtiss Aeroplane Company. United States District Court, Western District of New York.* [Hammondsport, N.Y.: January 11, 1915], 13 pp. and 11 photos. [Typescript.]

Extensive testimony on the assembling of the Langley flying machine and its testing on Lake Keuka, May–October 1914, by the official Recorder of the Smithsonian Institution's Langley Aerodynamical Laboratory.

Doherty, William E. Affidavit of William Elwood Doherty. In *The Wright Company, against The Curtiss Aeroplane Company. United States District Court, Western District of New York.* [Hammondsport, N.Y.: January 12, 1915], 3 pp. [Typescript.]

Testimony on the performance of the Langley flying machine by the pilot who flew it on Lake Keuka, June and September 1914.

[Statements on Flights of the Langley Aeroplane at Hammondsport, May 1914.] In *Annual Re-*

port of the Smithsonian Institution, 1914, Washington: Government Printing Office, 1915, pp. 4, 9.

Accuracy of this and similar statements by the Smithsonian Institution was later contested by Orville Wright.

[Statements on Flights of the Original Langley Machine at Hammondsport, 1914.] In *United States National Museum Report, 1914*, Washington: Government Printing Office, 1915, pp. 46, 47.

Accuracy of this and similar statements by the Smithsonian Institution was later contested by Orville Wright.

Zahm, Albert F. The First Man-Carrying Aeroplane Capable of Sustained Free Flight—Langley's Success as a Pioneer in Aviation. In *Annual Report of the Smithsonian Institution, 1914*, Washington: Government Printing Office, 1915, pp. 217–222, illus.

Also published in Zahm, Albert F., *Aeronautical Papers, 1885–1945*, Notre Dame, Ind.: University of Notre Dame, 1950, vol. 1, pp. 401–412.

Official report on the Hammondsport flights by the delegated observer of the Smithsonian Institution, the Recorder of the Langley Aeronautical Laboratory.

Accuracy of this report was later challenged by Orville Wright.

Eisenlohr, Roland. Neuere Versuche von Curtiss mit dem Langley-Tandemeindecker. *Motorwagen*, July 31, 1916, vol. 19, pp. 295–298.

The Title to an Honor. *Collier's*, Jan. 6, 1917, vol. 58, p. 11.

Reprinted with comment by A. I. Root, *Gleanings in Bee Culture*, Apr. 1917, vol. 44, pp. 300–301.

Editorial taking exception to an unidentified statement reportedly made by Dr. Charles W. Eliot, ascribing the invention of the aeroplane to Langley.

Butman, Carl H. Langley's Flying Machine. *Aviation*, Nov. 15, 1917, vol. 3, pp. 527–531, illus.

Includes account of the Hammondsport flights by a former Smithsonian staff member.

[Statements on Installation of Langley Machine of 1903 as Exhibit in National Museum.] In *Annual Report of the Smithsonian Institution, 1918*, Washington: Government Printing Office, 1920, pp. 3, 28, 114.

Orville Wright challenged the claim that "this was the first heavier-than-air man-carrying machine built."

Brewer, Griffith. Aviation's Greatest Controversy. *U.S. Air Services*, Oct. 1921, vol. 6, no. 3, pp. 9–17.

Also published with general discussion and comments by Dr. C. D. Walcott, Dr. A. F. Zahm, C. M. Manly, and Glenn H. Curtiss, in *The Aeronautical Journal*, Dec. 1921, vol. 25, pp. 620–664; abstracted in *Flight*, Oct. 27, 1921, vol. 13, pp. 703–704; summarized and discussed in *Aviation*, Nov. 7, 1921, vol. 11, pp. 532–535; in U.S. Congress. House. Committee on Military Affairs. *First Heavier-than-Air Flying Machine. Hearing . . . April 27, 1928*, Washington; United States Government Printing Office, 1928, pp. 15–25.

Paper read by Griffith Brewer before the Royal Society of Arts, October 20, submitting evidence to prove that the Langley machine was not capable of sustained free flight and was not successfully flown at Hammondsport, N.Y., on June 2, 1914.

[Finley, Earl N.] Langley Machine at Hammondsport. *U.S. Air Services*, Oct. 1921, vol. 6, no. 3, p. 7.
Editorial comment on paper by Griffith Brewer delivered before the Royal Society of Arts, London, October 20.

Walcott, Charles D. Smithsonian's Answer to Griffith Brewer. *U.S. Air Services*, Oct. 1921, vol. 6, no. 3, pp. 19–20.
Published also in *The Aeronautical Journal*, Dec. 1921, vol. 25, pp. 644–647.
Communication of October 10 by the Secretary of the Smithsonian Institution to the Royal Aeronautical Society with reference to Griffith Brewer's paper.

Zahm, Albert F. Review of Experiments with Rehabilitated Langley Airplane in 1914. *U.S. Air Services*, Oct. 1921, vol. 6, no. 3, pp. 21–24.
Published also in *The Aeronautical Journal*, Dec. 1921, vol. 25, pp. 647–651; Zahm, Albert F., *Aeronautical Papers, 1885–1945*, Notre Dame, Ind.: University of Notre Dame, 1950, vol. 2, pp. 633–636.
Statement by the representative of the Smithsonian Institution at the Hammondsport trials.

G[rey], C. G. On a Matter of Fraud. *Aeroplane*, Oct. 26, 1921, vol. 21, pp. 357–360, illus.
Editorial comment on and summary of Griffith Brewer's paper.

The Invention of the Aeroplane. *Engineering*, Oct. 28, 1921, vol. 112, p. 609.
Brief note on Griffith Brewer's paper.

Manly, Charles M. The Langley Machine at Hammondsport, Being a Reply to Griffith Brewer. *U.S. Air Services*, Nov. 1921, vol. 6, no. 4, pp. 21–26.
Published also in *The Aeronautical Journal*, Dec. 1921, v. 25, pp. 651–659.
Communication submitted to the Royal Aeronautical Society by Langley's assistant.

The Langley Flying Machine. *Nature*, Nov. 3, 1921, vol. 108, pp. 297–298.
Editorial comment on Griffith Brewer's paper.

Brewer, Griffith. Langley Machine and Hammondsport Trials. Replies to Walcott, Zahm, Manly, and Curtiss. *U.S. Air Services*, Dec. 1921, vol. 6, no. 5, pp. 26–29.
Also published in *The Aeronautical Journal*, Dec. 1921, vol. 25, pp. 660–664.

Curtiss, Glenn H. The Langley Machine at Hammondsport. *U.S. Air Services*, Dec. 1921, vol. 6, no. 5, p. 29.
Also published in *The Aeronautical Journal*, Dec. 1921, vol. 25, pp. 659–660.
Comment on Griffith Brewer's paper by Curtiss who had been commissioned by the Smithsonian Institution to test the Langley machine at Hammondsport, N.Y., in 1914.

The Langley Aeroplane. *World's Work*, Dec. 1921, vol. 43, pp. 128–130.
Editorial comment on Griffith Brewer's paper.

Wright ou Langley? *L'Aérophile*, Jan. 1–15, 1922, vol. 30, p. 11, illus.

Seely, Lyman J. The Wright-Langley Controversy. *Aeroplane*, Jan. 25, 1922, vol. 22, p. 75.
Letter to the editor from Curtiss Company representative in England during World War I.

The Langley Aeroplane and the Hammondsport Trials. *Nature*, Jan. 26, 1922, vol. 109, pp. 97–98.
Further editorial comment on Griffith Brewer's paper.

The Scandal of the First Man-Carrying Aeroplane. *Current Opinion*, Mar. 1922, vol. 72, pp. 373–376.
Editorial comment based on Griffith Brewer's paper before the Royal Society of Arts.

The Langley Machine and the Hammondsport Trials. *Nature*. Mar. 9, 1922, vol. 109, pp. 305–307.
Letter to the editor from Griffith Brewer regarding his article in this journal, January 26, 1922.

Hegener, Henri. Langley of Wright. *Het Vliegveld*, Feb. 1924, vol. 8, pp. 31–36, illus.
Second article in a series entitled "De Baanbrekers der Dynamische Luchtvaart."

On the Wright-Smithsonian Wrangle. *Slipstream*, Apr. 1925, vol. 6, no. 4, pp. 7, 21.

The Langley Plane. *Outlook*, May 13, 1925, vol. 140, pp. 50–51.
Editorial comment based on newspaper statement of Orville Wright, April 30, that he planned to send the Wright 1903 plane to England.

Walcott, Charles D. The Langley Plane. *Outlook*, May 13, 1925, vol. 140, pp. 54–56, illus.
Dr. Walcott's comment on Orville's announcement that he planned to send the original Wright aeroplane to the Science Museum in South Kensington, England.

The Wright-Langley Controversy. Both Sides Presented by Orville Wright and Dr. Walcott. *Aviation*, May 18, 1925, vol. 18, pp. 550–551, illus.
Abstract in *Literary Digest*, July 14, 1925, vol. 86. pp. 54–56.

[Findley, Earl N.] Orville Wright Gives Original Airplane to England. *U.S. Air Services*, June 1925, vol. 10, no. 6, p. 11.
Editorial comment on Orville Wright's decision to give the Wright 1903 aeroplane to the Science Museum, London.

——— Orville Wright to Give First Plane to England. Mutilation of Langley's Machine Permitted by Smithsonian Institution, for Purposes of Private Parties to a Patent Litigation, He Charges. *U.S. Air Services*, June 1925, vol. 10, pp. 31–33, illus.
Includes Orville Wright's reported statement to press, April 30, that the Wright 1903 aeroplane was to be sent to the Science Museum in London, statement of Dr. Walcott in reply, Orville's statement of May 2, detailing his previous charges, and statement of Dr. Walcott made public, May 4.

Grover Loening's Statement. *U.S. Air Services*, June 1925, vol. 10, no. 6, p. 34.
Reprinting, in part, of his statement on the controversy from the *New York Times*, May 4.

National Aeronautic Association Would Re-Label Langley Machine. *U.S. Air Services*, June 1925, vol. 10, no. 6, p. 34.
Statement issued May 12.

Wright First Plane May Remain in U.S. *Slipstream*, June 1925, vol. 6, no. 6, p. 5.

The Wright Machine. *Aviation*, June 8, 1925, vol. 18, p. 642.
Note on recent development in controversy.

Brewer, Griffith. Letter to the Editor. *The Journal of the Royal Aeronautical Society*, Mar. 1927, vol. 31, pp. 173–174.

Calls attention to change in label on Langley machine in Smithsonian Institution but states that it is still misleading and incorrect.

G[rey], C. G. The Original Wright Biplane. *Aeroplane*, Feb. 8, 1928, vol. 34, p. 162.

Author contends that Wright 1903 machine was the first aeroplane to fly but that Langley's was the first practical aeroplane.

First Wright Airplane sent to London Museum. *Current Events*, Feb. 13/17, 1928, vol. 27, p. 84.

Comments on recent shipment of Wright 1903 plane to Science Museum in London.

G[rey], C. G. That First Flying Machine. *Aeroplane*, Feb. 22, 1928, vol. 34, p. 228.

Author disparages Wright machine in a reply to a letter from J. H. Spottiswood.

Wright Plane in the Wrong Place? *Literary Digest*, Feb. 25, 1928, vol. 96, p. 14.

G[rey], C. G. The First Flying Machine Again. *Aeroplane*, Feb. 29, 1928, vol. 3, 4, pp. 268, 276.

In rebuttal of letter of F. Handley-Page asserting Wrights' contributions to aeronautical science, author contends that "Langley had a working knowledge of aerodynamics, which the Wrights evidently lacked."

U.S. Congress. House. *Joint Resolution to Ascertain Which Was the First Heavier-than-Air Flying Machine*. Washington: United States Government Printing Office, 1928, 2 pp. (70th Congress, 1st Session. H. J. Res. 224).

Introduced February 29 by John J. McSwain of South Carolina; referred to the Committee on Military Affairs, passed by the House of Representatives, May 16, 1928.

Provides for a commission of five persons to hear evidence on this question.

[Findley, Earl N.] The Wrong Placard Remains in America: the Wright Airplane Goes Abroad. *U.S. Air Services*, Mar. 1928, vol. 13, no. 3, p. 15.

Based on a statement by Orville Wright in *New York Times*, February 4, 1928.

McCormick, Anne O'Hare. America's Banishment of the Original Wright Airplane. *U.S. Air Services*, Mar. 1928, vol. 13, no. 3, pp. 32–35.

Based on interview with Orville Wright. Cites his letter of May 14, 1925, to Chief Justice Taft, Chancellor of the Smithsonian Institution.

Wright, Orville. Why the 1903 Wright Airplane is Sent to a British Museum. *U.S. Air Services*, Mar. 1928, vol. 13, pp. 30–31.

Published also in *U.S. Air Services*, Feb. 1948, vol. 33, no. 2, pp. 14–15.

Amplifies and emphasizes principal points brought out in Orville Wright's letter of May 14, 1925, to Chief Justice Taft.

Smithsonian Institution Secretary Makes an Offer to Orville Wright. *Aviation*, Mar. 19, 1928, vol. 24, p. 715.

Published also in U.S. Congress. House. Committee on Military Affairs. *First Heavier-than-Air Flying Machine. Hearing . . . April 27, 1928,*

Washington: United States Government Printing Office, 1928, pp. 27–30.

Smithsonian Institution statement issued to press, March 15, 1928.

Carll, George S., Jr. Congressman McSwain Explains His Bill. *U.S. Air Services*, Apr. 1928, vol. 13, no. 4, p. 28.

House Joint Resolution 224 introduced February 29 above.

[Findley, Earl N.] Smithsonian Statements Evade All Points at Issue. *U.S. Air Services*, Apr. 1928, vol. 13, no. 4, p. 17.

Editorial on Smithsonian Institution statement issued to the press, March 15, 1928.

Marshall, Fred A. Orville Wright Accuses Smithsonian. *Slipstream*, Apr. 1928, vol. 9, no. 4, pp. 7–8, illus.

Based largely on Orville Wright's article in *U.S. Air Services*, March, 1928.

The Original Wright Biplane. *The Journal of the Royal Aeronautical Society*, Apr. 1928, vol. 32, pp. 241–243.

Smithsonian Institution statement of March 3, 1928 with comment by editor and by Griffith Brewer in a letter to the editor dated, March 29, 1928.

Orville Wright Declines—Naturally. *U.S. Air Services*, Apr. 1928, vol. 13, no. 4, pp. 27–28.

Smithsonian Institution statement of March 3, 1928, including its invitation to have the Kitty Hawk aeroplane deposited in the United States National Museum and Orville Wright's refusal.

Test, Merlin E. Why the First Wright Plane Goes to an English Museum. *Air Travel News*, Apr. 1928, vol. 2, no. 4, pp. 5–6, illus.

Fitzgerald, Roy G. The Invention of the Aeroplane. *Congressional Record*, Apr. 20, 1928, vol. 69, pp. 6909–6910.

Includes short summary of points at issue, Orville Wright's letter of May 14, 1925, to Chief Justice Taft as Chancellor of the Smithsonian Institution asking for an investigation of controversy, and Taft's unfavorable reply of May 18, 1925.

U.S. Congress. House. Committee on Military Affairs. *First Heavier-than-Air Flying Machine. Hearing before Subcommittee No. 8 . . . April 27, 1928. Statements of Hon. Roy G. Fitzgerald, C. G. Abbot, Secretary Smithsonian Institution.* Washington: United States Government Printing Office, 1928, 56 pp.

Extensive discussion of points at issue with pertinent statements and documents introduced into the record.

Dacey, Norman F. The Man Who Successfully Flew the Langley Plane Speaks Up. *Air Travel News*, May 1928, vol. 2, no. 5, pp. 11–12, 49.

Claim is made that Walter Johnson flew the Langley machine at Hammondsport without mechanical changes.

Abbot, Charles G. Letter to the Editor. *Journal of the Royal Aeronautical Society*, June 1928, vol. 32, pp. 422–423.

Letter of April 27 offering further clarification of issues and facts discussed in the *Journal* for April 1928.

Hall, Norman A. Langley or Wright? The Facts About the Famous Controversy. *Liberty*, July 28, 1928, vol. 5, no. 30, pp. 68–70, illus.

Popular presentation of issues in controversy.

Shepherd, William G. Bring Home the Wright Plane. *Collier's*, Sept. 22, 1928, vol. 82, pp. 8–9, 38, 40, illus.

Summary of points at issue in controversy.

Abbot, Charles G. *The Relations Between the Smithsonian and the Wright Brothers.* Washington: The Smithsonian Institution, September 29, 1928, 27 pp. (Smithsonian Miscellaneous Collections, vol. 81, no. 5).

Also issued as Smithsonian Publication 2977.

Effort by the Secretary of the Smithsonian Institution to clarify the controversy and to correct errors and statements previously made. Renews invitation of March 4, 1928, to Orville Wright to deposit Kitty Hawk aeroplane in the United States National Museum.

Smithsonian Institution and Mr. Orville Wright. *Science*, Oct. 5, 1928, vol. 24, pp. 316–317.

Summarizes recent statement by Charles G. Abbot.

Shepherd, William G. The Road to Justice. *Collier's*, Dec. 8, 1928, vol. 82, pp. 28, 46.

Elaboration of his previous article on the controversy in the September 22d issue of this journal.

The Wright Brothers' and Langley's Aeroplanes. *Nature*, Dec. 15, 1928, vol. 122, p. 930.

Twenty-Five Years of Flight. *Nation*, Dec. 19, 1928, vol. 127, p. 674.

Editorial comment on Secretary Abbot's statement of September 29.

Arnold, Henry H. Who Flew First? *Modern Mechanics and Inventions Flying Manual*, 1929, pp. 6–9, illus.

Author contends that the Wrights were first to fly.

Goldstrom, John. The Wright-Smithsonian Dispute. In his *A Narrative History of Aviation*, New York: The Macmillan Company, 1930, pp. 46–54.

Summary of controversy to date.

The Government Denies Recognition to Wright and to North Carolina for First Flight. *Chapel Hill Weekly*, Jan. 27, 1933, vol. 10, no. 45, pp. 1, 2.

Based on article in *U.S. Air Services*, March 1928.

[Findley, Earl N.] Smithsonian ad Nauseam. *U.S. Air Services*, Feb. 1933, vol. 18, no. 2, pp. 6–7.

Editorial criticizing statements about Langley and the Wrights appearing in Charles G. Abbot's *Great Inventions*, published 1932 as volume 12 of the Smithsonian Scientific Series.

The Change of the Label. *Chapel Hill Weekly*, Feb. 10, 1933, vol. 10, no. 47, p. 21.

Editorial comment.

[Findley, Earl N.] Will 1934 See the 1903 Machine Back Home? *U.S. Air Services*, Jan. 1934, vol. 19, no. 1, p. 9.

Brief note concerning the proposed appointment of a committee of unbiased experts to decide the controversy on its merits.

Return the Wright Plane. *National Aeronautic Magazine*, Oct. 1934, vol. 12, no. 10, p. 16.

Text of resolution adopted by the Thirteenth Annual Convention of the National Aeronautic Association, October 11–13, 1934. Provides for the appointment of a committee to confer with Orville with a view to securing the return of the Wright 1903 plane to the United States.

Loening, Grover. Labels and Labels. In his *Our Wings Grow Faster*, Garden City, N.Y.: Doubleday, Doran & Co., Inc., 1935, pp. 184–185.

Author's account of his efforts to settle the controversy.

[Findley, Earl N.] Why Not Fix What is Wrong? *U.S. Air Services*, Jan. 1937, vol. 22, no. 1, p. 11.

Note on thirty-third anniversary celebration of first flight, including President Roosevelt's goodwill message to Orville Wright and author's statement urging that the President should take initiative in making arrangements for the early return of the Wright 1903 plane.

Start Drive to Bring World's First Plane Back to America. *Contact*, Jan. 2/9, 1937, vol. 3, no. 11, p. 15, illus.

Proposed movement by magazine *Contact* to bring the Wright 1903 plane back to America, to be launched January 9 at the Philadelphia Air Show. Further accounts: Jan. 28/Feb. 6, p. 3; Feb. 13/20, p. 3, 18; Mar. 13/20, p. 3; Feb. 12, 1938, pp. 11, 20; Feb. 26, p. 11.

Studer, Clara. Summer of 1914. In her *Sky Storming Yankee; the Life of Glenn Curtiss*, New York: Stackpole Sons, 1937, pp. 317–336.

Pages 322–326 refer to Curtiss' role in testing of Langley machine.

U.S. Congress. Senate. *Joint Resolution to Provide for the Safekeeping and Exhibit of the Airplane Used by the Wright Brothers in Making the First Successful Airplane Flight in History*. Washington: United States Government Printing Office, 1937, 2 pp. (75th Congress, 2d Session. Senate. J. Res. 237).

Introduced by Mr. Robert Reynolds, of North Carolina, November 16, 1937, and referred to the Committee on Military Affairs. Provides for $50,000 appropriation to be used to develop suitable site at Kitty Hawk, North Carolina.

Seek Wright Ship. *National Air News*, July 20, 1938, vol. 2, no. 29, p. 2, col. 5.

Reference to the formation of the Association of Men with Wings, chartered for the purpose of bringing the Wright 1903 aeroplane back to the United States from London.

[Findley, Earl N.] Why Not an Association to Get a Custodian for Our National Museum? *U.S. Air Services*, Aug. 1938, vol. 23, no. 3, pp. 29, 31.

Cites popular ignorance of reasons why the Wright 1903 aeroplane was sent abroad.

Kalb, Karl P. Why the Kitty Hawk Plane May Stay in England. *Liberty*, Aug. 6, 1938, vol. 15, no. 32, p. 52.

Take It and Welcome. *Aeroplane*, Aug. 17, 1938, vol. 55, p. 94.

Editorial comment on formation of "Association of Men with Wings." Minimizes importance of the Wright 1903 machine in the Science Museum.

[Findley, Earl N.] Airmen Move to Effect Return of Wright

Plane from England. *U.S. Air Services*, Sept. 1938, vol. 23, no. 9, p. 30.

Brief account of Association of Men With Wings, Inc. organized August 4. Includes text of petition addressed to Chief Justice Taft as Chancellor of the Board of Regents of the Smithsonian Institution asking that the Museum change "certain inaccuracies" in the records relative to the building and flying of the first aeroplane.

Is Paramount Financing Assoc. of Men with Wings? It's Your Guess Now. *American Aviation*, Sept. 1, 1938, vol. 2, no 7, p. 11.

States that Paramount Pictures put up $25,000 for the promotion of the organization.

Goldstrom, John. Bring Back Our Winged Exile. An Open Letter to President Roosevelt on the Kitty Hawk Plane. *Liberty*, Sept. 3, 1938, vol. 15, no. 36, p. 56.

Paramount Wonders why the Secrecy About Its Financing Men with Wings. *American Aviation*, Oct. 1, 1938, vol. 2, no. 9, p. 10.

Shades of Justice! The CAA Snubs the Smithsonian, Recognizes Wright Ship. *American Aviation*, Nov. 1, 1938, vol. 2, no. 11, p. 3.

Gray, "Jack" Stearns. Lest We Forget. In her *"Up"; a True Story of Aviation*, Strasburg, Va.: Shenandoah Publishing House, Inc., 1938, pp. 189–193.

Plea for the return of the Wright plane.

U.S. Congress. House. *Joint Resolution for the Return of the Wright Airplane to the United States of America, to be Placed on Permanent Exhibition, under such Conditions as may be Jointly Approved by Mr. Wright and the Congress. July 10, 1940.* Washington: United States Government Printing Office, 1940, 2 pp. (76th Congress, 3d Session. House. J. Res. 584).

Introduced by Harry R. Sheppard of California; referred to the Committee on the Library.

Sheppard, Harry R. Return of the Wright Airplane to the United States. Extension of Remarks . . . July 10, 1940. *Congressional Record*, July 10, 1940, vol. 86, Appendix, p. 4418.

Remarks made in connection with the introduction of the author's resolution in Congress. See above.

Hatch, Alden. [Testing of Langley Machine.] In his *Glenn Curtiss; Pioneer of Naval Aviation*, New York: Julian Messner, Inc., 1942, pp. 237–241.

Brief account of Hammondsport trials.

Abbot, Charles G. The 1914 Test of the Langley "Aerodrome." Washington: The Smithsonian Institution, October 24, 1942, 8 pp. illus. (Smithsonian Miscellaneous Collections, vol. 103, no. 8 and its Publication 3699).

Reprinted in *Annual Report of the Smithsonian Institution, 1942*, Washington: Government Printing Office, 1943, pp. 111–118; *U.S. Air Services*, Nov. 1942, vol. 27, no. 11, pp. 12–15; Kelly, Fred C., *The Wright Brothers*, New York; Harcourt, Brace and Company, 1943, pp. 324–333, and reprinted in part in *American Aviation Daily*, Oct. 30, 1942, vol. 23, pp. 290–291; *American Aviation*, Nov. 15, 1942, vol. 6, no. 12, pp. 17, 19; *Journal of the Aeronautical Sciences*, Jan. 1943, vol. 10, pp. 31–35; *Aerosphere 1943* . . .

edited by Glenn D. Angle, New York: Aerosphere, Inc., 1944, pp. CXIII–CXV.
Statement by the Secretary of the Smithsonian Institution correcting assertions and actions of former Smithsonian officials relative to the 1914 test of the Langley "aerodrome." Statement was submitted to Orville Wright who accepted it as basis for closing the prolonged Wright-Smithsonian controversy, provided it was "given adequate publication."

[Findley, Earl N.] Smithsonian Swings Into Step. *U.S. Air Services*, Nov. 1942, vol. 27, no. 11, pp. 7–8.
Editorial comment on publication of Smithsonian Institution's statement of October 24 (Its *Miscellaneous Collections*, vol. 103, no. 8).

Langley Dispute Ends. *Science News Letter*, Nov. 7, 1942, vol. 42, p. 292.

Dr. Abbot Ends Orville Wright-Smithsonian Controversy. *Museum News*, Nov. 15, 1942, vol. 20, no. 10, pp. 1, 4.

Good-bye to All That. *Flight*, Nov. 19, 1942, vol. 42, p. 542.

Future of the Wright Biplane. *Aeroplane*, Nov. 20, 1942, vol. 63, p. 580.

G[rey], C. G. "The First Aeroplane." *Aeroplane*, Dec. 4, 1942, vol. 63, p. 664.
Author contends that Wrights' 1903 flying machine was not a practical one.

Kelly, Fred C. Why the Wright Plane Was Exiled. In his *The Wright Brothers*, New York: Harcourt, Brace and Company, 1943, pp. 300–333, illus. and reprinted New York: Farrar, Straus and Young, 1951.
Extensive account of controversy.

Famous Aviation Controversies: Wright *vs.* Smithsonian. In *The Airman's Almanac*, edited by Francis Walton, New York: Farrar & Rinehart, Inc., 1945, pp. 421–422.
Brief summary.

[Findley, Earl N.] How Long, Oh Lord, How Long? *U.S. Air Services*, June 1946, vol. 31, no. 6, p. 9.
Editorial pointing out misstatements by Russell Owen in an article entitled "Trail-Blazers of the Blue" in the *New York Times Magazine*, May 4.

Brewer, Griffith. The Langley Machine and the Hammondsport Trials. In his *Fifty Years of Flying*, London: Air League of the British Empire, 1946, pp. 108–112.
Author's account of his role in controversy.

Noel, E. Percy. Remarks of President Noel on Mr. Nils H. Randers-Pehrson's Paper. *Columbia Historical Society Records*, Apr. 1947, vol. 46/47, pp. 60–79.
Discussion by the President of the Columbia Historical Society, of paper on "Aeronautics in the District of Columbia," with his observations on the Smithsonian Institution report issued October 24, 1942. Also included in his remarks is a statement by Dr. Albert F. Zahm on this report.

Hellman, Geoffrey T. Profiles [The Smithsonian Institution]. *New Yorker*, Dec. 3, 1966, vol. 42, pp. 66–150; Dec. 10, pp. 64–139; Dec. 17, pp. 58–112.

Included also in his *The Smithsonian; Octopus on the Mall*, New York: J. B. Lippincott, 1967, pp. 132–158.
The Smithsonian-Wright controversy is reviewed in the December 10 issue, pp. 100–139.

Vaeth, J. Gordon. *Langley, Man of Science and Flight*. New York: Ronald Press, 1966, 117 pp., illus.
The Wright-Smithsonian Institution controversy is discussed in the final chapter entitled "Epilogue," pp. 104–111

Monuments and Museums

Wright Memorial
(Proposed—Simms Station, Dayton, Ohio)

The Proposed Wright Memorial. *Aero Club of America Bulletin*, July 1912, vol. 1, no. 6, p. 5.
Recommendation by the Dayton Wright Memorial Commission that a memorial in the form of two Greek columns be erected at Huffman Prairie (Simms Station), Dayton, Ohio.

Wilbur Wright Monument, Auvours, France

The Wilbur Wright and Hubert Latham Monuments. *The Aero*, London, Dec. 1912, vol. 6, p. 352.
Brief note announcing the opening of subscriptions for the erection of a monument at Camp d'Auvours in memory of Wilbur Wright.

Veit, Sidney B. France and the Wright Brothers. *Légion d'honneur*, Apr. 1933, vol. 1, pp. 206–215, illus.
Includes photographs of Wright memorials at Auvours, Le Mans, and Pau.

Wilbur Wright Monument, Le Mans, France

Shaft to Wilbur Wright. *Flying*, New York, Jan. 1919, vol. 7, pp. 1166, 1169.
Account of the laying of the cornerstone, December 22, 1918.

Lafayette and Wilbur Wright Honored. *Flying*, New York, Feb. 1919, vol. 8, pp. 50–51, illus.
Another account reprinted from the Paris edition of the *New York Herald Tribune*.

Wilbur Wright Memorial. *Aeronautics*, July 22, 1920, vol. 19, p. 69.
Brief note on dedication exercises, July 18.

Béarn, C. de. A la mémoire des frères Wright. *Le Monde illustré*, July 24, 1920, vol. 127, pp. 62–63, illus.

L'Hermitte, J. Le Monument de l'aviation. *L'Illustration*, July 24, 1920, vol. 156, pp. 68–69, illus.
Translation with title, "Wilbur Wright in France," *Literary Digest*, Aug. 28, 1920, vol. 66, p. 32.

French Memorial to Wilbur Wright. *Flight*, July 29, 1920, vol. 12, p. 841.

Le Monument à Wilbur Wright et aux pionniers de l'aviation inauguré au Mans le 17 juillet 1920. *L'Aérophile*, Aug. 1920, vol. 28, pp. 246–248.
Extensive account of unveiling of the first notable memorial to the memory of Wilbur Wright. The monument by the French sculptor, Paul Landow-

ski, stands in the Place des Jacobins, before the Cathedral of St. Julien.

Wright Memorial Dedicated in France. *U.S. Air Services*, Aug. 1920, vol. 4, no. 1, p. 17.

Gives editorial comment on monument from New York *Sun* and *New York Herald*.

France's Tribute to Wilbur Wright, "Father of Aviation." *Literary Digest*, Aug. 28, 1920, vol. 66, p. 54.

Reprinted from Boston *Herald*.

Unveiling of the Monument to Wilbur Wright. *Flying*, New York, Sept. 1920, vol. 9, pp. 530–531, illus.

France's Tribute to the Wright Brothers. *U.S. Air Services*, Nov. 1920, vol. 4, no. 4, p. 21, illus.

Brief note on monument with speech given by Rear Admiral T. P. Magruder, American representative at unveiling ceremony.

The Wright Memorial. *Aircraft Year Book 1921*, Boston: Small, Maynard & Co., 1921, pp. 126–127.

Gilbert, Morris. America and Le Mans. *New York Times*, June 25, 1966, p. 30, col. 3–6.

Account of Wilbur Wright's early flights at Le Mans in 1908 and of the monument erected there in his honor in 1920.

Wilbur Wright Memorial, New Castle, Indiana

Wilbur Wright Memorial. [New Castle, Ind.] Circle Printing Service, [1923], 4 pp. illus.

Includes photograph of memorial tablet at Memorial Park, New Castle, Ind., erected by Phi Delta Kappa Fraternity, April 15, 1923, and dedicated in the presence of Orville and Katharine Wright.

Wright Brothers Monument, Pau, France

Le Monument de Wilbur Wright. Il a été inauguré le 30 janvier à Pau-Pont-Long. *Les Ailes*, Feb. 4, 1932, vol. 112, p. 14.

Brief note on dedication of Wright brothers monument, January 30, 1932, to commemorate the first flights of Wilbur at Pau in 1908 and the training of the first French aviation officers.

L'Inauguration du monument Wright à Pau. *L'Illustration*, Feb. 6, 1932, vol. 181, p. 164, illus.

The Monument to the Wright Brothers at Pau, France. *U.S. Air Services*, Apr. 1932, vol. 17, pp. 42, 44, illus.

Brief account of dedication including addresses delivered by Paul Tissandier and United States Ambassador Walter Edge.

France Remembers the Wrights. *National Aeronautics Magazine*, May 1932, vol. 10, pp. 16–18, illus.

Account of dedication of monument at Pau.

Wright Memorial, Kill Devil Hill, Kitty Hawk, North Carolina

U.S. Congress. House. *A Bill Authorizing an Appropriation of $50,000 for the Erection of a Memorial at Kitty Hawk, Dare County, North Carolina, to Commemorate the First Successful Airplane Flight Made by Wilbur and Orville Wright. December 17, 1926.* Washington: United States

Government Printing Office, 1926, 2 pp. (69th Congress, 2d Session. H. R. 15348).

Submitted by Congressman Lindsay Warren of North Carolina; referred to the Committee on the Library.

U.S. Congress. Senate. Committee on Military Affairs. *To Commemorate the First Successful Flight by Power-Driven Aircraft. Report [To accompany S. 4876]. Submitted by Mr. Robinson of Indiana. January 8, 1927.* Washington: United States Government Printing Office, 1927, 1 p. (69th Congress, 2d Session. Senate Report 1227).

Recommends passage of bill.

Monument on Kill Devil Hill, N.C. *Congressional Record*, Jan. 10, 1927, vol. 68, p. 1343.

Discussion of Senate bill 4876.

U.S. Congress. Senate. *An Act Providing for the Erection of a Monument on Kill Devil Hill at Kitty Hawk, North Carolina, Commemorative of the First Successful Attempt in History at Power-Driven Airplane Flight. January 11, 1927.* Washington: United States Government Printing Office, 1927, 2 pp. (69th Congress, 2d Session. S. 4876).

Introduced by Senator Hiram Bingham of Connecticut; referred to the Committee on the Library.

U.S. Congress. House. Committee on the Library. *Monument Commemorative of 1st Successful Attempt at Power-Driven Airplane Flight. Report [To accompany S. 4876]. Submitted by Mr. Luce. February 4, 1927.* Washington: United States Government Printing Office, 1927, 1 p. (69th Congress, 2d Session. House. Report 1989).

Recommends new section in bill providing that designs and plans of monument be subject to approval of the Commission of Fine Arts and the Joint Committee on the Library.

Warren, Lindsay. *The Memorial in Commemoration of the First Successful Attempt in All History at Power-Driven Airplane Flight, Achieved by Orville Wright on December 17, 1903, at Kitty Hawk, N.C. Speech . . . in the House of Representatives, Tuesday, February 8, 1927.* Washington: United States Government Printing Office, 1927, 8 pp.

Reprinted from *Congressional Record*, Feb. 8, 1927, vol. 68, pp. 3281–3282.

S. 4876 An Act Providing for the Erection of a Monument on Kill Devil Hill, at Kitty Hawk, N.C., Commemorative of the First Successful Human Attempt at Power-Driven Airplane Flight. Approved March 2, 1927. Washington: United States Government Printing Office, 1927, 1 p. (Public Law 668, 69th Congress)

Also in *United States Statutes at Large, 1927-1929*, vol. 44, pp. 1264-1265.

The Memorial to the First Airplane Flight. *Congressional Record*, Mar. 3, 1927, vol. 68, p. 5803.

Joint resolution by the General Assembly of North Carolina urging Congress to erect a memorial to the Wrights at Kitty Hawk; introduced into the record by Mr. Warren.

Memorial to Wright Brothers at Kitty Hawk. *U.S. Air Services*, Sept. 1927, vol. 12, p. 40.

Brief note on the formation of the Kill Devil Hills Memorial Association, August 16, 1927, for the purpose of erecting a monument commemorating the first flights of the Wrights at Kitty Hawk, N.C.

In Honor of the Wrights. *Slipstream*, Nov. 1927, vol. 8, no. 11, pp. 9–10, illus.

Editorial favoring Dayton, Ohio, over Kitty Hawk, North Carolina, as a site for Wright memorial.

Wright Memorial Site Criticized. *Slipstream*, Jan. 1928, vol. 9, no. 1, pp. 7–8, illus.

Further editorial favoring erection in Dayton of a suitable Wright Memorial for housing the first Wright machine and other Wright trophies.

Monument on Kill Devil Hill, Kitty Hawk, N.C. In U.S. Congress. House. Committee on Appropriations. *War Department Appropriations Bill 1929. Hearings. January 19, 1928.* Washington: United States Government Printing Office, 1928, pt. 2, pp. 420–421.

An Act Making Appropriations for the Military and Non-military Activities of the War Department for the Fiscal Year June 30, 1929, and for Other Purposes. Approved March 23, 1928. In *United States Statutes at Large, 1927–1929*, vol. 44, pp. 326–365.

Includes an appropriation of $25,000 for the Kitty Hawk monument, page 357.

Wright Brothers to be Honored by NAA. *Aeronautic Review*, Nov. 1928, vol. 6, p. 173, illus.

Announces planning of a memorial by the National Aeronautic Association on the spot from which the first flight was made at Kitty Hawk, North Carolina, on December 17, 1903.

Status of Kitty Hawk Monument, N.C. In U.S. Congress. House. Committee on Appropriations. *War Department Appropriations Bill for 1930. Hearings . . . November 15, 1928.* Washington: United States Government Printing Office, 1928, pt. 2, pp. 53–54.

Twenty-Fifth Anniversary of the First Airplane Flight. Proceedings at the Exercises Held at Kitty Hawk, N.C., on December 17, 1928, in Commemoration of the Twenty-Fifth Anniversary of the First Flight of an Airplane Made by Wilbur and Orville Wright. Washington: United States Government Printing Office, 1929, 29 pp. (70th Congress, 2d Session. House. Document no. 520).

Proceedings included are those relating to the laying of the cornerstone of the Wright Memorial and the unveiling of the memorial erected by the National Aeronautic Association on the spot from which the Wrights made their December 1903 flights.

Neely, Frederick R. N.A.A. Marks Site of the First Airplane Flight with Impressive Ceremonies at Kitty Hawk. *Aeronautics Review*, Jan. 1929, vol. 7, no. 1, pp. 4–7, illus.

Account of unveiling of bronze tablet and boulder erected by the National Aeronautic Association on the site of the first flight, and of laying of cornerstone of Wright Memorial, Kill Devil Hills, N.C., December 17, 1928, in the presence of Orville Wright.

Monument on Kill Devil Hill, Kitty Hawk, N.C. In U.S. Congress. House. Committee on Appropriations. *War Department Appropriations Bill for 1931. Hearings . . . November 18, 1929.* Washington: United States Government Printing Office, 1929, pt. 2, pp. 69–71.

Reynolds, Carolyn L. Kill Devil Will Do No More Wandering Now That It Is Firmly Anchored With

269-517—68——11

Grass—Shrubs, Grass, and Vegetables Now Growing on Sandy Desert. *Congressional Record*, Jan. 8, 1930, vol. 72, pp. 1256–1258.

Reprinted from the Raleigh, North Carolina *News and Observer*, August 18, 1929.

Introduced into the record by Mr. Warren. Account of the work of the United States Army Quartermaster Corps in "anchoring" Kill Devil Hill.

Wright Memorial Competition. *Pencil Points*, Apr. 1930, vol. 11, pp. 304–306, illus.

Winning design sketches by architects Robert Pliny Rodgers and Alfred Eastin Poor.

U.S. Bureau of the Budget. *Monument on Kill Devil Hill, N.C.* Communication from the President of the United States Transmitting Supplemental Estimates of Appropriation for the War Department for the Fiscal Year 1930, to Remain Available Until June 30, 1932, Amounting to $225,000 for Monument on Kill Devil Hill, Kitty Hawk, N.C., April 25, 1930. Washington: United States Government Printing Office, 1930, 2 pp. (71st Congress, 2d Session. House. Document No. 369)

Wright, Hamilton M. Chaining a Mountain of Sand. *Popular Mechanics*, July 1930, vol. 54, pp. 99–100, illus.

Account of the work of the United States Army Quartermaster Corps in their efforts to stabilize sand so as to provide a permanent base for the monument.

Monument on Kill Devil Hill, Kitty Hawk, N.C. In U.S. Congress. House. Committee on Appropriations. *War Department Appropriations Bill for 1932. Hearings . . . November 17, 1930.* Washington: United States Government Printing Office, 1930, pt. 2, pp. 83–84.

The Government's Memorial to the Wright Brothers. *U.S. Air Services*, Dec. 1930, vol. 15, no. 12, p. 42.

Government Memorial for Aviation's Birthplace. *Southern Aviation*, Aug. 1931, vol. 2, no. 12, p. 6, illus.

Sharp, Edward R. A Nation's Tribute to the Wrights. *National Aeronautics Magazine*, July 1932, vol. 10, no. 7, pp. 14–17.

Summarizes progress made to date on monument.

Wright Memorial to be Dedicated This Month. *U.S. Air Services*, Nov. 1932, vol. 17, no. 11, p. 25.

A Fitting Memorial to the Pioneers of Flight. *Air Corps News Letter*, Nov. 30, 1932, vol. 16, pp. 458–459.

Slightly abridged with title, "The Monument at Kitty Hawk," *Popular Aviation*, Feb. 1933, vol. 12, no. 2, pp. 99–100, 133, illus.

Account of dedication exercises held November 19, 1932.

Wright Memorial Dedicated. *U.S. Air Services*, Dec. 1932, vol. 17, no. 12, pp. 20–21, illus.

Account of dedication exercises attended by Orville Wright.

The Granite Wing at Kitty Hawk. *U.S. Naval Institute Proceedings*, Jan. 1933, vol. 59, pp. 140–141.

Reprinted from *New York Herald Tribune*, November 20, 1932.

Fitzgerald, Francis V. Shifting Sands. How the Wright Memorial Was Built. *Quartermaster Review*, Jan.–Feb. 1933, vol. 12, pp. 45–48, illus.

Graves, Louis. The Wright Memorial and Its Interesting Custodian. *U.S. Air Serices*, June 1933, vol. 18, no. 6, p. 31.

Reprinted from *Chapel Hill Weekly*.

Saunders, W. O., ed. *A Souvenir Handbook of the Wright Memorial*. Elizabeth City, N.C.: The Independent, 1935, 29 pp., illus.

A descriptive brochure including the act of Congress creating the monument and special contributions on "The Granite Man's Job" by John P. Frank, "Orville Wright's Own Story," and the author's "America's First Airplane Casualty" [John T. Daniels], reprinted from *Collier's*, September 17, 1927.

———. *Two Historic Shrines. The Wright Memorial and Fort Raleigh on Roanoke Island*. Elizabeth City, N.C.: W. O. Saunders, 1937, 30 pp.

"The Wright Memorial," pages 5–25.

World's First Airport Deserves a Landing Field. *U.S. Air Services*, Dec. 1937, vol. 22, no. 12, pp. 7–8.

Plea for establishment of an airport near the Kitty Hawk monument.

Doors of Wright Memorial, Kill Devil Hill, N.C. From a Photograph by F. S. Lincoln '22. *Technology Review*, Jan. 1939, vol. 41, cover.

U.S. Dept. of the Interior. *Kill Devil Hill National Memorial*. [New York]: Polygraphic Company of America, Apr. 1942, 6 pp., illus.

Reprinted Washington: United States Government Printing Office, 1948 and 1949.

Descriptive leaflet issued by the National Park Service which administers the Memorial.

Saunders, Keith. The Wright Memorial Museum. *National Aeronautics and Flight Plan*, Feb. 1953, vol. 32, p. 1.

Announcement of plans for the establishment of a memorial museum at Kill Devil Hills.

Brown, Aycock, and Whitener, Ralph V. Where It All Began. *Air Force*, Nov. 1953, vol. 36, pp. 47, 63.

Discusses plans for the 1953 fiftieth anniversary celebration of the Wright brothers' 1903 flights at Kill Devil Hill, N.C., including an account of the plans by the Kill Devil Hills Memorial Society, the National Park Service, the Air Force Association, and the North Carolina Fiftieth Anniversary of Powered Flight Commission to reconstruct the Wrights' original site at Kill Devil Hill.

Fifty Years of Flight. *Travel*, Nov. 1953, vol. 100, pp. 17–19, illus.

Deals with the Wright Brothers National Memorial at Kitty Hawk, N.C., and the annual commemorative ceremonies held there.

Restoring Wright Brothers' Camp of 1903. *Journal of the Society of Architectural Historians*, Oct. 1954, vol. 13, pp. 28–29, illus.

Describes the two original Wright buildings at Kill Devil Hills, N.C., restored by the National Parks Service, as a part of the fiftieth anniversary of the first powered flights by the Wright brothers.

And Kitty Hawk It Will Remain. *U.S. Air Services*, Jan. 1955, vol. 40, p. 6.

Editorial quoting extensively from a letter by Marvin W. McFarland, editor of *The Papers of Wilbur and Orville Wright*, to Aycock Brown regarding the proper designation, Kitty Hawk or Kill Devil Hills, for the area in North Carolina where the Wrights conducted their early experiments and flights.

U.S. Congress. House. Committee on Interior and Insular Affairs. *Revising Boundaries of Wright Brothers National Memorial, North Carolina. Report [To Accompany H.R. 5488]. April 16, 1959.* Washington: United States Government Printing Office, 1959. 3p. (86th Congress, 1st Session. House. Report No. 274).

H.R. 5488 was submitted by Rep. Herbert C. Bonner of North Carolina, March 10, 1959. The bill was referred to the Committee on Interior and Insular Affairs, passed the House May 4, and the Senate, June 12.

Provides for the addition of approximately 11 acres of land. One tract of approximately 95 acres contains the landing site of the fourth and longest of the Wright brothers' historic flights on December 17, 1903.

U.S. Congress. Senate. Committee on Interior and Insular Affairs. *Revising the Boundaries of Wright Brothers National Memorial, North Carolina. Report [To Accompany H.R. 5488]. June 9, 1959.* Washington: United States Government Printing Office, 1959. 3p. (86th Congress, 1st Session. Senate. Report No. 377).

Similar to House Report No. 274.

An Act to Revise the Boundaries of Wright Brothers National Memorial, North Carolina, and for Other Purposes. *United States Statutes at Large*, 1959, vol. 73, p. 91.

Approved June 23, 1959 (Public Law 86–59).

East, Omega G. *Wright Brothers National Memorial.* Washington: U.S. Govt. Print. Off., 1961. 64p. (National Park Service. Historical Handbook Series. No. 34).

A guide book succinctly presenting the achievements of the Wright brothers and the significant events in their lives.

Originally authorized by Congress on March 2, 1927 as the Kill Devil Hills Monument National Memorial to commemorate the Wrights' first successful flights in a man-carrying, power-driven heavier-than-air aeroplane, the name was changed to the Wright Brothers National Memorial, December 1, 1953.

Originally administered by the War Department, the area transferred to the National Park Service, August 10, 1933, includes the reconstructed Wright brothers' living quarters and hangar, a granite memorial placed by the National Aeronautic Association in 1928 to mark the take-off point of the 1903 flights, a reconstruction of the original single-rail starting track, Kill Devil Hill, used by the Wrights during their gliding experiments, 1900–1903, and the Wright memorial shaft, dedicated November 19, 1932.

Wright Brothers Home and Shop, Greenfield Village, Dearborn, Michigan

Ford Purchases Wright Building. *The Air Line Pilot*, July 1936, vol. 5, no. 8, p. 7.

Announcement of the purchase of the building for the purpose of restoring it as a memorial to the Wrights.

Living Memorial to Faith, Industry, and Foresight of Wright Brothers Assured by Purchase.

Chirp, Aug. 1936, no. 17, pp. 4–5, illus.

Bauer, Charles J. Birthplace of the Airplane. *Popular Aviation*, Dec. 1936, vol. 19, no. 6, pp. 17–18, 64–65, illus.
Written on occasion of removal of Wright bicycle shop to Dearborn, Michigan for restoration.

A Celebration in Honor of Wilbur and Orville Wright. Dearborn, Mich.: The Edison Institute, 1938. [13]p., illus.
A program issued for the dedication exercises held April 16, 1938, at the Edison Institute, when the restored Wright home and bicycle shop were opened to the public.

Kresin, William. Wright Home and Workshop Dedicated. *Herald* [publication of Edison Institute], Apr. 29, 1938, vol. 5, no. 7, pp. 1, 3, 11, illus.
Full account of dedication exercises.

Ford Dedicates Wright Shrine. *U.S. Air Services*, May 1938, vol. 23, no. 5, pp. 8–9.
Editorial note on dedication.

The Wright Dedication. *Chirp*, Aug. 1, 1938, no. 22, pp. 1–4.
Account of participation of Early Birds organization in exercises.

Atkinson, Elizabeth. The Wright Homestead. *Herald* [publication of the Edison Institute], July 4, 1941, vol. 8, no. 11, pp. 1, 3, 18, illus.
Description of home as restored.

Pennington, John. The Wright Bicycle Shop. *Herald* [publication of the Edison Institute], July 18, 1941, vol. 8, no. 12, pp. 1, 3, 12–15, illus.
Description of bicycle shop as restored.

Wilbur and Orville Wright Memorial, Dayton, Ohio

Dedication of Wright Brothers Hill by the Wilbur and Orville Wright Memorial Commission. National Aviation Day. 2:30 P.M., August 19, 1940. [Dayton, 1940], 4 pp.
Dedication program.

Have You Visited "Wright Brothers Hill"? *NCR* [National Cash Register] *Factory News*, Aug.-Sept. 1940, pp. 1–6, illus.
Special issue giving pictorial account of dedication ceremonies.

Wright Hill Dedicated at Dayton. *U.S. Air Services*, Sept. 1940, vol. 25, no. 9, pp. 10–11, illus.
The Wilbur and Orville Wright Memorial, a North Carolina marble shaft, on Wright Brothers Hill, was dedicated August 19, 1940. It stands on a high ridge between Wright and Patterson Air Force Bases and overlooks the site of Huffman Prairie where the Wrights experimented with their planes of 1904 and 1905 and where many of the early Army flyers were trained.

Dedication of the Wright Brothers Monument. *Air Corps News Letter*, Sept. 1, 1940, vol. 23, no. 17, p. 7.
Brief note on dedication ceremonies.

Dedication of Wilbur and Orville Wright Memorial at Dayton, Ohio. Extension of Remarks of Hon. Harry N. Routzohn of Ohio . . . September 5, 1940. *Congressional Record*, Sept. 5, 1940, vol. 86, appendix pp. A5468–A5469.

Address of Gov. James M. Cox at the dedication, August 19, 1940.

Wright Hall, Carillon Park, Dayton, Ohio

The Wright Brothers. Dayton, Ohio: Carillon Park [1950], 26 pp., illus.

An illustrated biographical brochure which includes an account of Wright Hall, Carillon Park, built by Col. E. A. Deeds, of National Cash Register Company, especially to provide a home for the restored 1905 Wright aeroplane.

Wilbur Wright Memorial (Indiana)

Harvey, Ralph. Harvey Names Wright Memorial Backers. *Congressional Record*, May 25, 1953, vol. 99, pp. A2888–A2889.

Lists names of individuals who are engaged in establishing a permanent memorial to Wilbur Wright at his birthplace in Henry County, Indiana, together with the text of a resolution adopted by the Indiana General Assembly calling for the establishment of such a memorial.

——— Wilbur Wright. *Congressional Record*, May 25, 1953, vol. 99, pp. 5526–5527.

Fiftieth anniversary tribute to Wilbur. Reports formation of a Wilbur Wright Memorial Commission for the purpose of establishing a memorial to Wilbur in Indiana.

Indiana. General Assembly. House. Joint Resolution Designating the Wilbur Wright Birthplace as a State Memorial. In Indiana. General Assembly. House. *Journal, 1953 Session.* Indianapolis, 1953, pp. 300–301. (88th Session. Joint Resolution 15)

Introduced by Rep. Clem Conway, February 3, 1953, passed House, February 11, and Senate, February 28, and approved by Gov. George M. Craig, March 9.

Memorials

Wilbur Wright Chair of Aerodynamics

(Proposed)

Recommends Wilbur Wright Chair. *Aero*, St. Louis, June 22, 1912, vol. 4, p. 276.

Recommendation by the Aero Club of Philadelphia to the aero clubs of the country that a Wilbur Wright Chair of Aerodynamics be established in some American college.

A Communication to the Aero Club [Signed Committee on Memorial to Wilbur Wright]. *Fly Magazine*, July 1912, vol. 4, no. 9, p. 19.

Letter dated June 7, 1912, recommending that the Aero Club of Pennsylvania take steps to create a Wilbur Wright Chair of Aerodynamics.

Wilbur Wright Memorial Lecture
(Royal Aeronautical Society, London)

Wilbur Wright Memorial. *Aeronautic Journal*, July 1912, vol. 16, no. 63, p. 146.

Announcement of the opening

of a subscription fund for the establishment of a memorial to Wilbur Wright in "appreciation of his great work and in recognition of the support he gave to the Aeronautical Society of Great Britain." This was to take the form of an annual lecture called the "Wilbur Wright Lecture."

Wilbur Wright Memorial Lecture. *Flight*, May 24, 1913, vol. 5, p. 556.
Editorial comment on establishment of lecture series.

Ruck, R. M. Introductory Statement Made at First Wilbur Wright Memorial Lecture. *Aeronautical Journal*, July 1913, vol. 17, p. 170.
Brief statement on purpose of lecture series.

The Wilbur Wright Memorial Fund. *Journal of the Royal Aeronautical Society*, Aug. 1925, vol. 29, pp. 335–337.
Published also in *U.S. Air Services*, Dec. 1925, vol. 10, no. 12, p. 34.
Reports progress of the fund and of the lectures up to June 30, 1925.

Pritchard, J. Laurence. In Memory of Wilbur Wright. *Airways and Airports*, June 1934, vol. 11, pp. 92–93.
Brief note on significance of Wilbur Wright Memorial Lecture.

U.S.S. Wright
(aircraft carrier)

U.S.S. *Wright*—Our First Balloon-and-Airplane Carrier. *Scientific American*, Apr. 1922, vol. 126, p. 267, illus.
Description of ship named in honor of Wilbur Wright and commissioned December 1921.

Turnbull, Archibald, and Lord, Clifford L. U.S.S. *Wright*. In their *History of United States Naval Aviation*, New Haven: Yale University Press, 1949, pp. 152, 230, 261.
Brief references to ship.

Wilbur Wright
(flying boat)

Miss Wright Christens Our Boat. *Wright Engine Builder*, Oct. 1922, vol. 2, no. 4, p. 8, illus.
Account of christening September 26 by Katharine Wright of the Wright Aeronautical Corporation flying boat *Wilbur Wright*.

Wright Brothers' Medal
(Society of Automotive Engineers)

Wright Brothers' Medal. *Journal of the Royal Aeronautical Society*, Aug. 1924, vol. 28, p. 503.
Announces forthcoming inauguration of an annual medal award by the Dayton Section, Society of Automotive Engineers, to commemorate the pioneer aeronautical achievements of the Wright brothers (actually delayed until 1928).

The Wright Brothers Medal. *SAE Journal*, Mar. 1928, vol. 22, pp. 382–383, illus.
Announcement of the rules for the award of the medal which state that "The Wright Brothers Medal, originally donated by the Dayton Section of the Society of Automotive Engineers, shall be awarded annually to the author of the best paper on aerodynamics or structural theory or research, or aeroplane design or construction, which shall have been presented at a meeting of the Society or

any of its sections during the calendar year."

Society of Automotive Engineers. *The Wright Brothers Medal.* [New York: 1945], 10 pp.
Brochure giving history of the medal awards, rules for award of medal, and list of recipients, 1928–1944. Earlier editions were published in 1930 and 1932.

Wright Field

(Dayton, Ohio)

World's Greatest Air Post Christened "Wright Field." *Slipstream*, Sept. 1925, vol. 6, no. 9, p. 8.
Announces adoption of name by headquarters of the Army Air Service.

Wright Field is Dedicated. *Aviation*, Oct. 24, 1927, vol. 23, pp. 995–997.
Account of dedication ceremonies, October 12, 1927, when field was dedicated to Wilbur and Orville Wright, in the presence of the latter, who raised the flag.

Dedication of Wright Field. *U.S. Air Services*, Nov. 1927, vol. 12, no. 11, pp. 32–33, illus.
Report on dedication ceremonies.

Jacobs, A. M. The Dedication of Wright Field. *Air Corps News Letter*, Nov. 10, 1927, vol. 11, pp. 314–316.
Includes address of Secretary of War, F. Trubee Davison, delivered at dedication.

The Story of Wright Field. In *The Materiel Center and You; a Handbook for Your Guidance*, Wright Field, Dayton, Ohio: 1943, pp. 18–21, illus.
Brief history.

Wilbur Wright Elementary and Junior High School

(Dayton, Ohio)

The New Wilbur Wright Elementary and Junior High School. *School Progress*, Dayton, Mar. 1926, vol. 4, no. 6, pp. 1, 2, illus.

Wright Brothers Lecture

(Institute of the Aeronautical Sciences, now American Institute of Aeronautics and Astronautics)

Wright Brothers Lecture. *Journal of the Aeronautical Sciences*, May 1937, vol. 4, p. 301.
Note announcing inauguration of a new annual lecture to be known as the "Wright Brothers Lecture."

Wright Brothers Memorial Wind Tunnel

(Massachusetts Institute of Technology)

The Wright Brothers Wind Tunnel. *Technology Review*, June 1938, vol. 40, p. 362, illus.
Note on new wind tunnel under construction.

Lewis, George W. The Value of the Wind Tunnel in Aeronautical Research and Design. *U.S. Air Services*, Oct. 1938, vol. 23, no. 10, pp. 25–27.
Published also with illustrations of the wind tunnel with title, "Why Wind Tunnels," *Technology Review*, Nov. 1938, vol. 41, pp. 24–25, 50–54.
Address delivered on September 12, at the dedication of the Wright Brothers Memorial Wind Tunnel at the Massachusetts Institute of Technology.

Wright Brothers High Pressure Wind Tunnel. *Aero Digest*, Oct. 1938, vol. 33, no. 4, p. 63.

Wright Brothers Wind Tunnel. *Aero Equipment Review*, Nov. 1938, vol. 5, no. 2, p. 4, illus.

Pan American Aviation Day
(December 17)

U.S. Congress. House. *Joint Resolution Authorizing the Participation of the United States in the Celebration of a Pan American Aviation Day, to be Observed on December 17, of Each Year, the Anniversary of the First Successful Flight of a Heavier-than-Air Machine.* [Washington: United States Government Printing Office, 1940], 2 pp. (76th Congress, 3d Session. House J. Res. 595).

Introduced August 27, 1940, by Robert L. Mouton of Louisiana; referred to the Committee on the Judiciary. An identical bill, H. J. Res. 597, was introduced August 29 by Charles A. Plumley of Vermont and also referred to the Committee on the Judiciary.

U.S. Congress. Senate. *Joint Resolution Authorizing the Participation of the United States in the Celebration of a Pan American Aviation Day, to be Observed on December 17 of Each Year, the Anniversary of the First Successful Flight of a Heavier-than-Air Machine.* [Washington: United States Government Printing Office, 1940], 2 pp. (76th Congress, 3d Session. Senate. J. Res. 295).

Introduced September 6, 1940, by Mr. William H. Smathers of New Jersey; reported (No. 2169) with amendment, submitted by Bennett Champ Clark, September 24, 1940; passed Senate September 30; passed House October 2; approved October 10 and published in *United States Statutes at Large*, 1939–1941, vol. 54, pt. 1, p. 1093.

U.S. Congress. House. *Joint Resolution Authorizing the Annual Issue of a Series of Air Mail Stamps on Pan-American Aviation Day.* [Washington: United States Government Printing Office, 1939], 2 pp. (76th Congress, 3rd Session. House. J. Res. 615).

Introduced October 14, 1940, by Mr. J. Hardin Peterson of Florida; referred to the Committee on Post Office and Post Roads.

Closer Relationships Stressed in Addresses on the Occasion of Pan American Aviation Day. Extension of Remarks of Hon. Jennings Randolph. *Congressional Record*, Dec. 18, 1940, vol. 86, appendix pp. A6905–A6906.

Includes addresses by Dr. L. S. Rowe and Thomas Burke, delivered December 17.

Borges, Ivo. Protesto. *Asas*, Jan. 1941, vol. 10, p. 1.

Author protests the naming of December 17 as Pan American Aviation Day.

Celebration of Pan American Aviation Day. Extension of Remarks of Hon. J. Sparkman. *Congressional Record*, Jan. 2, 1941, vol. 86, pp. 7039–7040.

Account of programs held December 17.

Pan American Aviation Day. In *United States Statutes at Large*, 1937–1941, vol. 54, pt. 2, pp. 2765–2766.

Proclamation of President Roosevelt, November 18, 1940, designating December 17, 1940, and December 17, of each succeeding year as Pan American Aviation Day in accordance with Public Resolution No. 105, approved October 10, 1940.

Suggestions for Pan American Activities in Observance of Pan American Aviation Day, December 17 in Chicago Public Schools. Chicago: Bureau of Curriculum, Board of Education, 1944, 28 pp.

Aviation Day and National Aviation Day
(August 19)

Aviation Day. Extension of Remarks of Hon. Robert R. Reynolds of North Carolina. *Congressional Record*, Jan. 28, 1939, vol. 84, appendix pp. A314–A315.
Reprints article from St. Petersburg, Fla., *Independent*, January 12, 1939, proposing the designation of an Aviation Day in honor of American air heroes, particularly Wilbur and Orville Wright.

Aviation Day in America. Extension of Remarks of Hon. Jennings Randolph. *Congressional Record*, Feb. 28, 1939, vol. 84, appendix pp. A750–A751.
Statement of J. E. Myers favoring the designation of Orville Wright's birthday as an annual aviation day.

U.S. Congress. Senate. *Joint Resolution Designating August 19 of Each Year as National Aviation Day.* [Washington: United States Government Printing Office, 1939], 1 p. (76th Congress, 1st Session. Senate. J. Res. 111).
Introduced April 3, 1939, by Mr. Claude Pepper of Florida; passed Senate May 4; passed House May 5.
Numerous similar bills, Senate Joint Resolution 53 and House Joint Resolutions 134, 147, 229–240, 251, and 253, also were introduced at this session.

National Aviation Day. In *United States Statutes at Large*, 1939, vol. 53, pt. 3, p. 2548.
Published also in *Code of Federal Regulations of the United States . . . 1939 Supplement*, Washington: United States Government Printing Office, 1940, pp. 36–37.
Text of President Roosevelt's proclamation signed July 25, 1939, designating August 19 as National Aviation Day, as provided in Public Resolution No. 14, 76th Congress, approved May 11, 1939.

U.S. Congress. Senate. *Joint Resolution Authorizing the Issuance of an Air Mail National Aviation Day Stamp.* [Washington: United States Government Printing Office, 1940], 1 p. (76th Congress, 3rd Session. Senate. J. Res. 265).
Introduced May 27, 1940, by Mr. Robert R. Reynolds of North Carolina; referred to the Committee on Post Office and Post Roads.

Wright
(aircraft carrier)

Carrier *Wright* Launched. *New York Times*, Sept. 2, 1945, sec. I, p. 26, col. 2.
Brief note on launching, September 1, of the carrier *Wright* named for Wilbur Wright and sponsored by his niece, Mrs. Harold S. Miller. The carrier was commissioned February 9, 1947.

Wright Skyway
(Washington-Los Angeles)

Wright Skyway, Four Others to be Dedicated April 24–25. *Na-*

tional Aeronautics, Apr. 1948, vol. 27, no. 4, p. 15.

Announces plans for the dedication of the "Wright Skyway" between Los Angeles and Washington, including the erection of a bronze tablet at Wright Field, Dayton, Ohio.

First Skyways Dedicated Across Nation. "Wrightway" Gains Fame. *Aviation News Beacon*, Apr. 22, 1948, vol. 3, no. 17, p. 1.

Announcement of plans for dedication, April 24.

Wright Memorial Trophy
(National Aeronautics Association)

New Wright Memorial Trophy Goes to Dr. Durand. *National Aeronautics*, Dec. 1948, vol. 27, no. 12, p. 5, port.

Announces presentation for the first time of a Wright trophy founded by Dr. Godfrey Lowell Cabot to be awarded annually by the National Aeronautics Association for "significant public service of enduring value to aviation in the United States."

Victory, John F. Wright Brothers Memorial Award. *Pegasus*, Dec. 1949, vol. 14, no. 6, pp. 12–13, illus.

Wright Memorial Trophy Facts. *National Aeronautics*, Jan. 1963, vol. 42, p. 13.

Lists recipients, 1948–1962.

Wright Brothers Airmail Commemorative Stamp
(1949)

Wright Brothers Air Mail Stamp to be Placed on First-Day Sale at Kitty Hawk, N.C., Dec. 17. *Stamps*, Nov. 5, 1949, vol. 69, p. 225, illus.

Brief description of stamp.

Ellis, F. Some Notes on the Wright Brothers and Stamps Honoring Their Aeroplane. *Stamps*, Dec. 10, 1949, vol. 69, pp. 454–455, illus.

Note on the 2 cent International Civil Aeronautics Conference stamp issue of 1928, issued on the twenty-fifth anniversary of the Wright brothers' first flight, and the forthcoming 6 cent airmail stamp, authorized by the Post Office Dept. August 15, 1949, both of which show the Wright 1903 aeroplane in flight.

Glass, Sol. Wright Brothers Airmail Commemorative Stamp, 6c Red—Issued December 17, 1949. *Bureau Specialist*, Aug. 1950, vol. 21, p. 181, illus.

Gives technical details.

Wilbur and Orville Wright Laboratory of Physics
(Oberlin College)

Wilbur and Orville Wright Laboratory of Physics. *Oberlin College Bulletin*, July 1950, vol. 48, no. 7, pp. 1–40.

Announcement of naming of New Physics Laboratory at Oberlin College, Oberlin, Ohio, for Wilbur and Orville Wright.

Fiftieth Anniversary of Powered Flight Stamp
(1953)

U.S. Congress. House. *A Bill to Provide for the Issuance of a Special Air-Mail Postage Stamp in Commemoration of the Fiftieth Anniversary of the Wright Brothers' Flight at Kitty Hawk, North Carolina.* Washington: [United States Government Printing Office, 1953] 2 pp. (83rd Congress, 1st Session. H.R. 4217)

Introduced March 25, by Mr. Peter F. Mack of Illinois; referred to the Committee on Post Office and Civil Service.

Official Post Office Department Notice Concerning New 6¢ Air Mail Stamp. *Airpost Journal*, Apr. 1953, vol. 24, no. 7, p. 220 and cover.

Details on stamp commemorating the 50th anniversary of powered flight.

Gatchell, L. B. Sidelights on the Campaign for a Wright Commemorative Stamp. *Airpost Journal*, May 1953, vol. 24, pp. 266–267, illus.

Published also in *Stamps*, May 16, 1953, vol. 83, pp. 236–237.

Discusses plans and designs, 1943–1953, for a stamp honoring the Wrights.

Glass, Sol. Fiftieth Anniversary of Powered Flight Issue. *Bureau Specialist*, Sept. 1953, vol. 24, pp. 191, 193, 200, illus.

Technical details on commemorative 6-cent air mail stamp issued May 9, 1953. Shows Wright 1903 aeroplane in silhouette.

Wright Brothers Day
(December 17)

U.S. Congress. House. Committee on the Judiciary. *Wright Brothers Day. Report [To Accompany H. J. Res. 513]. September 2, 1959.* Washington: United States Government Printing Office, 1959. 1 p. (86th Congress. House. Report no. 1130).

Introduced by Rep. Joseph W. Martin, Jr. of Massachusetts, August 31, 1959. Referred to the Committee on the Judiciary, passed House September 3, and Senate September 9.

Designates December 17, 1959, as "Wright Brothers Day."

Wright Brothers' Day Proclamation. *National Aeronautics*, Nov. 1959, vol. 38, p. 2.

President Eisenhower's proclamation issued September 21, 1959.

Joint Resolution Designating the 17th Day of December 1959 as "Wright Brothers Day." *United States Statutes at Large*, vol. 73, 1959, p. 583.

House Joint Resolution 513, approved and proclaimed September 21, 1959 (Public Law 86–304).

U.S. Congress. House. Committee on Judiciary. *Wright Brothers Day. Report [To Accompany H. J. Res. 109]. May 22, 1961.* Washington: United States Government Print. Office, 1961, 2p. (87th Congress, 1st Session. House. Report No. 423).

Introduced by Rep. Joseph W. Martin, Jr., of Massachusetts, January 6, 1961. Referred to Committee on Judiciary, passed House June 5 and Senate September 11.

Designates December 17, 1961, as "Wright Brothers Day."

U.S. Congress. Senate. Committee on Judiciary. *Wright Brothers Day. Report [To Accompany H. J. Res. 109]. September 7, 1961.* Washington: United States Government Printing Office, 1961, 1 p. (87th Congress, 1st Session. Senate. Report No. 885).

Similar to House Report No. 423.

Whitener, Ralph V. Wanted—a Day for the Wright Brothers. *National Aeronautics*, Sept. 1961, vol. 40, p. 4.

A plea for the establishment of December 17, each year, as "Wright Brothers Day."

Joint Resolution Designating the 17th Day of December 1961 as "Wright Brothers Day." *United*

States Statutes at Large, vol. 75, 1961, p. 611.

House Joint Resolution 109, approved and proclaimed September 22, 1961 (Public Law 87–291).

U.S. Congress. House. Committee on Judiciary. *Wright Brothers Day. Report [To Accompany H. J. Res. 335]. September 17, 1963.* Washington: United States Government Printing Office, 1963, 1 p. (88th Congress, 1st Session. House. Report No. 752).

Introduced by Rep. Joseph W. Martin, Jr., of Massachusetts, March 21, 1963. Referred to Committee on Judiciary, passed House October 7 and Senate December 6.

Authorizes the observance of a "Wright Brothers Day" on December 17 of each year.

Joint Resolution Designating the 17th Day of December Each Year as "Wright Brothers Day." *United States Statutes at Large*, vol. 77, 1963, p. 402.

House Joint Resolution 335, approved and proclaimed December 17, 1963 (Public Law 88–209).

Wright Brothers Day, 1966. Proclamation 3757. December 1, 1966. *Weekly Compilation of Presidential Documents*, Dec. 5, 1966, vol. 2, pp. 1750–1751.

President Johnson's proclamation designating December 17, 1966, as Wright Brothers Day.

Medals and Honors

General

Deposition of William J. Hammer, January 28, 1911. In The Wright Company *vs.* Herring Curtiss Co. and Glenn H. Curtiss, *Complainant's Record*, New York: 1912, pp. 20–208, 833, illus.

Summarized also in The Wright Company *vs.* Claude Grahame-White, *Brief for Complainant on Final Hearing*, New York: 1911, pp. 3–8.

Includes enumeration of recognitions and honors tendered Wrights in 1908 and 1909, pages 24–34, with an accompanying photographic reproduction of many of them.

Académie des Sports Medal

L'Aéronautique à l'Académie des Sports. *L'Aérophile*, Nov. 1, 1908, vol. 16, p. 429.

Includes announcement of the award, October 16, of the Académie des Sports medal to Wilbur and Orville Wright.

Aéro-Club de France Gold Medal

Ehrungen Wilbur Wrights. *Illustrierte Aeronautische Mitteilungen*, Nov. 4, 1908, vol. 12, p. 695.

Includes announcement of the award in September of the Aéro-Club of France's gold medal to Wilbur and Orville Wright.

Aeronautical Society of Great Britain Medal

Letter from Mr. Wilbur Wright. *Aeronautical Journal*, Jan. 1909, vol. 13, p. 3, illus. (facing p. 2).

Wilbur Wright's letter from Le Mans, December 3, 1908, acknowledging that the Wright brothers had been voted the gold medal of the Aeronautical Society at its November 9 meeting, "in recognition of their distinguished services to aeronautical science."

Presentation of the Aeronautical Society's Medal. *Flight*, May 8,

1909, vol. 1, pp. 260–261.
Account of ceremonies at the Institution of Civil Engineers, London, May 3, 1909, when the medal was presented to Wilbur and Orville Wright.

Presentation of the Gold Medal of the Aeronautical Society of Great Britain to Messrs. Wilbur and Orville Wright. *The Aeronautical Journal*, July 1909, vol. 13, pp. 76–79, illus.
Includes brief speeches of acceptance by Wilbur and Orville Wright.

Académie des Sciences Gold Medal

Les Médailles de l'Académie des Sciences. *L'Aérophile*, Dec. 1, 1909, vol. 17, p. 545.
Announcement of the award of an Académie des Sciences medal to Wilbur and Orville Wright.

Médaille de l'Aéronautique. *Comptes rendus . . . de l'Académie des Sciences*, Dec. 20, 1909, vol. 149, p. 1297.
Announcement of award of its gold medal to Wrights.

Aero Club of America Medal

Aero Club Medal. *Bulletin of the Aerial Experiment Association*, Jan. 4, 1909, no. XXVI, p. 2.
Report on visit of Alexander Graham Bell and Aero Club of America's Committee on Medals to the White House, December 16, 1908, to invite President Roosevelt to attend a banquet and present a medal to the Wrights on their return to America.

Taft to Present Wright Medals. *Aeronautics*, New York, Apr. 1909, vol. 4, pp. 153–154.
Announcement of plans for presentation of Aero Club of America medals.

Gold Medals for the Great Aviators. *Numismatist*, May 1909, vol. 22, p. 134, illus.
Description of medal designed by the sculptor Victor D. Brenner for the Aero Club of America which had sponsored a public subscription of funds for it.

Taft Presents Wright Medals. *Aeronautics*, July 1909, vol. 5, pp. 25–26.
Account of the presentation ceremonies at the White House, June 10.

Wright Memorial Book. Compiled by the Aero Club of America to Commemorate the Discovery by Wilbur and Orville Wright of the Correct Principles of Maintaining Equilibrium in the Air. [New York], 1913, 103 pp., illus.
Edition limited to three copies, first presented to Orville Wright, December 17, 1913, second preserved in Aero Club of America archives, third given to Smithsonian Institution. Includes resolutions of Congress, photographs of medals, President Taft's speech of presentation, messages from the Governors of ten states, thirteen scientific institutions, and numerous editorials and cartoons marking the occasion.

Congressional Gold Medal

U.S. Congress. Senate. *Joint Resolution Authorizing the Secretary of War to Award Gold Medals to Orville Wright and Wilbur Wright*. [Washington: United States Government Printing Office, 1909], 2 pp. (60th Congress, 2d Session. S. J. R. 119).
Introduced January 25, by

Joseph B. Foraker of Ohio; passed Senate January 25.

U.S. Congress. House. *Joint Resolution Authorizing the Secretary of War to Award Gold Medals to Orville Wright and Wilbur Wright.* [Washington: United States Government Printing Office, 1909], 2 pp. (60th Congress, 2d Session. H. J. Res. 246).

Introduced January 25 by J. Eugene Harding of Ohio; referred to the Committee on Military Affairs; reported with amendments (House Report 2042) February 4; passed the House March 3; approved March 4 and published in *United States Statutes at Large, 1907–1909*, vol. 35, pt. 2, p. 1627.

Gold Medal by Congress to Wright Brothers. *Numismatist*, Aug. 1909, vol. 22, p. 231, illus.

Description of special congressional medal designed by Messrs. Barber and Morgan of the United States Mint and an account of its presentation by General James Allen at Dayton, June 18.

Ohio Medal

Ohio. Senate. Providing for the Presentation of a Medal to Orville and Wilbur Wright, of Dayton, Ohio, in Recognition of Their Great Genius, Displayed by Their Invention of the Aeroplane. In Ohio. Senate. *Journal*, Feb. 23, Mar. 2, 12, 1909, pp. 115, 126, 147, 153, 246, 248, 272. (Ohio. Senate. S. B. No. 107)

Introduced by Sen. George K. Cetone, February 23, 1909. Referred to Committee on Finance, February 24, passed Senate March 2 and the House, March 12. The medal was presented by Gov. Judson Harmon in Dayton on June 18, 1909.

Langley Medal
(Smithsonian Institution)

Smithsonian Medal for Wrights *Aeronautics*, New York, Mar. 1909, vol. 4, p. 118.

Announcement that the first award of the Langley Medal is to go to Wilbur and Orville Wright.

Langley Medal and Memorial Tablet. In *Annual Report of the Smithsonian Institution, 1909*, Washington: Government Printing Office, 1910, pp. 22, 107.

Resolution adopted by the Board of the Regents of the Smithsonian Institution, December 15, 1908, establishing the Langley Medal "to be awarded for specially meritorious investigation in connection with the science of aerodromics and its application to aviation."

Award of Langley Medal. In *Annual Report of the Smithsonian Institution, 1909.* Washington: Government Printing Office, 1910, p. 111.

Report of committee of award and resolution, Octave Chanute, chairman, of February 10, awarding first Langley medal to the Wright brothers.

Langley Medal Presented to W. and O. Wright. *Aeronautics*, London, Mar. 1910, vol. 3, no. 3, pp. 40–41, illus.

Brief account of presentation ceremonies.

Wrights Get First Langley Medal. Aviators' Work Honored by Smithsonian Institution. *Fly*, Mar. 1910, vol. 2, pp. 7–8, illus.

Presentation of the Langley Medal to the Wright Brothers. Historical Address at the Smithsonian Institution, Feb. 10, 1910, by Alexander Graham Bell.

Science, Mar. 4, 1910, vol. 31, pp. 334–337.
Account of presentation ceremonies, February 10, 1910, at the Smithsonian Institution.

Langley Medal Presented to Wright Bros. *Flight*, Mar. 5, 1910, vol. 2, p. 160, illus.
Brief report.

Presentation of Langley Medal to Messrs. Wilbur and Orville Wright. In *Annual Report of the Smithsonian Institution, 1910.* Washington: Government Printing Office, 1911, pp. 104–110, illus.
Includes addresses by Alexander Graham Bell, Senator Henry Cabot Lodge, and remarks by Wilbur Wright at presentation ceremonies.

Collier Trophy
(Aero Club of America)

Stabilizer Qualifies Wright for Trophy. *Aero and Hydro*, Jan. 10, 1914, vol. 7, p. 179.

The Collier Trophy of the Aero Club of America for 1913 Awarded to Mr. Orville Wright for the Development and Demonstration of the Wright Stabilizer. *Flying*, Feb. 1914, vol. 3, no. 1, pp. 6–7, illus.
Account of demonstrations by Orville Wright before a special committee of the Aero Club at Simms Station, December 31, 1913, which led to the award.

Elliott Cresson Medal
(Franklin Institute)

Award of the Elliott Cresson Medal to Distinguished Scientists and Technologists. *Journal of the Franklin Institute*, July 1914, vol. 178, pp. 105–115.
Includes award to Orville Wright of medal, May 20, "in recognition of the epoch-making work accomplished by him, at first together with his brother Wilbur and latterly alone, in establishing on a practical basis the science and art of aviation."

Albert Medal
(Royal Society of Arts)

Albert Medal. *Journal of the Royal Society of Arts, June 29*, 1917, vol. 65, p. 564.
Announces award of distinguished British medal to Orville Wright "in recognition of the value of the contributions of Wilbur and Orville Wright to the solution of mechanical flight."

Lord Northcliffe Presents Albert Medal to Orville Wright. *Aerial Age Weekly*, Nov. 12, 1917, vol. 6, p. 372.
Account of presentation ceremonies held in Memorial Hall, Dayton, October 27, 1917.

Presentation of the Society's Albert Medal to Mr. Orville Wright. *Journal of the Royal Society of Arts*, Jan. 25, 1918, vol. 66, p. 167.

John Fritz Medal
(American Society of Electrical Engineers)

John Fritz Medal Awarded to Orville Wright. *Journal of the American Institute of Electrical Engineers*, Apr. 1920, vol. 39, p. 418.
Announces award of medal to Orville Wright for noteworthy work in the development of the aeroplane.

Orville Wright Awarded John Fritz Medal. *American Machinist*, May 1920, vol. 52, p. 1118.
Account of presentation ceremonies in New York, May 17.

Orville Wright presented with John Fritz Medal. *Power*, May 18, 1920, vol. 51, pp. 823–824.

John Fritz Medal Presented to Orville Wright. *Journal of the American Institute of Electrical Engineers*, June 1920, vol. 139, p. 601.

John Fritz Medal Presented to Orville Wright. *Mechanical Engineering*, June 1920, vol. 42, p. 364.

Orville Wright Honored. *U.S. Air Services*, June 1920, vol. 3, no. 5, p. 17.

Orville Wright Receives John Fritz Medal. *Mining & Metallurgy*, June 1920, no. 162, pp. 11–12.

Presentation of John Fritz Medal to Orville Wright. *Society of Automotive Engineers Journal*, June 1920, vol. 6, pp. 394–396.

Washington Award
(Western Society of Engineers)

Orville Wright Receives Washington Award. *Journal of the Western Society of Engineers*, June 1927 (news section), vol. 32, pp. 75–78.

Includes presentation address of Mr. Paul Westburg and Orville Wright's acceptance speech, June 1, on receipt of award, "in recognition of devoted, unselfish, and pre-eminent service in advancing human progress."

Distinguished Flying Cross

U.S. Congress. House. *A Bill to Authorize the President to Present the Distinguished-Flying Cross to Orville Wright.* [Washington: United States Government Printing Office, 1928], 1 p. (70th Congress, 1st Session. H.R. 13990).

Introduced May 23, 1928, by W. Frank James of Michigan; referred to Committee on Military Affairs; reported (House Report 1946) with amendments December 11 (adding words "and to Wilbur Wright, deceased"); passed House December 13, 1928.

An Act to Authorize the President to Present the Distinguished-Flying Cross to Orville Wright and to Wilbur Wright, Deceased. *United States Statutes at Large, 1927–1929*, vol. 45, pt. 2, p. 2036.

Approved December 18, 1928.

Wright Gets Flying Cross. *New York Times*, Feb. 28, 1929, p. 2.

Report of the presentation of the Distinguished-Flying Cross to Orville Wright by Secretary of War Davis at the War Department, Washington, D.C., February 27.

Daniel Guggenheim Medal

Orville Wright Presented the Daniel Guggenheim Medal for 1929. *Mechanical Engineering*, May 1930, vol. 52, p. 521.

Account of presentation, April 8, of the first Daniel Guggenheim Medal for 1929 "for design and construction, with his brother now deceased, of the first successful engine-propelled airplane."

Franklin Medal
(Franklin Institute)

Award of Franklin Medals. *Journal of the Franklin Institute*, Aug. 1933, vol. 216, pp. 239–240.

Includes account of award of medal, May 17, 1933, to Orville

269-517—68——12

Wright in absentia "in recognition of the valuable investigations carried out by him and his brother Wilbur."

Aircraft Pilot's Certificate No. 1

U.S. Congress. Senate. *A Bill Authorizing the Issuance to Orville Wright of Honorary Aircraft Pilot's Certificate Number 1.* [Washington: United States Government Printing Office, 1939], 1 p. (76th Congress, 1st Session. S. 2735).

Introduced June 30, 1939, by Mr. Claude Pepper of Florida; referred to the Committee on Commerce; reported (report No. 992), July 27, 1939; passed Senate August 1, 1939.

U.S. Congress. House. Committee on Interstate and Foreign Commerce. *Authorizing the Issuance of Honorary Aircraft Pilot's Certificate No. 1 to Orville Wright. Report (to accompany S. 2735).* [Washington: United States Government Printing Office, 1940], 1 p. (76th Congress, 3d Session. House. Report No. 1911).

Submitted by Mr. Clarence F. Lea of California, April 2, 1940; passed by House June 6, 1940.

An Act Authorizing the Issuance to Orville Wright of Honorary Aircraft Pilot's Certificate Numbered 1. *United States Statutes at Large, 1939–1941*, vol. 54, pt. 2, p. 1283.

Approved June 13, 1940.

Orville Wright Presented with Honorary Pilot's License No. 1. *Air Line Pilot*, July 1940, vol. 9, no. 6, p. 1, port.

States that Air Line Pilot's Association was co-sponsor of bill which authorized issuance of license.

Orville Wright Gets Certificate No. 1. *Civil Aeronautics Journal*, Sept. 15, 1940, vol. 1, p. 429.

Announcement of presentation of certificate at ceremonies dedicating Wright Brothers' Hill, Dayton, Ohio, August 19.

Aviation Hall of Fame (Air Force Magazine)

Aviation's Hall of Fame. *Air Force*, Dec. 1953, vol. 36, p. 32, illus.

Announces the establishment by *Air Force* of an Aviation Hall of Fame with Wilbur and Orville Wright as the first two nominations.

Hall of Fame for Great Americans (New York University)

Wright Brothers Accomplishments to be Commemorated in New York University Hall of Fame. *Mechanical Engineering*, Aug. 1958, vol. 80, p. 124.

Reports that the Senate of New York University waived the 25-year eligibility rule to permit the nomination of Orville Wright in the 1960 elections of the Hall of Fame for Great Americans. Orville was nominated in 1960 and elected on October 28, 1965.

New York University. Hall of Fame for Great Americans. Wilbur Wright. In its *Hall of Fame for Great Americans at New York University; Official Handbook.* New York: New York University Press, 1962, p. 94.

Wilbur Wright was elected to the Hall of Fame for Great Americans in 1955.

Memorabilia

Aeroplanes

The Wright Brothers. Washington: National Air Museum, Smithsonian Institution, 1959. [11] p., illus. (*Its* Information Leaflet 8 (rev.).)

Concise factual informational leaflet about the Wrights and exhibits in the National Air Museum (now National Air and Space Museum) pertaining to the Wright brothers, including the Wright 1903 aeroplane, the Military Flyer, Type A, 1909, and Transcontinental Flyer, Type EX, "Vin Fiz," 1911.

1903 Machine

The Original Wright Aeroplane, 1903. In Science Museum, *Handbook of the Collections Illustrating Aeronautics*, London: His Majesty's Stationery Office, 1929, vol. 1, p. 72.

Included also in 1935 edition of the *Handbook*, vol. 1, p. 76.

Descriptive note on Wright 1903 aeroplane exhibited in the Science Museum, 1929–1948.

Williams, Al. Bring Home the One and Only Kitty Hawk Plane. *U.S. Air Services*, Mar. 1946, vol. 31, no. 3, p. 20.

Reprinted from his syndicated column in the Scripps-Howard newspapers.

Kitty Hawk Biplane Awaits Suitable Home. *Aviation News*. Nov. 18, 1946, vol. 6, no. 21, pp. 11–12.

Brief note on Orville's current views.

[Findley, Earl N.] Orville Wright Ordered Return to America of Original Airplane. *U.S. Air Services*, Feb. 1948, vol. 33, no. 2, pp. 15–16.

Gives text of letters exchanged, December 8, 1943 and January 5, 1944, between Colonel E. E. Mackintosh, Director of the Science Museum, London, and Orville in which latter asks return of Wright 1903 plane.

McSurely, Alexander. Orville Wright's Death May Return Kitty Hawk Plane to U.S. Museum. *Aviation Week*, Feb. 9, 1948, vol. 48, no. 6, pp. 13–14.

Nephews Will Decide Wright Plane Date. *Aviation Week*, Feb. 16, 1948, vol. 48, no. 7, p. 12.

Note on Orville Wright's will and expressed wishes regarding return of the 1903 Wright aeroplane to the U.S.

Picture Story of the Week; Kitty Hawk Will Come Home. *Scholastic*, Feb. 23, 1948, vol. 52, p. 6.

Wright Biplane May Return to U.S., August 19. *Aviation Week*, Feb. 23, 1948, vol. 48, no. 8, p. 7.

Departure of the Pioneer. *Flight*, Oct. 21, 1948, vol. 54, p. 476, illus.

Account of the ceremony October 18, of the removal of the Wright 1903 plane from exhibit at the Science Museum and its handing over to Mr. L. Satterthwaite, American civil air attaché, who received it on behalf of the American government.

The Wright Biplane Goes Home. *Aeroplane*, Oct. 22, 1948, vol. 75, p. 523.

Brief note on removal ceremony at Science Museum, October 18.

Back to the Beginning. *Flight*, Oct. 28, 1948, vol. 54, pp. 505–507, illus.

Further note on ceremonies held at Science Museum, October 18.

Kitty Hawk in Museum. *Aviation Week*, Nov. 29, 1948, vol. 49, no. 22, p. 15.
Announces the arrival of the Wright 1903 plane at the Smithsonian Institution.

[Findley, Earl N.] The "Kitty Hawk" Comes Home at Last. *U.S. Air Services*, Dec. 1948, vol. 33, no. 12, pp. 5–6.
Editorial comment on return of Wright 1903 plane to America.

Kitty Hawk's Last Landing. *Air Force*, Dec. 1948, vol. 31, no. 12, pp. 18–19.

Wright Plane Return was Featured Event of 45th Anniversary. *National Aeronautics and Flight Plan*, Dec. 1948, vol. 27, no. 12, pp. 6–7.

McSurely, Alexander, Wright Plane Back Home at Last. *Aviation Week*, Dec. 13, 1948, vol. 49, no. 24, pp. 16–18, illus.
Brief history of the 1903 Wright plane.

U.S. National Museum is Given Wright Aeroplane. *Museum News*, Jan. 1, 1949, vol. 26, no. 13, pp. 1–2, illus.

Franks, Oliver. It is a Little as if We had Before Us the Original Wheel. The Most Remarkable Example of the Audacity of Man. *U.S. Air Services*, Mar. 1949, vol. 34, no. 3, pp. 11–12, illus.
Address delivered by the British Ambassador at ceremony marking formal installation of the 1903 Wright aeroplane in the National Air Museum of the Smithsonian Institution, December 17, 1948.

America Welcomes the Kittyhawk. Some Extracts from the American Press on the Return of the Aeronautical Beau Geste. *Pylon*, June 1949, vol. 8, no. 2, p. 21.

True, Webster P. Operation "Homecoming." *Sperryscope*, Winter 1949, vol. 11, no. 8, pp. 2–3, illus.
Account of shipment of 1903 plane to U.S. from England.

Exhibition [of the Wright Brothers 1903 Aeroplane]. In *Annual Report of the Smithsonian Institution, 1949*, Washington: United States Government Printing Office, 1950, pp. 117–118.
Brief report by the curator of the National Air Museum, Paul E. Garber, on the shipment of the Wright 1903 aeroplane from Nova Scotia to Washington and its installation in the Museum for the presentation ceremonies, December 17, 1948.

Presentation of the Wright Brothers' Aeroplane of 1903 to the United States National Museum. In *Annual Report of the Smithsonian Institution, 1949*, Washington: United States Government Printing Office, 1950, pp. 3–5, 20.
Brief report on presentation ceremonies, December 17, 1948.

Beck, Mabel. The First Airplane—After 1903. *U.S. Air Services*, Dec. 1954, vol. 39, pp. 9–10.
An account by the secretary of the Wright brothers, 1910–1948, of the history of the original Wright 1903 aeroplane—its storage, renovation, various exhibitions, 1916–1924, until the aeroplane was shipped to England on January 28, 1928, to be exhibited in the Science Museum, South Kensington.

Reproductions

Thirty-Eight Years of Flight. [*Franklin*] *Institute News*, Dec. 1941, vol. 6, no. 8, p. 7, illus.

Brief note on the Franklin Institute Hall of Aviation and mention of its scale model of the Wright 1903 aeroplane, built with the aid of suggestions of Orville Wright.

Wright, H. D. The Wright Biplane Replica. *Pylon*, June 1949, vol. 8, no. 2, pp. 17–20, illus.

Account of the building of the replica by the students of the De Havilland Aeronautical Technical School for installation in the Science Museum.

Replica of Wright Aeroplane 1903. Constructed by the De Havilland Aeronautical Technical School. In Davy, M. J. B., *Aeronautics: Heavier-Than-Air Aircraft; Their History and Development as Illustrated by the National Collection. Part II, Catalogue of the Exhibits With Descriptive Notes*, London: His Majesty's Stationery Office, 1949, p. 28.

Johnston, S. Paul. Wright Replica. [Signed S.P.J.] *Aeronautical Engineering Review*, July 1953, vol. 12, no. 7, pp. 22–23, illus.

Brief report on full-scale reproduction of the Wright 1903 aeroplane built cooperatively by 24 West Coast manufacturers and assembled by the Northrop Aeronautical Institute for display at the Los Angeles Headquarters Building of the Institute of the Aeronautical Sciences (now American Institute of Aeronautics and Astronautics).

Replica of the Kitty Hawk Aeroplane. *Western Aviation*, July 1953, vol. 33, p. 7, illus.

The reproduction was built through the cooperation of twenty industrial organizations in Southern California in observance of the fiftieth anniversary of powered flight.

Full-Scale Replica Original Wright Airplane. *U.S. Air Services*, Aug. 1953, vol. 38, p. 6.

Reports the unveiling on July 15, 1953, in Los Angeles, of the only full-scale reproduction, at that time, of the original Wright aeroplane in the United States, a project of the Institute of the Aeronautical Sciences.

Dodge, Beverly A. Wright Reproduction. *Aeronautical Engineering Review*, Oct. 1953, vol. 12, pp. 24–27, illus.

Describes the cooperative effort which resulted in the building of a full-scale reproduction of the Wright brothers 1903 aeroplane. The model was installed on permanent exhibition in the W. F. Durand Aeronautical Museum of the Institute of the Aeronautical Sciences (now American Institute of Aeronautics and Astronautics) in Los Angeles in July 1952 and was officially dedicated by Lt. Gen. James H. Doolittle, USAF (Ret.), on July 15, 1953.

The Wright Flyer. *Flight*, Dec. 11, 1953, vol. 64, p. 787–788, illus.

Includes three-view drawing and data on the Wright 1903 aeroplane based on information available from the staff of the Science Museum and the De Havilland Technical School which constructed the reproduction of the Wright machine on display in the Museum.

1903 Wright Flyer. *Aerospace*, Dec. 1963, vol. 1, pp. 18–26 (and cover), illus.

Presents details and photographs of the reconstruction of a Wright "Flyer" by the National Capitol Section of the American Institute of Aeronautics and Astronautics which was presented to the Wright National Memorial Museum at Kill Devil Hills, North Carolina.

A Wright Replica in Los Angeles. *Esso Air World*, Mar./Apr. 1954, vol. 6, p. 127, illus.

Brief report on the building of a full-scale reproduction of the Wright 1903 biplane.

Maycock, C. B. Prototypes Worth Modeling. No. 37—The Wright Biplane. *Model Aircraft*, Dec. 1953, vol. 12, pp. 582–583, illus.

1905 Machine

The Wright Brothers. Dayton, Ohio: Carillon Park [1950]. 26 p. illus.

The restored 1905 Wright aeroplane is in Wright Hall in Carillon Park and is discussed, pp. 15–17.

1908 Machine (France)

Wright Aeroplane in the French Museum. *Aeronautics*, New York, June 1909, vol. 4, p. 191.

States that the 1908 aeroplane used by Wilbur Wright in France has been presented by the Weiler syndicate to the Arts et Métiers Museum in Paris.

1909 Machine (Germany)

Hildebrandt, Alfred. *Vom Flugahnen zum Höhenflug*, Berlin: VDI-Verlag GmbH, 1933, 93 p., illus. (Deutsches Museum. Abhandlung und Berichte. 5 Jahr., Heft 3).

The Wrights are discussed, pp. 71–72, with a photograph of their model A aeroplane flown by Orville at Tempelhof, Germany, in August 1909, now in the Deutsches Museum, Munich.

1909 Signal Corps Machine

Chandler, Charles D., and Lahm, Frank P. Signal Corps No. 1 to Smithsonian. In their *How Our Army Grew Wings*, New York: The Ronald Press Company, 1943, p. 187.

Note on circumstance leading to the deposit of the Wright 1909 aeroplane in the Smithsonian Institution, October 1911.

Wright Military Flyer Type "A" 1909. Wright-Patterson Air Force Base, Ohio, [1960]. 4p. (Air Force Museum Folder No. 1).

Consists of three-view drawings and specifications of a reproduction of a Wright-built, modified Model "A" aeroplane on exhibit in the Air Force Museum.

Motors

1903 Motor

The Original Wright Aero-Engine, 1903. In Science Museum, *Handbook of the Collections Illustrating Aeronautics*, London: His Majesty's Stationery Office, 1930, vol. 3, p. 60.

Included also in 1936 edition of the *Handbook*, vol. 3, p. 66.

Brief description of the Wright 1903 engine exhibited in the Science Museum, 1929–1948.

Andrews, J. R. A 1903 Engine Re-Born. Working Replica of Wright

Brothers' Power Unit Constructed in D. H. Technical School. *Flight*, July 13, 1961, vol. 60, p. 49, illus.
Reprinted from *Pylon*.

Brodie, J. L. P. Testing a Wright Engine. *Aeroplane*, Dec. 18, 1953, vol. 85, p. 827, illus.
Describes test run conducted November 1950 of the reproduction of the Wright 1903 aeroplane engine which was presented to the Science Museum, South Kensington, London, April 25, 1951.

4-Cylinder Motor
(1909)

Wright-Bollée Engine, 1909. In Science Museum, *Handbook of the Collections Illustrating Aeronautics*, London: His Majesty's Stationery Office, 1930, vol. 3, p. 60.
Included also in 1936 edition of the *Handbook*, vol. 3, p. 67.
Brief description of the French-built Wright engine presented to the Science Museum by Alec Ogilvie.

4-Cylinder Motor
(1910)

Wright Brothers [Engine]. *Notes*, Museum of Science and Industry, Chicago, Apr. 1938, vol. 1, no. 5, p. 39.
A Wright 4-cylinder engine, 1910.

6–60 Motor

60 H. P. Wright Engine 1915. In Science Museum, *Handbook of the Collections Illustrating Aeronautics*, London: His Majesty's Stationery Office, 1930, vol. 3, p. 61.
Included also in the 1936 edition of the *Handbook*, vol. 3, p. 67.
Brief description of engine loaned for exhibit purposes by the Imperial War Museum.

Wind Tunnel Apparatus

McClarren, Ralph. The Wright Brothers' Aeronautical Engineering Collection at the Franklin Institute, Philadelphia, Pa. *Journal of the Franklin Institute*, Aug. 1951, vol. 252, pp. 175–196, illus.
Detailed account and inventory of the original wind tunnel apparatus, model airfoils, test data, and drawings of the Wright brothers' early aeroplanes deeded to the Franklin Institute by Orville Wright.

Barnaby, Ralph S. Wright Material at the Franklin Institute. *U.S. Air Services*, Mar. 1954, vol. 39, p. 11.
Report on the formal opening on Dec. 17, 1953, of an exhibition of material deeded to the Institute by Orville Wright, comprising all original wind-tunnel apparatus, model airfoils, test data, and drawings of the Wright brothers' early aeroplanes and engines, some airfoil models and aircraft models tested for the Wright Company at McCook Field, during 1919, 1920, and 1921, as well as some of Orville Wright's later experimental aviation devices.

Eckhardt, George H. Work Sheets of the Wright Brothers. *Science Digest*, Oct. 1961, vol. 50, pp. 7–12.
Popular account of Wright materials in the collections of the Franklin Institute, Philadelphia, comprising drawings, work sheets, data books, the original 1901 lift and drag balances, and a model of the Wright 1903 biplane, stated by Orville Wright to be even more

accurate than the original aeroplane, on which later changes were made.

Medals

Dayton Art Institute Receives All Medals Awarded to Wright Brothers. *Museum News*, Mar. 15, 1948, vol. 25, p. 2.

Announces receipt by bequest from Orville Wright of all the bronzes and all the gold and other medals owned by him.

Dayton Marks a Famous Flight. *Art Digest*, Feb. 1, 1954, vol. 28, p. 25.

Brief note on exhibition by the Dayton Art Institute, Ohio, entitled "Flight, Fantasy, Faith, Fact," commemorating the fiftieth anniversary of the first Wright brothers' powered flights. Exhibits included the Institute's collection of medals, awards, citations, and degrees conferred on the Wrights for their achievements.

Papers

The Hart O. Berg Collection. *Journal of the Aeronautical Sciences*, Aug. 1939, vol. 6, p. 427.

Collection of early aeronautical materials of Hart O. Berg, business associate of the Wrights, including valuable and rare photographs, books, and clippings which contain much unique material on the early work of the Wright brothers. Presented to the Institute of the Aeronautical Sciences.

Diary of Orville Wright at Library of Congress. *Airpost Journal*, Nov. 1948, vol. 20, p. 70.

Reports showing of a page, entry of December 17, 1903, from Orville Wright's diary on the occasion of the meeting of the American Association for the Advancement of Science, September 13–20.

Wright Brothers' Papers to Library of Congress. *U.S. Air Services*, June 1949, vol. 34, no. 6, p. 6.

Announcement of acquisition of the Wright Papers from the Orville Wright Estate, June 5, 1949.

Eells, Richard and staff. Wright Brothers Scrapbooks. *Library of Congress Quarterly Journal of Current Acquisitions*, Aug. 1949, vol. 6, pp. 37–39.

Report by the Aeronautics Division of the Library of Congress on the acquisition of a microfilm of the eleven-volume scrapbook collection maintained by the Wrights, 1902–1948. The original volumes were presented to the Institute of the Aeronautical Sciences, May 1949, by the Orville Wright Estate and transferred to the Library of Congress in 1964.

New Print of Photograph of Wright Brothers' First Power Flight Made by Library of Congress. *U.S. Air Services*, Apr. 1953, vol. 38, no. 4, pp. 8–9, illus.

Reprinting of Library of Congress press release announcing the making of an improved print from an original glass-plate negative given to the Library of Congress in 1949 by the Orville Wright Estate.

McFarland, Marvin, and Renstrom, Arthur. The Papers of Wilbur and Orville Wright. *Library of Congress Quarterly Journal of Current Acquisitions*, Aug. 1950, vol. 7, pp. 23–34, illus.

Extensive account of the Wright brothers' papers received by the Library of Congress, May 27, 1949, from the Estate of Orville Wright, giving history of acquisition and outline of contents and materials in the collection.

Watches

Wright Brothers' Watches Exhibited in Aeronautical Archives. *Aeronautical Engineering Review*, Dec. 1949, vol. 8, no. 12, p. 9, illus.

Announcement of the bequest to the Institute of the Aeronautical Sciences by the Estate of Orville Wright of watches, medals, and other Wright memorabilia. The watches were transferred in 1965 to the National Air and Space Museum.

Art

Bronze Busts of Wright Brothers. *Air Corps News Letter*, July 1, 1937, vol. 20, no. 13, p. 7.

Note on busts, by the sculptor, Seth Velsy, which were installed in the rotunda of the Army Aeronautical Museum, Dayton, June 15, 1937. Several sets were cast from the original bronzes, one of which was presented to the University of Maine in October 1938. Another set is in Wright Hall, Carillon Park, Dayton.

Italians Honor Memory of Wilbur Wright. *U.S. Air Services*, Sept. 1947, vol. 32, no. 9, p. 33.

Note on forthcoming aeronautical festival at Centocelle, Italy, to be opened by the unveiling of a marble statue of Wilbur Wright.

Wilbur Wright Honored in Rome, Bust Unveiled. *New York Times*, Nov. 2, 1947, p. 47, col. 6.

Opening Up in Italy. *Aeroplane*, Nov. 28, 1947, vol. 73, p. 693.

Includes account of ceremonies on Aviation Day, November 1, at Centocelle Airport, near Rome at which a marble bust of Wilbur Wright, the work of sculptor Pier Gabrielle Vangelli, was unveiled. It was presented by Gianni Caproni in the name of Italian pilots and aviation pioneers. At Centocelle the first Italian military pilot, Lt. Mario Calderara, received instruction from Wilbur Wright.

Portrait by Lewis Eugene Thompson as Displayed at the Institute's New York Headquarters. *Aeronautical Engineering Review*, Mar. 1948, vol. 7, no. 3, p. 14, illus.

Portrait of Orville with bust of Wilbur, and Kitty Hawk aeroplane in background.

The Kitty Hawk Plane. Painting by Melbourne Brindle. *Colliers*, Dec. 25, 1948, vol. 22, no. 26, pp. 10, 32–33, illus.

Also reproduced in *Sperryscope*, Winter 1949, vol. 11, no. 8, cover.

Reproduction of water-color painting, original of which was presented to the Smithsonian Institution on December 17, 1948, on the occasion of the forty-fifth anniversary of the first Wright 1903 flights and now on exhibit in the National Air and Space Museum.

The Wright Brothers. *Collier's*, Dec. 25, 1948, vol. 122, no. 26, p. 10 and cover.

Painting of the Wright brothers by Arthur Lidov from a composite portrait photograph, by Hollinger & Company, 1907. Donated by Orville Wright to the Institute of the Aeronautical Sciences.

[Bronze Bust of Wilbur Wright]. *In Annual Report of the Smithsonian Institution, 1950*, Washington: United States Government Printing Office, 1951, pp. 125, 132.

Brief descriptive note on bust of Wilbur Wright by the sculptor, Oskar J. W. Hansen, presented to the Smithsonian Institution, January 27, 1950, by Mr. and Mrs. Elmer F. Weiboldt.

[Oil Portrait of Wilbur Wright]. In *Annual Report of the Smithsonian Institution, 1951*, Washington: United States Government Printing Office, 1952, pp. 127, 132.

Note on receipt of oil portrait done from life by J. A. Herve Mathe. Commissioned by Frank S. Lahm and given to Smithsonian Institution by his son and daughter, Gen. Frank P. Lahm and Mrs. Frank Parker.

"Wilbur and Orville Wright and Their Accomplishments," an Oil Painting By Dwight Mutchler. Dedication, December 17, 1959. Columbus: The F. J. Heer Printing Company, 1959, 9 p.

Descriptive booklet produced by the Public Works Department of Ohio and the Ohio Historical Society on the occasion of the unveiling of the painting. The painting was authorized by the Ohio General Assembly, May 1957, to be hung in the Ohio State Capitol Building and the commission awarded to Dwight Mutchler of Athens, Ohio, October 11, 1958.

Sweet, Floyd J. SSA to Participate at Kitty Hawk. *Soaring*, Dec. 1963, vol. 27, p. 21.

Announcement of bronze memorial plaque, the work of Capt. Ralph S. Barnaby, gift of the Soaring Society of America, honoring the Wright brothers, to be unveiled December 17, 1963, at Kitty Hawk, N.C.

SSA Installs Plaque at Kitty Hawk. *Soaring*, Mar. 1964, vol. 28, pp. 8–9, illus.

The plaque consists of the likenesses of Wilbur and Orville Wright in bas-relief and the caption "They Taught Us To Fly." Accurately depicted on the background of the plaque are the gliders which the Wrights flew on the Kitty Hawk dunes in 1901, 1902, and 1911.

Haggerty, James J. and Warren Reiland Smith. *The U.S. Air Force; a Pictorial History in Art.* New York and Washington: Books, Inc., 1966. 261p., illus.

Comprises reproductions from the Air Force Art Collection. Included, pp. 2–7, are "The Wright Brothers' First Powered Flight," by Harvey Kidder; "Lieutenant Lahm's First Flight [with Orville Wright]", by Richard Green; and "The Wright Brothers at Fort Myer," by John McCoy.

New York University. The Hall of Fame for Great Americans. *Unveiling of the Busts and Tablets for Wilbur Wright and Orville Wright in the Auditorium of the Library of New York University, University Heights, New York, May 7, 1967* . . . New York: 1967. 24p., illus.

Program issued for the occasion, setting forth and illustrating some of the highlights in the career of the Wright brothers. The bust of Wilbur Wright is the work of Vincent Glinsky, and that of Orville Wright the work of Paul Fjelde. A Wright brothers medal designed by Paul Fjelde was also issued in commemoration of the event.

Poetry

Andrews, John W. *The Story of Orville and Wilbur Wright at Kitty Hawk, North Carolina.* [Sixtieth Anniversary Edition]. Westport, Conn.: Pavilion Press, 1963. 31p.

Originally published as a part of his poem entitled "*Prelude to Icarus*," New York: Farrar & Rinehart, 1936, pp. 115–134; also published in 1962 in "Cape Hatteras Edition," Westport, Conn.: Pavilion Press, 1962, 29 p. Brief extract published in *Wings: an Anthology of Flight*, edited by H. G. Bryden, London: Faber and Faber, 1942, p. 128.

Based on early experiments of the Wright brothers at Kitty Hawk, N.C.

Baker, Joseph B. The Aviator. *Aeronautics*, June 1909, vol. 4, p. 174.

On Wilbur Wright.

Benét, Rosemary, and Benét, Stephen Vincent. Wilbur and Orville Wright. In their *A Book of Americans*, New York: Farrar and Rinehart, 1933, pp. 106–107.

Juvenile book.

Benét, William R. Kitty Hawk. In his *With Wings as Eagles; Poems and Ballads of the Air*, New York: Dodd, Mead, 1940, pp. 3–5.

Commander, Kingsmill. The Flagship. A Song of Nineteen-Three. In his *Vikings of the Stars*, New York: Harold Vinal, 1928, pp. 14–15.

Crane, Hart. Cape Hatteras [passage on Wrights beginning "There, from Kill Devils Hill at Kitty Hawk"]. In his *The Bridge*. New York: Horace Liveright, 1930, p. 48.

Included also in *The Collected Poems of Hart Crane*, edited by Waldo Frank, New York: Liveright, 1933, p. 34; in *The Complete Poems and Selected Letters and Prose of Hart Crane*, New York: Liveright, 1966 and Garden City, N.Y.: Anchor Books, 1966, p. 90; and in *Verse of Our Day*, by M. Gordon and M. B. King, New York: D. Appleton-Century, 1935, p. 195.

Dunbar, Paul L. [Poem on Orville Wright.] In McSpadden, J. Walker. *How They Blazed The Way; Men Who Have Advanced Civilization*, New York: Dodd, Mead, 1939, p. 269.

Author quotes four lines of doggerel verse about Orville, purportedly written by Dunbar.

Dunkle, Meryl. The Wright Brothers. *Aeronautics*, Oct. 1909, vol. 5, p. 131.

Frost, Robert. Kitty Hawk. *Atlantic Monthly*, Nov. 1957, vol. 200, pp. 52–56.

Published also in his *In the Clearing*, New York: Holt, Rinehart and Winston, 1962, pp. 41–58.

Tribute to the Wright brothers by poet friend of Orville Wright.

——— The Wrights' Biplane. In his *A Further Range. Book Six*, New York: Henry Holt, 1936, p. 69.

Included also in his *Complete Poems*, 1939, 1949, and 1956; in his *Selected Poems*, 1963; and reprinted in *Wings; an Anthology of Flight*, edited by H. G. Bryden, London: Faber and Faber, 1942, p. 124.

MacKaye, Percy W. The Air Voyage up the Hudson. In his *Poems*, New York: The Macmilland Company, 1909, pp. 21–22.

Published also in later editions of his *Poems* and in *U.S. Air Services*, Dec. 1922, vol. 7, no. 11, p. 11.

Phillips, H. I. Bicycles Repaired. *U.S. Air Services*, May 1938, vol. 38, no. 5, p. 31.

Written on the occasion of the restoration of the old Wright bicycle workshop at Greenfield Village, Dearborn, Michigan.

Rodman, Selden. The Boyhood of the Wright Brothers. *Saturday Review of Literature*, Sept. 14, 1940, vol. 22, p. 7.

Excerpt from Part III of his *The Airmen; a Poem in Four Parts*. Included also in *The Saturday Review Treasury*, New York: Simon and Schuster, 1957, pp. 168–170.

——— The Brothers. In his *The Airmen; a Poem in Four Parts*, New York: Random House, 1941, pp. 69–106.

Skinner, George W. The Crest of Fame. *Fly*, July 1909, vol. 1, no. 9, p. 18.

A poetic tribute to the Wright brothers.

Smart, Douglas A. Wilbur Wright. *Flight*, June 8, 1912, vol. 4, p. 514.

Published also in *Aero Club of America Bulletin*, July 1912, vol. 1, p. 5 and in Payne, E. George and Barrows, H. R., *The Story of American Aviation*, New York: American Viewpoint Society, 1930, p. 222.

Written on the occasion of Wilbur's death, May 30, 1912.

Throm, Edward L. Kitty Hawk. In Throm, Edward L., and Grenshaw, James S. *Popular Mechanics Aviation Album*, Chicago: Popular Mechanics Company, 1953, pp. 191–192.

"Touchstone." Wilbur Wright. *Daily Mail*, London, May 31, 1912, p. 6, col. 6.

Reprinted with title, "The Father of Flight," in *Aero Club of America Bulletin*, July 1912, vol. 1, no. 6, p. 9, and in *Fly Magazine*, July 1912, vol. 4, no. 9, p. 10.

Written on the occasion of Wilbur's death, May 30, 1912.

The Wright Brothers. *Aeronautics*, Sept. 1909, vol. 5, no. 3, facing p. 81.

Music

Knostman, Mary E. *Song of the Wright Boys*. Composed by Mary E. Knostman. Dayton, O.: Reisbach & Knostman, 1909, 5 pp.

Three stanzas and chorus for voice and piano, 4/4 time.

Guiterman, Arthur. The Sons of an Eagle-Bird. Dedicated to the Wright Brothers. (Air—"The Son of a Gambolier"). *Aero Club of America Bulletin*, Feb./Mar. 1912, vol. 1, no. 2, suppl., p. [4]

Sung at the sixth annual banquet of the Aero Club of America, January 27, 1912, at which Wilbur Wright was present. Text published also in *U.S. Air Services*, Aug. 1951, vol. 36, p. 10.

Térès, Louis. *Wilbur Wright March. Marche américaine*. Paris: A. Costet, 1908, [19 pp.]

Orchestral parts with piano-conductor score.

Térès, Louis. *Wilbur Wright March. Marche américaine*. Pour piano. Paris: A. Costet, 1908, 3 pp.

Piano solo arrangement of preceding entry.

Motion Pictures and Film Strips

Dare, Birthplace of Aviation. The People of Dare County, N.C. Made and Released by Communication Center, University of North Carolina, 1952. 22 min., sd., color, 16 mm.

Includes the first flights by the Wright brothers, which were made in Dare County.

The Day Man Flew. Go Pictures. Released by McGraw-Hill Book Co., 1962. 17 min., sd., b&w, 16 mm.

Deals with the Wright brothers. Explains how they solved the problems of lift and balance, describes the building of their first engine, and tells about their early flights.

The First Flight of the Wright Brothers. CBS Television. Released by Young America Films, 1955. 28 min., sd., b&w, 16 mm. (You Are There).

Telecast, January 16, 1955, on the CBS television program "You Are There." Reconstructs the events of December 17, 1903.

Flight History at Kitty Hawk, December 17, 1903. Richard B. Morros, Inc., in Association with Hearst Metrotone News. Released by Official Films, 1960. 5 min., sd., b&w, 16 mm. (Almanac Newsreel).

Describes the flights made by the Wrights at Kitty Hawk, N.C., December 17, 1903. Lists some of the honors given to the Wright brothers, including the annual tribute made at the Wright Memorial at Kitty Hawk.

Wings Over Kitty Hawk. Movietonews, 1954. 13 min., sd., b&w, 16 mm. (Greatest Drama).

Discusses events in the lives of the Wright brothers and includes an authentic account of their first historic flight December 17 ,1903.

The Wright Brothers. Jam Handy Organization, 1957. 42 fr., color, 35 mm. (Famous Americans, no. 2).

Describes the childhood and youth of Wilbur and Orville Wright, and shows how their early experiments led them to build an aeroplane and to become American aviation pioneers.

Wright Brothers Fly. Filmrite Associates. Released by Official Films, 1960. 3 min., sd., b&w, 16 mm. (Greatest Headlines of the Century).

Portrays events in the lives of the Wright brothers, showing them in their bicycle shop as they experiment with flying machines and endeavor to understand the science of aerodynamics. Shows the first successful flight of a heavier-than-air mechanically propelled aeroplane by Orville Wright on December 17, 1903.

Wright Brothers National Memorial, North Carolina. Eye Gate House, 1961. 47 fr., color, 35 mm. (National Landmarks, Memorials, and Historic Shrines, no. 6).

Describes the first aeroplane flights made by Wilbur and Orville Wright in December 1903, and explains how the historic event is commemorated in the Wright Brothers National Memorial in North Carolina.

The Wright Brothers, Pioneers of American Aviation. David J. Goodman, Inc., 1957. 47 fr., color, 35 mm.

Adapted from book of the same title by Quentin Reynolds (New York: Random House, 1950). Shows how the Wright brothers develop an interest in the principles of flying through construction of a sled, kites and bicycles, work toward controlled flight, and develop their first aeroplane.

Wynne, Hugh. Historical Aviation Films. *American Aviation Historical Society Journal*, Oct./Dec. 1958, vol. 3, pp. 226–230.

Lists three films in the Motion Pictures Branch, National Archives which include pictures of Orville Wright. One is entitled "First Army Aeroplane Flight, Ft. Myer, Virginia."

Juvenile Publications

Allen, Carl B., and Lyman, Lauren D. Man Flies. In their *The Wonder Book of the Air*, Chicago, Philadelphia: John C. Winston, 1936, pp. 72–85, illus.

Reprinted 1938, 1939, 1941.

Arnold, Henry H. *Bill Bruce and the Pioneer Aviators.* New York: A. L. Burt Company, 1928, 250 pp. (His Aviators Series).

Includes four chapters dealing with Wrights entitled "The Wright Flyer," "Wilbur Wright," "The Unwelcome Visitor," and "The Grant's Tomb Flight," pages 24–56.

Bailey, Carolyn S. Tag-Along Boy; Orville Wright. In her *A Candle for your Cake: Twenty-Four Birthday Stories of Famous Men and Women*, Philadelphia: J. B. Lippincott, 1952, pp. 161–168.

Barksdale, Lena. Wilbur and Orville. In her *Daring Riders and Other Tales of Young America.* Illustrated by Frank Nichols, New York: Alfred A. Knopf, 1946, pp. 79–86.

Bixby, William. The Wright Brothers: Men with Wings. In his *Great Experimenters*, New York: David McKay, 1964, pp. 105–131.

Bolton, Sarah. The Wright Brothers. In her *Lives of Poor Boys Who Became Famous.* Illustrated by Constance Joan Naar, New York: Thomas Y. Crowell Company, 1962, pp. 299–320, illus.

Included also in earlier 1947 printing.

Byrd, Richard E. Our First Air Pioneers. *Boy's Life*, July 1928, vol. 18, no. 7, pp. 8–9, illus.

Published also in Mathiews, Franklin K., ed., *Flying High; a Book of Aviation Stories and Model Airplanes for Boys*, New York: Grosset & Dunlap, 1930, pp. 16–21.

Catherall, Arthur. Wilbur and Orville Wright: Conquerors of the Air. In Duthie, Eric, ed. *Children's Book of Famous Lives*, London: Odhams, 1958, pp. 407–416.

Charnley, Mitchell V. *The Boys' Life of the Wright Brothers.* Illustrated. New York and London: Harper & Brothers, [1928], 291 pp.

Slightly different version of a series of articles originally published in the *American Boy*, August–November, 1928, with title "They Gave the World Wings; the Story of the Wright Brothers," see below.

"Material for this book has come largely from the few published writings of Wilbur and Orville Wright . . . and the miscellaneous writings about them": page v.

——— They Gave the World Wings; the Story of the Wright Brothers. Illustrated by Ernest Fuhr. *American Boy*, Aug. 1928, vol. 29, no. 10, pp. 11–13, 46–47; Sept., no. 11, pp. 6–7, 30, 32, 37; Oct., no. 12, pp. 22–24, 63; Nov., vol. 30, no. 1, pp. 13–14, 32–34, illus.

Clark, Leonard. The Wright Brothers. In his *When They Were Children*, New York: Roy Publishers, 1964, pp. 113–120.

Claudy, Carl H. Two American Conquerors of the Air. *St. Nicholas*, July 1909, vol. 36, pp. 785–787, illus.

Claxton, William J. The Wright Brothers and Their Secret Experiments, The Wright Biplane, and How the Wrights Launched Their Biplane. In his *The Mastery of the Air*, London: Blackie and Son Limited, 1916, pp. 102–106, 123–133.

Clifford, Harold B. Wilbur and Orville Wright. In his *American Leaders*, New York: American Book Company, 1953, pp. 258–267.

Cohen, Rose N. The Wrights Show How! In her *The Men Who Gave Us Wings*, New York: The Macmillan Company, 1944, pp. 115–136, illus.

Cottler, Joseph, and Jaffe, Haym. Wright Brothers. *Child Life*, Sept. 1931, vol. 10, no. 9, pp. 444–445, 471, illus.

Craig, Barbara. *The Wright Brothers and Their Development of the Airplane*. Raleigh: State Dept. of Archives and History, 1960, 23p.

Crowther, James G. The Wright Brothers. In his *Six Great Inventors; Watt, Stephenson, Edison, Marconi, Wright Brothers, [and] Whittle*, London: Hamish Hamilton, 1954, pp. 163–201. (The "Six Great" Series).

Curtin, Andrew. Wright Brothers. In his *Gallery of Great Americans*, New York: Franklin Watts, Inc., 1965, p. 101.

Darrow, Floyd L. Masters of the Air [Wright Brothers]. In his *Builders of the Empire*, New York: Longmans, Green, 1930, pp. 85–90.

——— [Wright Brothers]. In his *Masters of Science and Invention*, New York: Harcourt, Brace and Company, 1923, pp. 315–325.

Delacombe, Harry. The Wrights, The First Flights on Record, and The Wright Aeroplane. In his *The Boys' Book of Airships*, New York: Frederick A. Stokes Company, 1909, pp. 176–177, 199–201, 213.

DeWitt, William A. Wilbur and Orville Wright. In his *Illustrated Minute Biographies . . .*, New York: Grosset & Dunlap, 1949, p. 160, illus.
Also included in revised ed., 1953.

Dolin, Arnold. The Wright Brothers; Pioneers of Flight. In his *Great Men of Science*, New York: Hart Publishing Company, 1962, pp. 175–181.

Eberle, Irmengarde. Wilbur and Orville Wright. In her *Famous Inventors for Boys and Girls*, New York: A. S. Barnes, 1941, pp. 111–118, illus.

Egermeier, Elsie E. The Wright Brothers. In her *Stories of Great Men and Women*, Anderson, Ind.: Warner Press, 1961, pp. 138–144. (Stories for Boys and Girls).

Evans, Idrisyn O. The Airplane; Wilbur and Orville Wright. In his *Inventors of the World*, London, New York: Frederick Warne & Company, 1962, pp. 119–133.

Everett, Carroll, and Reed, C. F. Wilbur and Orville Wright. In their *When They Were Boys*, Dansville, N.Y.: F. A. Owen Publishing Co., 1922, pp. 38–44.
Also included in revised ed., 1932.

Fanning, Leonard M. The Wright Brothers; Fathers of the Airplane Industry. In his *Fathers of Industries*, Philadelphia: J. B. Lippincott, 1962, pp. 194–203.

Federau, Wolfgang. *Die Gebrüder Wright, Pioniere der Luftfahrt.* Nürnberg: Olympia-Verlag, 1952, 149pp., illus. (Biographische Jugendreihe).

Fellowes-Gordon, Ian. Wilbur and Orville Wright. In Canning, John, ed., *100 Great Modern Lives; Makers of the World Today from Faraday to Kennedy*, New York: Hawthorn Books, 1966, pp. 317–322.

Gardner, Jeanne L. *Sky Pioneers, the Story of Wilbur and Orville Wright.* Illustrated by Douglas Gorsline. New York: Harcourt, Brace & World, 1963, 62p.
Includes bibliography, pp. 61–62.

Gates, Arthur I., and Ayer, Jean. The Flying Brothers. In their *Let's Go Ahead*, New York: The Macmillan Company, 1940, pp. 367–391, illus.

Gilmartin, John G., and Skehan, Anna M. Wilbur and Orville Wright, Pioneers in Aviation. In their *Great Names in American History*, Chicago: Laidlaw Bros., 1946, pp. 335–342, illus.

Goebel, Edmund J., and others. Wilbur and Orville Wright; Pioneers in Aviation. In their *Builders of Our Country*, Chicago: Laidlaw Bros., 1951, pp. 345–352. (Catholic School History Series).

Grahame-White, Claude, and Harper, Harry. Wilbur and Orville Wright. In their *Heroes of the Air, a Book for Boys.* Illustrated in Colour by Cyrus Cuneo and with Numerous Portraits, London: Henry Froude, 1912, pp. 55–93.

Griffith, Ward. Orville and Wilbur Wright. In his *Fifty Famous Americans.* Illustrated by Henry E. Vallely, Racine, Wis.: Whitman Publishing Company, 1946, pp. 10–15 (Classics Series).

Guggenheim, Harry. Giving Wings to the World. *St. Nicholas*, Dec. 1928, vol. 56, p. 88.

Hagedorn, Hermann. Wilbur and Orville Wright. In his *The Book of Courage*, Chicago: John C. Winston Co., 1942, pp. 293–305.
Included also in earlier editions.

Hall, Charles G. The Bishop and the Boys and The Wonderful Year of Nineteen Three. In his *Skyways*, New York: The Macmillan Company, 1938, pp. 44–58, 59–64.

Harney, Laura B. The Wright Brothers. In her *The Skycraft Book*, New York: D. C. Heath and Company, 1932, pp. 20–26, illus.

Harper, Harry. Wilbur and Orville Wright. In his *Riders of the Sky; the Saga of the Flying Men*, London: Hodder and Stoughton [1936], pp. 21–25.

Hartman, Gertrude. Man Learns to Fly. In her *Machines and the Men Who Made the World of In-*

dustry, New York: The Macmillan Company, 1939, pp. 237–242.

Heard, Sarah Dow, and King, M. W. The First Airplane. The Wright Brothers. In their *Stories of American Leaders*, Philadelphia: John C. Winston Company, 1934, pp. 307–318, illus.

Heath, Monroe. Orville Wright and Wilbur Wright. In his *Great Americans at a Glance*, vol. 2, *Inventors, Scientists*, Redwood City, Calif.: Pacific Coast Publishers, 1956, pp. 16–17.

Holland, Rupert S. Wilbur and Orville Wright. In his *Historic Airships*. Illustrated by Manning deV. Lee, Philadelphia: Macrae-Smith Company, 1928, pp. 75–89.

Horsfall, Jessie E. The First Aeroplane Flight. In French, Joseph L., ed., *The Big Aviation Book for Boys*, Springfield, Mass.: McLoughlin Bros., Inc., 1929, pp. 58–69.

Hough, Richard A. *Wright Brothers*, by Bruce Carter [pseud.]. London: Newnes Educational Publishing Co., Ltd., 1955, 45p. ("Men of Speed" Series).

Humphrey, Grace. The Secret of the Bird; Wilbur Wright, Orville Wright. In her *Children of Necessity*, Indianapolis: Bobbs-Merrill, 1925, pp. 263–295.

Iseman, John W., and Taylor, Sloan. The First Flight and Gliding Experiments. In their *The Book of Airplanes*, New York: Oxford University Press, 1929, pp. 48–50, 54–58.

Jerome, Lucy B. The First Man to Fly. *Boys' World*, Sept. 14, 1912, vol. 11, no. 37, p. 3, illus.

Kaufman, Mervyn D. *The Wright Brothers; Kings of the Air*. Illustrated by Gray Morrow, Champaign, Ill.: Garrard Publishing Company, 1964, 80p. (A Discovery Book).

Large, Laura A. The Bird Men. In her *Little Stories of Well-Known Americans*, New York: Platt & Munk Co., Inc., 1935, pp. 113–122, illus.

——— The Wright Brothers. In her *Air Travelers from Early Beginnings to Recent Achievements*. Illustrated by Harold Cue, Boston: Lothrop, Lee & Shepard Co., 1932, pp. 65–70.

Law, Frederick H. Wilbur and Orville Wright, Inventors of the Airplane. *St. Nicholas*, June 1926, vol. 53, pp. 793–796.

——— Wilbur and Orville Wright. In his *Great Lives; Life Stories of Great Men and Women*, New York: Globe Book Company, 1952, pp. 45–57.

Lehrburger, Egon. Wilbur and Orville Wright; the Men Who Gave Us Wings. In his *Men Who Changed the World; Stories of Invention and Discovery*, by Egon Larsen [pseud. 2d ed.], New York: Roy Publishers, 1952, pp. 121–143.

McGuire, Edna. Wilbur and Orville Wright; Masters of the Air. In her *They Made America Great; a First Book in American History*, New York: Macmillan, 1957, pp. 238–244. (Macmillan Elementary History Series).

Macmillan, Norman. Wilbur and Orville Wright; First to Fly. In his *Great Airmen*, London: G. Bell, 1955, pp. 14–34.

Maizlish, I. Leon. Wings for Men. In his *Wonderful Wings, the Story of Aviation*. Illustrated by Barry Bart, Evanston, Ill., etc.: Row,

269–517—68——13

Peterson and Company, 1941, pp. 25–33, illus.

Martin, Rudolph, and Schalk, Gustav. Die Gebrüder Wright. In their *Von Ikarus bis Zeppelin; ein Luftschifferbuch für die Jugend*, Berlin, Leipzig: Brandus'sche Verlagsbuchhandlung, 1908, pp. 54–68.

Mason, Miriam E. and Cartwright, William H. The Wright Brothers. In their *Trail Blazers of American History*, Boston: Ginn and Company, 1961, pp. 315–324.

Mills, Lois. *Three Together; the Story of the Wright Brothers and their Sister*. Illustrated by William Moyers, New York: Follett Publishing Company, 1955, 160 p.

Montgomery, David H. The Wright Brothers, Wilbur and Orville. In his *Beginner's American History*, 2d rev. ed., Boston: Ginn and Company, 1945, pp. 335–342, illus.

Montgomery, Elizabeth R. The Third Rudder [1903 Airplane of Wilbur and Orville Wright]. In her *The Story Behind Great Inventions*. Rev. ed., New York: Dodd, 1953, pp. 241–244.

Mooney, James E. It Happened at Last. In his *Wings Away*. Illustrated by Paul Laune, New York: Thomas Nelson and Sons, 1937, pp. 21–25.

Moore, Patrick. *Conquest of the Air: the Story of the Wright Brothers*. London: Lutterworth Press, 1961, 94 p. (Courage and Conquest Series no. 6.)

Morrill, Madge H., and Morrill, Leslie. *The Wright Brothers, First to Fly*. Illustrated by Lee J. Ames, Nashville: Abingdon Press, 1955, 128p.

Mowbray, Jay H. Early Experiments of Wright Brothers. In his *Conquest of the Air by Airships and Other Flying Machines*, Philadelphia: National Publishing Co., 1910, pp. 156–175, illus.

Nida, William L., and Nida, Stella H. The Wright Brothers and the Aeroplane. In their *Pilots and Pathfinders*, New York: Macmillan, 1934, pp. 395–399.

Norris, Geoffrey. *Wright Brothers*. Illustrated by John Norbury. New York: Roy Publishers, 1963, 159p. (Peoples, Places, and Things).

Paris, Leonard. Birth of the Air Age. *Senior Scholastic*, Feb. 1, 1957, vol. 70, p. 17.

An account of the Wright brothers' December 17, 1903 flights in the magazine's "Words That Shaped America" series, erroneously quoting them in a telegram to their sister Katharine as saying "We Have Done It."

——— They Gave Us Tomorrow; Wilbur and Orville Wright. *Senior Scholastic*, Apr. 11, 1958, vol. 72, p. 11.

Thumbnail sketch, no. 22 in the magazine's "Creative Americans" series.

Pringle, Patrick. The First to Fly. In his *They Were the First*, New York: Roy Publishers, 1965, pp. 57–65.

——— Wilbur and Orville Wright. In his *When They Were Boys; Sixteen Boyhood Stories of Famous Men*, New York: Roy Publishers, 1954, pp. 197–209.

Pratt, Fletcher. [Wright Brothers]. In his *Famous Inventors and Their Inventions*, New York: Random House, 1955, pp. 40–44.

Reynolds, James J., and others. The Wright Brothers. In their *Short Stories of Famous Men*, New York: Noble and Noble, 1946, pp. 279–285.
Included also in revised editions, 1948 and 1953, pages 251–257.

Reynolds, Quentin. Wright Brothers. In Evans, Pauline R., ed., *Best Book of Heroes and Heroines*, Garden City, N.Y.: Doubleday & Company, 1964, pp. 192–205.

——— *The Wright Brothers, Pioneers of American Aviation.* Illustrated by Jacob Landau. New York: Random House [1950], 183 p., illus. (Landmark Books. [10]).
Dramatized and produced as phonodisc in 1953 by Howard Tooley, Enrichment Records, LLP 104 (3104B), 1s., 10 in., 33⅓ rpm.

Rhodes, James A. The Wright Brothers. In his *Teenage Hall of Fame*, Indianapolis: Bobbs-Merrill, 1960, pp. 57–59.

Romer, A. Ralph, and Romer, Margaret. The Wright Brothers. In their *Sky Travel*, New York, etc.: Rand McNally & Company, 1929, pp. 146–154.

Ross, Frank, Jr. The First Heavier-than-Air Flying Machine—1903. In his *Trail Blazers of the Sky*, Santa Barbara: Wallace Hebberd, 1945, pp. 3–10, illus.

Sanford, Chester M., and Owen, Grace A. Wilbur and Orville Wright. In their *Modern Americans*, New York: Laurel Book Co., 1921, pp. 99–107.

Schirmer, Mathilda, ed. Conquerors of the Air, Orville and Wilbur Wright. In *Builders for Progress*, Chicago: Beckley-Cardy, 1950, pp. 145–162, illus.

Sobol, Donald J. *The Wright Brothers at Kitty Hawk.* Illustrated by Stewart Mackenzie, New York: T. Nelson, 1961, 143 p., illus.
Reprinted: Englewood Cliffs, N.J.: Scholastic Book Services, 1965.

Southworth, Gertrude V. D., and Southworth, James V. D. The Wright Brothers. In their *Heroes of Our America*, Syracuse, New York: Iroquois Publishing Co., 1952, pp. 329–333.

Stevenson, Augusta. *Wilbur and Orville Wright, Boys with Wings.* Illustrated by Paul Laune. Indianapolis: Bobbs-Merrill [1951], 192 p., illus. (The Childhood of Famous Americans Series).
Slightly revised edition, illustrated by Robert Doremus, published in 1959.

Sutton, Felix. *We Were There at the First Airplane Flight.* Historical consultant: Grover Loening. Illustrated by Laszlo Matulay, New York: Grosset & Dunlap, 1960, 179 p. (We Were There Books, 28).

Tharp, Edgar. Wilbur Wright, Orville Wright; Man Learns to Fly. In his *Giants of Invention*, New York: Grosset & Dunlap, 1963, pp. 101–103. (Illustrated True Books).

Thomas, Eleanor, and Kelty, Mary G. The Wright Brothers. In their *Heroes, Heroines, and Holidays*, Boston: Ginn and Company, 1947, pp. 55–63, illus.
Included also in 1952 edition.

Thomas, Henry. *The Wright Brothers.* Illustrated by Charles

Beck, New York: Putnam, 1960, 126 p. (Lives to Remember).

Thomson, Jay E. The Wrights Invent the First Airplane. In his *Aviation Stories*, New York: Longmans, Green and Co., 1937, pp. 171–180.

Tinsley, Frank. He Saw the Wrights Fly. *Air Progress*, 1953–1954, pp. 39–41.
Fiction.

Turner, Charles C. Wilbur and Orville Wright. In French, Joseph L., ed., *The Big Aviation Book for Boys*, Springfield, Mass.: McLoughlin Bros., Inc., 1929, pp. 45–57.

——— Wilbur and Orville Wright. In his *The Romance of Aeronautics*, London: Seeley, Service & Co., Limited, 1912, pp. 166–199.

Verrill, Dorothy. Man Finds his Wings; How the Wright Brothers Made the First Flight. In her *Aircraft Book for Boys*, New York and London: Harper & Brothers, 1930, pp. 1–16, illus. (Harper's Practical Book Series).

Visiting the Wright Boys. *St. Nicholas*, Nov. 1910, vol. 38, pp. 76–78.

Wade, Mary H. The Wright Brothers. In her *The Light-Bringers*, Boston: Little, Brown, 1914, pp. 112–141.

Walters, David W. Wilbur and Orville Wright; They Taught the World to Fly. In his *Modern Lives*, London: Collins, 1954, pp. 53–60.

[Watson, Thomas] Wilbur and Orville Wright. In *Pioneers of Progress*, Glasgow: W. & R. Holmes [1950] pp. 85–88, illus.

Welch, Helena. Wilbur and Orville's Toy. In her *When They Were Children*, Nashville, Tenn.: Southern Publishing Association, 1965, pp. 127–129.

White, D. Thompson. The Wright Brothers, The First Successful Flyers. In Humphreys, Pauline A. and Hosey, Gertrude. *Romance of the Airman*, Boston: Ginn and Company, 1931, pp. 185–195, illus.

Whitehouse, Arch. Success at Kitty Hawk. In his *The Real Book about Airplanes*. Illustrated by Albert Orbaan, Garden City, N.Y.: Garden City Books, 1952, pp. 55–66, illus.
Included also in 1961 edition, pp. 63–74.

Williams, Walter R., Jr. The Wright Brothers. In his *Exploring The Arts and Industries*, Scranton, Pa.: International Textbook Company, 1940, pp. 247–251, illus.

Winslow, John. The Wright Brothers Plane. In his *Famous Planes and Famous Flights*. Illustrations by Irvin L. Holcombe, New York: The Platt & Munk Co., Inc., 1940, pp. 7–10, illus.

Wright, Elsie. The Wright Brothers. In her *Boys' Book of Famous Fliers* [by] Captain J. J. Grayson [pseud.], Cleveland: World Publishing Co., 1951, pp. 32–45.
Included also in 1932 edition with title, *Famous Flyers and Their Famous Flights.*

Wymer, Norman. *Wright Brothers.* London: Oxford University Press, 1957. 32p. (Lives of Great Men and Women. Ser. 3: Great Inventors).

Index

269-517—68——13

U.S. GOVERNMENT PRINTING OFFICE: 1968

THE LIBRARY OF CONGRESS